FOOD

&

PROCESS

ENGINEERING

TECHNOLOGY

Luther R. Wilhelm, Professor
Biosystems Engineering and Environmental Science Department
The University of Tennessee, Knoxville

Dwayne A. Suter, Professor Emeritus
Biological and Agricultural Engineering Department
Texas A&M University, College Station

Gerald H. Brusewitz, Regents Professor Emeritus
Biosystems and Agricultural Engineering Department
Oklahoma State University, Stillwater

Contents

Introductory Comments

This work is intended as a textbook for non-engineers who are interested in the application of engineering concepts to food processing, handling, and storage. While several good food engineering textbooks are available, none were fully suitable for the needs of students in our courses for non-engineers. Thus, over the years, each of us developed class notes for distribution to our classes. These notes were incomplete, covering only selected topics in these courses. The impetus for combining our notes into a textbook was spurred by receipt of a USDA Higher Education Challenge Grant led by the second author.

This book presents each chapter as a more-or-less stand-alone unit. Some chapters do have brief references to other units; but, insofar as possible, each chapter is presented independently of others, since each of us had somewhat different emphases in our courses and we wanted to be able to use only the chapters needed by our students. It is our hope that the material will be useful to other instructors of food engineering technology topics. Like any book, it remains a work in progress. Some suggested topics have not been included, while others have been only briefly covered. As with any document of this magnitude, some errors may still remain. We solicit your comments for correcting, clarifying, and otherwise improving this document.

This material is not to be reproduced without permission from the authors.

Luther R. Wilhelm
Dwayne A. Suter
Gerald H. Brusewitz   September 2003

Introduction: Problem-Solving Tools

Abstract. This chapter provides a general introduction to common mathematical concepts used in engineering applications. Simple algebraic applications, including exponents and logarithms, are reviewed. Other useful topics include: interpolation, graphical presentations, the rate equation, and the concept of mass and energy balances.

Keywords. Equations, graphs, interpolation of tabular data, logarithms, mass balances, rate equation, significant digits, spreadsheets.

1.1 Introduction

Knowledge of basic problem-solving principles is essential for understanding many of the engineering applications in food engineering. This unit includes a review of several basic problem-solving topics needed to understand subjects covered in subsequent units. Guidelines for presentation of information are also included. The material is presented as a review only. If you understand the topics, you do not need to read this unit. If you do not understand them, you should read the unit, study the examples, and work the problems given at the end of the unit.

1.2 Significant Digits

The writing of any number indicates a certain degree of precision for that number. This is best shown by the use of examples as shown below.

Table 1.01. Significant digit examples.

Number	Tolerance	Significant Digits
2.2	2.2 ± 0.05	2
2.20	2.20 ± 0.005	3
3.1416	3.1416 ± 0.00005	5
2	2 ± 0.5	1
0.0030	0.0030 ± 0.00005	2
2200	2200 ± 50	2
2200	2200 ± 5	3
2200	2200 ± 0.5	4

Note the significance of the zeros in the examples above. The numbers 2.2 and 2.20 represent different degrees of precision because the added zero is a significant digit. On the other hand, zeros following a decimal but preceding the first non-zero digit are not significant digits since they only serve to place the decimal. The last number (2200) is ambiguous since it may have been rounded to the nearest whole number (4 significant digits) or the nearest 10 or the nearest 100. This ambiguity can be eliminated by the use of scientific notation (e.g., 2.200×10^3 and 2.2×10^3 show four and two significant digits respectively.)

The precision of results from any arithmetic calculation depends upon the precision of the least precise number used in the calculations. Thus if two numbers are multiplied (i.e., 2.2×3.1416) the result, 6.9115, implies false precision because it contains more significant digits than the least accurate factor in the multiplication. Thus the result in this example should be rounded to 6.9. This procedure applies identically for division. For addition and subtraction, the results should be rounded to the number of decimal points included in the least precise number.

The above comments represent the official guidelines for significant digits. In actual practice, these rules are not always followed. For example, a length may be expressed as 1 m when it is actually 1.0 m or 1.00 m. Because numbers are often presented in less than the true number of significant digits, it is common practice to present calculated results as 3 significant digits—even though the rules may call for only one or two significant digits.

You should also be cautious in rounding numbers. A series of numerical calculations should be carried out with several significant digits and the final answer rounded to an appropriate number of significant digits. For example, 10/3 equals 3.33333..., not 3 or 3.3.

1.3 Unit Factors

Numerical quantities without units generally carry little meaning in engineering problems. Consequently, including the correct units with the numerical answer to a problem is just as important as arriving at the correct numerical value. A brief discussion of units and a list of many common unit conversion factors are included in the appendix.

Unit analysis affords a valuable aid in solving many physical problems. Some problems require only the conversion of units for a solution. Others may require a more thorough analysis of the problem before finding the number and units for the solution. Virtually all problems involving food engineering applications involve numbers with units. Thus, close monitoring of units is essential.

The conversion of units is accomplished by the use of **unit factors**, defined as ratios whose actual value is unity, or one. Consider the following:

Equation	Ratio	Unit Factor
1 hr = 3600 s	$\dfrac{1\,\text{hr}}{3600\,\text{s}} = 1$	$\dfrac{1\,\text{hr}}{3600\,\text{s}}$
1 hr = 3600 s	$\dfrac{3600\,\text{s}}{1\,\text{hr}} = 1$	$\dfrac{3600\,\text{s}}{1\,\text{hr}}$
$1\,\text{m}^3 = 1000\,\text{L}$	$\dfrac{1000\,\text{L}}{1\,\text{m}^3} = 1$	$\dfrac{1000\,\text{L}}{1\,\text{m}^3}$

The combination of numbers and units in the numerator of a unit factor is equal to the combination of numbers and units in the denominator. Thus, the actual value of the ratio is one, or unity. The numerical values alone are usually not equal to one since they serve as conversion multipliers for the units involved.

The following example shows how a unit factor problem can be set up for a systematic solution. The steps may seem unnecessary for this simple problem; however, you can avoid difficulties with more complicated problems by following this procedure.

Example 1.1

A conveyor belt moves 3 ft in 15 s. What is the belt speed in meters per hour?

Solution:
First enter a blank followed by the final desired units. An equality sign should follow this, and then enter the pertinent information needed for the solution:

$$\underline{\quad}\ \frac{m}{hr} = \frac{3\ ft}{15\ s}$$

Once the pertinent information is included, the solution consists of multiplying the basic data on the right hand side of the equation by appropriate unit factors to obtain the desired final results. Many different unit factors can usually be used to obtain the desired results; however, the better solutions will be those that produce a logical solution with a minimum number of unit factors. The following is one such "better" solution:

$$\underline{\quad}\ \frac{m}{hr} = \frac{3\ ft}{15\ s} \times \frac{1\ m}{3.281\ ft} \times \frac{3600\ s}{1\ hr} = 219.4$$

The units on the right side of the equation are canceled to produce the resulting units on the left side of the equation. The numeric answer is then written in the blank on the left side of the equation.

1.4 Algebraic Equations

An equation is a statement of equality between one or more expressions involving variables and constants. The equation for a straight line ($y = ax + b$) is a simple example. We solve equations by manipulating them such that the equality of the equation is not affected. Such changes are: addition or subtraction of the same number or variable to each side ($y - y = ax + b - y$ and $b + y = ax + b + b$); multiplication of each side by the same number or variable ($ky = kax + kb$); or dividing each side by the same non-zero number or variable ($y/a = x + b/a$).

Algebraic equations are used extensively in analysis of food processing operations. To adequately use such equations, one must:

1. Be able to perform simple algebraic manipulations that change the form of the equation;
2. Be able to interpret graphical representations of these equations; and
3. Be able to solve the equations for unknown parameters.

Introductory coverage of these topics is presented in this and subsequent units.

Several geometric formulas commonly used in food engineering applications are shown below. More extensive lists of formulas are available in physics and mathematics texts, mathematical handbooks, and other similar sources.

Circle $\qquad A = \dfrac{\pi D^2}{4} = \pi r^2 \qquad\qquad C = \pi D$

Sphere $\qquad A = \pi D^2 \qquad\qquad V = \dfrac{4}{3}\pi r^3 = \dfrac{\pi D^3}{6}$

Cylinder $\qquad A = 2\pi rh = \pi Dh \qquad V = \pi r^2 h$

where: A = area
   D = diameter
   C = circumference
   r = radius
   V = volume

1.5 Exponents and Logarithms

Relationships involving roots, exponents, and logarithms are common in food engineering applications. Since roots are actually exponents ($\sqrt{2} = 2^{1/2}$), we will examine briefly the rules for exponents and logarithms. An understanding of these rules is essential to understanding the governing equations applicable to many food-engineering analyses. Food sterilization and drying processes are two major applications that involve logarithmic (and thus exponential) applications in their analyses.

1.5.1 Exponents

In many mathematical operations we must raise a constant or variable to a power. This power may be an integer or decimal value, and it may be positive or negative. We use exponents to identify these powers. In the relationships given below a may be a constant or a variable while m and n are integer or decimal exponents.

$$a^{-n} = \frac{1}{a^n} \qquad\qquad \sqrt[n]{a} = a^{\frac{1}{n}}$$

$$a^m \times a^n = a^{m+n} \qquad\qquad \frac{a^m}{a^n} = a^{m-n}$$

$$\left(a^m\right)^n = a^{mn} \qquad\qquad \sqrt[n]{a^m} = a^{\frac{m}{n}}$$

1.5.2 Logarithms

The logarithm of X to the base b is the exponent to which b must be raised to get X. Thus:

$$10^2 = 100 \qquad \Rightarrow \qquad \log_{10}(100) = 2$$

$$\log_{10}(10) = 1 \qquad \Rightarrow \qquad 10^1 = 10$$

$$\log_{10}(3.162) = 0.5 \qquad \Rightarrow \qquad 10^{0.5} = 3.162.$$

We commonly use two bases for logarithms: **common logarithms,** or logarithms to the base 10, and **natural logarithms,** logarithms to the base e. The number e (2.718 281 828 459 ...) is a constant that occurs frequently in mathematical problems. If a subscript is not given, $\log X$ usually means $\log_{10} X$, and $\ln X$ means $\log_e X$.

Three simple rules involving logarithms are given in the equations below. These rules are often very useful in working with logarithmic equations.

$$\log XY = \log X + \log Y$$

$$\log \frac{X}{Y} = \log X - \log Y$$

$$\log X^n = n \log X$$

Most logarithmic calculations are now performed using hand calculators or computers. Calculations can also be made manually using logarithmic tables. Table 1.02 is an abbreviated table of natural logarithms (base e). Common logarithms (base 10) are given in Table 1.03. Typical tables of common logarithms do not show that the numbers in the table header row are decimal. In typical tables, these numbers are written as whole numbers $0 - 9$ rather than $0.00 - 0.9$. In addition, all numbers in the table are assumed to be decimal values and the "1." is not shown. Table 1.03 is read by finding the intersection of the whole number and the decimal value. Thus, $\log_{10}$ 12.6 = 1.1004. Hand-held calculators are commonly used for problem solving. Most now include logarithmic functions; however, the specific computational procedure differs among calculators. One useful application of the logarithmic tables is to verify

Table 1.02. Natural (base e; e = 2.71828) logarithm of selected numbers.

n	$\log_e n$	n	$\log_e n$	n	$\log_e n$	n	$\log_e n$
0.0		2.0	0.6931	11	2.3979	40	3.6889
0.1	-2.3026	2.5	0.9163	12	2.4849	50	3.9120
0.2	-1.6094	3.0	1.0986	13	2.5649	60	4.0943
0.3	-1.2040	3.5	1.2528	14	2.6391	70	4.2485
0.4	-0.9163	4.0	1.3863	15	2.7081	80	4.3820
0.5	-0.6931	4.5	1.5041	16	2.7726	90	4.4998
0.6	-0.5108	5.0	1.6094	17	2.8332	100	4.6052
0.7	-0.3567	6.0	1.7918	18	2.8904	200	5.2983
0.8	-0.2231	7.0	1.9459	19	2.9444	300	5.7038
0.9	-0.1054	8.0	2.0794	20	2.9957	400	5.9915
1.0	0.0000	9.0	2.1972	25	3.2189	500	6.2146
1.5	0.4055	10.0	2.3026	30	3.4012	1000	6.9078

Table 1.03. Four-place common (base 10) logarithms.

N	0	0.1	0.2	0.3	0.4	0.5	0.6	0.7	0.8	0.9
0		--	--	--	--	--	--	--	--	--
		1.0000	0.6990	0.5229	0.3979	0.3010	0.2218	0.1549	0.0969	0.0458
1	0	0.0414	0.0792	0.1139	0.1461	0.1761	0.2041	0.2304	0.2553	0.2788
2	0.3010	0.3222	0.3424	0.3617	0.3802	0.3979	0.4150	0.4314	0.4472	0.4624
3	0.4771	0.4914	0.5051	0.5185	0.5315	0.5441	0.5563	0.5682	0.5798	0.5911
4	0.6021	0.6128	0.6232	0.6335	0.6435	0.6532	0.6628	0.6721	0.6812	0.6902
5	0.6990	0.7076	0.7160	0.7243	0.7324	0.7404	0.7482	0.7559	0.7634	0.7709
6	0.7782	0.7853	0.7924	0.7993	0.8062	0.8129	0.8195	0.8261	0.8325	0.8388
7	0.8451	0.8513	0.8573	0.8633	0.8692	0.8751	0.8808	0.8865	0.8921	0.8976
8	0.9031	0.9085	0.9138	0.9191	0.9243	0.9294	0.9345	0.9395	0.9445	0.9494
9	0.9542	0.9590	0.9638	0.9685	0.9731	0.9777	0.9823	0.9868	0.9912	0.9956
10	1.0000	1.0043	1.0086	1.0128	1.0170	1.0212	1.0253	1.0294	1.0334	1.0374
20	1.3010	1.3032	1.3054	1.3075	1.3096	1.3118	1.3139	1.3160	1.3181	1.3201
30	1.4771	1.4786	1.4800	1.4814	1.4829	1.4843	1.4857	1.4871	1.4886	1.4900
40	1.6021	1.6031	1.6042	1.6053	1.6064	1.6075	1.6085	1.6096	1.6107	1.6117
50	1.6990	1.6998	1.7007	1.7016	1.7024	1.7033	1.7042	1.7050	1.7059	1.7067
60	1.7782	1.7789	1.7796	1.7803	1.7810	1.7818	1.7825	1.7832	1.7839	1.7846
70	1.8451	1.8457	1.8463	1.8470	1.8476	1.8482	1.8488	1.8494	1.8500	1.8506
80	1.9031	1.9036	1.9042	1.9047	1.9053	1.9058	1.9063	1.9069	1.9074	1.9079
90	1.9542	1.9547	1.9552	1.9557	1.9562	1.9566	1.9571	1.9576	1.9581	1.9586
100	2.0000	2.0004	2.0009	2.0013	2.0017	2.0022	2.0026	2.0030	2.0035	2.0039

Table 1.04. Logarithms of selected numbers.

$\ln 0.1 = -2.3026$	$\log_{10} 0.1 = -1.00$
$\ln 0.5 = -0.6931$	$\log_{10} 1 = 0.000$
$\ln 1.0 = 0.000$	$\log_{10} 50 = 1.6990$
$\ln 50 = 3.9120$	$\log_{10} 50.5 = 1.7033$
$\ln 100 = 4.6052$	$\log_{10} 43576 = 4.6392$

$$\ln 1000 = \ln (10 \times 100) = \ln 10 + \ln 100$$
$$= 2.3026 + 4.6052 = 6.9078$$

Table 1.05. Calculation of logarithms.

Problem	Logarithmic Calculations		Answer
$55^{\frac{1}{2.1}}$	$\Rightarrow \ln(55)^{\frac{1}{2.1}} = \dfrac{\ln(55)}{2.1} = \dfrac{4.0073}{2.1} = 1.9083$	$\Rightarrow e^{1.9083}$	6.74
$55^{\frac{1}{2.1}}$	$\Rightarrow \log(55)^{\frac{1}{2.1}} = \dfrac{\log(55)}{2.1} = \dfrac{1.7404}{2.1} = 0.8287$	$\Rightarrow 10^{0.8287}$	6.74
$(3.5)^3$	$\Rightarrow \ln(3.5)^3 = 3\ln(3.5) = 3(1.2528) = 3.758$	$\Rightarrow e^{3.758}$	42.9
$(3.5)^3$	$\Rightarrow \log(3.5)^3 = 3\log(3.5) = 3\log\dfrac{35}{10} = 3(\log(35) - \log(10))$ $= 3(1.5441 - 1) = 3(0.5441) = 1.632$	$\Rightarrow 10^{1.632}$	42.9

correct use of your calculator. Table 1.04 shows examples of logarithmic table values that could be used for such verification. Examples in Table 1.05 demonstrate the use of logarithms to solve other problems.

1.6 Graphs and Coordinate Systems

Graphs are used to present data in visual form and to show relationships between equation variables. We are often interested in obtaining an equation to relate experimental data. A straight line can represent many such experimental data if plotted on an appropriate graph. Table 1.06 summarizes three types of graphs, the equation type, and examples of each. Many different coordinate systems are used in the scientific and business world. Most graphs, however, are presented as standard rectilinear X-Y (Cartesian), semi-logarithmic (semi-log), or full logarithmic (log-log) graphs. These

Table 1.06. Straight-line relationships for common graph types.

Graph Type	Rectilinear	Semi-log	Log-log
Equation Type	Linear	Exponential	power law
General Form of Equation	$y = mx + b$	$y = be^{mx}$ $y = b10^{mx}$	$y = bx^m$
Intercept [a]	$b = y - mx$	--	--
Slope [b]	$m = \dfrac{y_2 - y_1}{x_2 - x_1}$	$m = \dfrac{\ln y_2 - \ln y_1}{x_2 - x_1}$ or $m = \dfrac{\log y_2 - \log y_1}{x_2 - x_1}$	$m = \dfrac{\log y_2 - \log y_1}{\log x_2 - \log x_1}$

[a] Intercept has meaning only for rectilinear coordinates. The value of y is never equal to zero for semilog and log-log graphs.

[b] A common way of stating the slope for semi-log graphs is the change in x corresponding to a full log cycle on the y-axis.

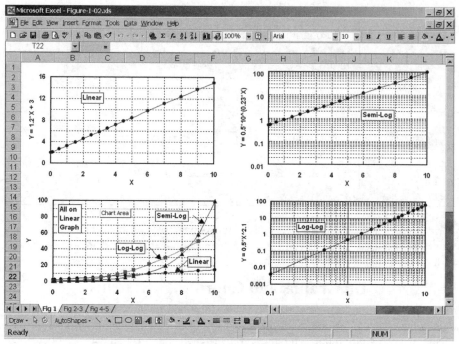

Figure 1.01. Examples of linear, semi-log, and log-log graphs.
(Image from a Microsoft Excel worksheet.)

are the only three types of graphs we will consider. Figure 1.01 shows examples of these three graphs. Actual curves plotted are:

$$\text{Linear:} \quad y = 0.5x + 10$$

$$\text{Semi-log:} \quad y = 0.5 \times 10^{0.23x}$$

$$\text{Log-log:} \quad y = 0.5x^{0.21}$$

1.6.1 General (Cartesian) Coordinates

This type of graph uses equal increments for all measurements along an axis. The scales along the vertical and horizontal axes may be different but the grid (lines along each axis) usually has uniform spacing. Figure 1.02 is an example of a graph in Cartesian coordinates. This type of graph, commonly called an X-Y graph, is perhaps the most common graph type for presenting engineering data. The curve shapes in this figure indicate that the data could also be printed on a semi-logarithmic graph.

1.6.2 Logarithmic Graphs

Logarithmic graphs present data along an axis that is scaled by taking the logarithms (base 10) of the numbers to be plotted. For example: log 1 = 0; log 2 = 0.301; log 4 = 0.602; log 9 = 0.954; log 10 = 1.00; log 20 = 1.301; log 40 = 1.602; and log 100 = 2.00. We can see from these values that each multiple of 10 begins a new cycle on a logarithmic scale.

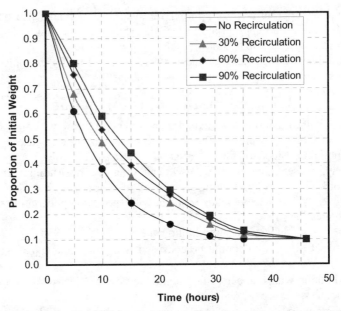

Figure 1.02. Moisture removal as a function of time for peaches dried with recirculated air.

Logarithmic graphs may use logarithmic scales on both axes (called log-log) or on only one axis with a standard scale on the other (called semi-log). We will be concerned only with semi-log graphs—a graph type used extensively in thermal processing analysis. An example of a semi-logarithmic graph is shown in Figure 1.03.

1.6.3 Plotting Graphs

Certain general rules should be followed when plotting all graphs. The first rule is that a graph should clearly present the desired information. This requires that appropriate X and Y values must be shown on the axes. In addition each axis should have a

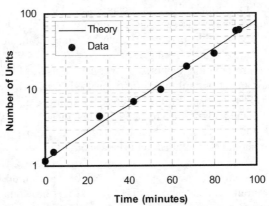

Figure 1.03. Example of a semi-logarithmic plot.

title and units as appropriate. An appropriate overall title should also be included. Other items that may be appropriate to include are legends (for multiple line plots), symbols indicating data points, notes highlighting certain features of a graph, equations defining lines shown, etc. Refer to Figures 1.02 and 1.03 for examples of graphs that present some of the information types noted above.

1.7 Presentation of Information

We transmit information in text, tables, pictures, and various graph forms. We should always attempt to present this information as accurately, clearly, and completely as possible. Much of the information we transmit involves numerical data. Unfortunately, presentation methods used can often be misleading. An excellent discussion of such misleading techniques is given in *How to Lie With Statistics* (Huff, 1954). Petroski (1995) discusses this problem with specific application to writing for technical publication.

Some specific guidelines we should follow are:
- Significant digits used should be consistent with the accuracy of the data presented.
- Include units with numbers unless units are already clear or the number is dimensionless.
- Avoid ambiguity. "Average" can be used to imply mean (arithmetic average of all values); median (half of values are above, half are below); or mode (most frequently occurring value). Mean and median are the most commonly used "averages."

Graphs are perhaps the most common medium for misleading presentations. Many misleading or poorly presented graphs—including some computer-generated graphs— are simply the result of careless preparation.

Graphs should be clear and easily understood. An appropriate overall title should be included. The graph should be appropriate for the data presented. Pie charts are often used to show distribution percentages, such as budget distribution by category. Bar charts are useful for presentation of discreet values. Plots of data reported monthly (electrical consumption, store sales, plant production, etc.) are excellent candidates for bar charts. Three-dimensional (3-D) bar charts can be used to compare similar monthly data for more than one year. Surface plots provide a 3-dimensional surface plot of a continuously variable parameter, such as temperature distribution along a plane through a bread loaf as it is baking.

Each graphical representation, as noted above, can be useful for a specific application. However, the most commonly used (and misused) graph is the simple *X-Y* plot. This plot (Figure 1.02 is an example) often presents multiple lines on a single graph. The graph should "stand alone" as presented. This means that, in addition to an appropriate title, *X* and *Y* axes should be labeled, curves (if more than one) should be labeled or a legend should be included, and scales should be selected to appropriately present the data.

Figure 1.04 is an example of how data should NOT be presented. The figure title is very general. Time units are not shown. The time scale shows no increments. Two lines are shown, using the same line type and no indication of what each represents.

The *Y*-axis scale is divided into increments that make chart reading very difficult. All numbers on the *Y*-axis are shown to two decimal places. (A value of 2.33 probably implies an accuracy far better than the data represented. The limited range of the *Y*-axis is also a problem with the graph. It does not begin at zero and greatly exaggerates the difference between the two curves. In some instances, where the purpose is to show small perturbations to a large value, such a range may be suitable. In most cases, it is not appropriate. Figure 1.05 corrects the problems noted above and presents a very different visual image. Now we see that customer satisfaction is, indeed greater for Product B. However, the difference is noticeably less than implied in Figure 1.04.

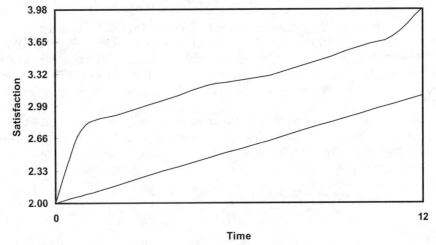

Figure 1.04. Customer satisfaction.

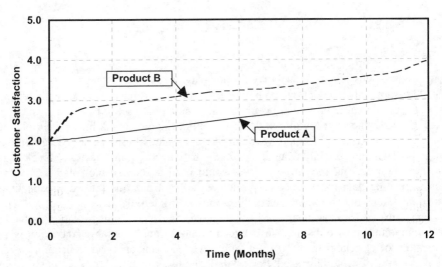

Figure 1.05. Customer satisfaction for two Acme Widget products.

1.8 Interpolation of Tabular Data

Tabular data are widely used for many applications. This use often involves interpolation between two values in a table. Consider these tabular values taken from a table of thermodynamic properties of water (Table 9.05). Values in this table are given in 5° increments.

$t\,(°C)$	k	Pr
0	0.558	13.7
5	0.568	11.4
10	0.577	9.5

If we need values at temperatures between the tabulated values, we must interpolate. We can broadly define three degrees of difficulty (and precision) in interpolation. The easiest (and least precise) is an approximate interpolation. For example, we can say by inspection that the Prandtl number (Pr) at 2.5°C is approximately 12.5. We know that 2.5 is midway between 0 and 5 and 12.5 is approximately midway between 13.7 and 11.4.

A second and more precise calculation can be made using linear interpolation. This is equivalent to plotting the above data, drawing straight lines between the points, and reading the interpolated value from the chart. We can express this mathematically as a relationship between ratios as shown in the following equation:

$$\frac{x_1 - x}{x_1 - x_2} = \frac{y_1 - y}{y_1 - y_2} \quad \text{or} \quad y = y_1 - (y_1 - y_2) \times \left(\frac{x_1 - x}{x_1 - x_2}\right)$$

Now, if we think of the x values as temperature and the y values as Prandtl numbers, we can repeat the above interpolation to find the Prandtl number at 2.5°C.

$$Pr = 13.7 - (13.7 - 11.4) \times \left(\frac{0 - 2.5}{0 - 5}\right) = 13.7 - 2.3 \times 0.5 = 13.7 - 1.15 = 12.55$$

This linear procedure is widely used to interpolate between tabulated values. It typically provides sufficient accuracy for most applications. One precaution, however, should be noted. If the relationship between x and y is not linear and the Δx increment is large, considerable error can occur. In these situations, a third approach must be used. Consider the semi-log plot in the lower left of Figure 1.01. A linear interpolation for y between x-values of 4 and 8 would give a substantial error, since the graph has substantial curvature in that range. In this situation we would need to develop an equation representing the curve, or we would need a detailed plot of the curve to permit reading data more closely. While we will not use this third approach, it is mentioned to point out potential errors in some linear interpolations.

The term *precision* has been used above in our discussion of interpolation methods. It is important that we distinguish between precision and accuracy. **Accuracy** is an indication of closeness to the correct value, while **precision** is an indication of the number of significant digits used. For example, let us assume that the correct value for some parameter is exactly 22.5. Two individuals calculate the parameter value as 22.4

and 22.2576 respectively. Even though the second value (22.2576) indicates more precision, the first value (22.4) is closest to the correct value and is more accurate.

1.9 Mass and Energy Balances

Many engineering analyses involve mass and/or energy balances. These balances are simply accounting processes that account for all material or energy in processes of interest. For flow processes the general balance equations is *input − output = accumulation*. In mass balances, this equation applies for mass of each component involved in a process and for the total mass of all components. Mass balances are essential in processes involving material flow. For example, liquid handling systems and dehydration systems must be analyzed using mass balances.

Example 1.2

A food leather is dried in a continuous-flow dehydrator. The wet leather contains 0.80 kg H_2O/kg wet leather while the dry leather contains 0.20 kg H_2O/kg dry leather. Heated drying air flows opposite to the flow of the leather. Flow rates are as shown below. What is the flow rate of drying air?

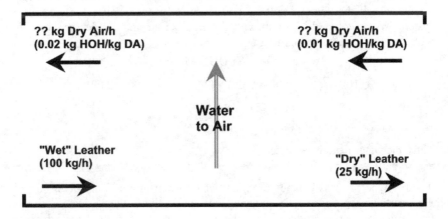

Solution:

This system has no accumulation. Thus, input must be equal to output for all components: water, dry air, solids in the leather, and for the sum of all these. The airflow must be sufficient to remove all the water evaporated from the leather. We begin by looking at the moisture and dry matter of the wet and dry leather. The 100 kg/hr of wet leather is 80% water. Thus we have an input of 80 kg H_2O/hr and 20 kg solids/hr. The dried leather contains 20% water, giving outputs of 5 kg H_2O/hr and 20 kg solids/hr. Thus, the solids balance was indirectly accounted for in the problem statement. The water removed is $80 - 5 = 75$ kg H_2O/hr (or $100 - 25 = 75$, if we look at the total water plus solids balance). This water is added to the air. Thus the airflow must be sufficient to remove the water. A water balance for the air can be written as:

$$\text{water in air IN} + \text{water added (75)} = \text{water in air OUT}$$

$$X\left(\frac{\text{kg dry air}}{\text{hr}}\right) \times 0.01\left(\frac{\text{kg } H_2O}{\text{kg dry air}}\right) + 75\left(\frac{\text{kg } H_2O}{\text{hr}}\right) = X\left(\frac{\text{kg dry air}}{\text{hr}}\right) \times 0.02\left(\frac{\text{kg } H_2O}{\text{kg dry air}}\right)$$

$$X\left(\frac{\text{kg dry air}}{\text{hr}}\right) \times 0.01\left(\frac{\text{kg } H_2O}{\text{kg dry air}}\right) + 75\left(\frac{\text{kg } H_2O}{\text{hr}}\right) = X\left(\frac{\text{kg dry air}}{\text{hr}}\right) \times 0.02\left(\frac{\text{kg } H_2O}{\text{kg dry air}}\right)$$

Solving for X,

$$X = \frac{75\left(\dfrac{\text{kg } H_2O}{\text{hr}}\right)}{0.02 - 0.01\left(\dfrac{\text{kg } H_2O}{\text{kg dry air}}\right)} = \frac{75}{0.01}\left(\frac{\text{kg dry air}}{\text{hr}}\right) = 7500\left(\frac{\text{kg dry air}}{\text{hr}}\right)$$

ANSWER

We have now completed all the calculation necessary for the answer. However, we can check the above result by performing a water balance for the entire system. Water enters the system with the entering air and wet leather. It exits with the "dry" leather and exiting air. Thus the balance is:

$$\text{water IN} - \text{water OUT} = 0$$

$$(100 \times 0.8 + 7500 \times 0.01) - (25 \times 0.2 + 7500 \times 0.02)$$

$$= (80 + 75) - (5 + 150)$$

$$= 155 - 155 = 0$$

Thus, the water mass is balanced.

Another type of mass balance problem occurs when products are being mixed to obtain a certain proportion of components. One application is the blending of sorghum syrup. Sorghum syrup is produced from the juice of sweet sorghum. It has a distinctive flavor that makes it desirable as a cooking additive. For use as a syrup, many prefer a modified product with milder flavor. This is accomplished by mixing the pure sorghum syrup with other syrups, such as corn syrup, to produce a sweetener with a lower percentage of the flavor components found in the pure syrup. Example 1.3 demonstrates this application.

Example 1.3

A blend of sorghum syrup is to be produced by mixing pure syrup with corn syrup and a semi-syrup to produce 100 kg of blended product. Properties of the three syrups are shown in the following table. All percentages are by mass.

Component	% Water	% Sugar	% Flavor	kg
Sorghum syrup (S)	23.0	75.5	1.5	???
Corn syrup (C)	20.0	80.0	0.0	???
Semi-syrup (P)	40.0	59.0	1.0	???
Desired blend	24.0	75.0	1.0	100.0

Solution:
Three mass balances are needed: sugar; flavor; and total mass. Using the symbol following each syrup name in the table, we write the mass balances as follows:

$$\text{Total:} \quad S + C + P = 100$$
$$\text{Sugar:} \quad 0.755\,S + 0.8\,C + 0.59\,P = 0.75 \times 100 = 75$$
$$\text{Flavor:} \quad 0.015\,S + 0\,C + 0.01\,P = 0.01 \times 100 = 1$$

Rearranging the flavor balance and solving for P in terms of S gives:

$$P = 100 - 1.5\,S$$

Substituting this relationship for P into the total mass balance equation given:

$$S + C + 100 - 1.5\,S = 100$$
$$C = 0.5\,S$$

Substituting for C and P in the sugar balance equation given:

$$0.755\,S + 0.8\,(0.5\,S) + 0.59\,(100 - 1.5\,S) = 75$$
$$0.27\,S = 15$$
$$S = 55.56$$

Solving for C and P:

$$C = 0.5\,S = 0.5\,(55.56) = 27.78$$
$$P = 100 - 1.5\,S = 100 - 1.5\,(55.56) = 16.66$$

Checking the results against the total mass balance equation, we see that

$$S + C + P = 55.56 + 27.78 + 16.66 = 100$$

Note: This combination of ingredients can be used to produce the desired blend. Some ingredient combinations are not possible. For example, if the corn syrup of the above problem contained a 1.1% flavor level, no combination of ingredients could reduce the flavor level to 1%. In general, if a solution of the mass balance equations results in a negative value for at least one ingredient, this indicates that the desired blend is not possible.

Energy balances are handled in the same manner as mass balances, but we must account for all forms of energy: thermal, kinetic, and potential energy. Heat generation and/or storage, if present, must also be considered. In most applications, energy balances involve application of thermal property data discussed in subsequent units. Watson and Harper (1988) present additional examples of mass and energy balances for food engineering applications.

1.10 The Rate Equation

We frequently encounter applications where we are interested in the rate at which something occurs: heat transfer, diffusion, electrical flow, and similar applications. A single basic equation form applies for all these processes. The general form of the equation is:

$$\text{Flow rate} = \frac{\text{Driving force}}{\text{Resistance}}$$

Specific forms of this equation for different applications are:

Ohm's law (for electricity) $I = \dfrac{E}{R}$

Fick's first law (for diffusion) $J = -D\dfrac{dC}{dx} = -\dfrac{\frac{dC}{dx}}{D}$

Fourier's law (for heat transfer) $\dot{q} = -k\dfrac{dt}{dx} = -\dfrac{\frac{dt}{dx}}{k}$ or $\dot{q} = \dfrac{\Delta t}{R_T}$

While these equations may look different, they all have the same form. The terms dx/D and dx/k represent resistances to diffusion and heat transfer respectively. The minus sign is present simply to indicate the direction of diffusion or heat transfer. Thus, all equations above are of the same form as the general equation.

> *Historical Note*: J. B. J. Fourier proposed the heat transfer relationship now known as Fourier's law in 1822. Five years later Georg S. Ohm, a German professor of mathematics, proposed a similar relationship (Ohm's law) for electrical flow. Fick's law for diffusion was proposed much later (Crew, 1928).

1.11 Spreadsheets—A Problem-Solving Tool

In the early 1980s, a new computer program became number one in sales for several months. That software package, Lotus 1-2-3, represented the first widespread use of spreadsheets as a problem-solving tool. The success of Lotus 1-2-3 spawned a number of imitators. Several spreadsheet packages are now available. The current packages represent great improvements in features and ease of use over the original version of 1-2-3. These packages differ in some advanced features, but the basic spreadsheet principles are the same for all.

The basic feature of a spreadsheet is its tabular format. It is made up of rows, numbered 1 to 8192 or more, and columns identified as A, B, ... Z, AA, AB, ...IU, IV, or more. Each intersection of a row and column is identified as a cell with the column letter and row number as an address. The "home" cell in the upper left corner has the address A1. Figure 1.06 shows a spreadsheet arrangement for a block of cells from A1 to G16. We will use this figure to provide a quick overview of some spreadsheet applications.

The cell contents of Figure 1.06 show a simple application of spreadsheets. They represent calculations of surface area and volume for several can sizes. Whole numbers, not actual can sizes, are used here for simplicity. Formulas in columns C, D, E, and F perform the calculations based upon numbers given in Columns A and B. For other sizes, the numbers in the first two columns can be replaced with new numbers, or additional numbers can be added below the current values. Formulas for the calculations can then be copied to provide additional results. (As you use spreadsheets, review the effect of relative and absolute cell addressing upon copied formulas. This is a very important, and useful, feature of spreadsheets.) Formulas in Cells C through F of Row 3 are given below, with an explanation of each. Note the unit conversion for Column F.

	A	B	C	D	E	F	G
1	Radius	Height	End Area	Side Area	Tot Area	Volume	COMMENTS
2	(mm)	(mm)	(Sq mm)	(Sq mm)	(Sq mm)	(L)	
3	30	20	5655	3770	9425	0.0565	End Area = 2 ends
4	30	60	5655	11310	16965	0.1696	Side Area = can walls
5	30	100	5655	18850	24504	0.2827	
6	50	20	15708	6283	21991	0.1571	Note units for Volume
7	50	60	15708	18850	34558	0.4712	
8	50	100	15708	31416	47124	0.7854	
9	70	20	30788	8796	39584	0.3079	
10	70	60	30788	26389	57177	0.9236	
11	70	100	30788	43982	74770	1.5394	
12	90	20	50894	11310	62204	0.5089	
13	90	60	50894	33929	84823	1.5268	
14	90	100	50894	56549	107442	2.5447	
15	60	60	25761	22619	48381	0.7728	Averages of above
16	60	60	22619	22619	45239	0.6786	A & V using Avg. R & H

Figure 1.06. Example of a spreadsheet application.

Col	Equation	Comment
C3	=2*PI()*A3^2	$(2\pi A3^2)$, where A3 represents the content of cell A3. The PI() is a spreadsheet function that gives the value of π. The * represents multiplication and the ^ indicates raising to a power.
D3	=2*PI()*A3*B3	$(2\pi A3 \times B3)$
E3	=C3+D3	Each formula must begin with = to indicate that what follows is a formula rather than a text string.
F3	=PI()*(A3^2)*B3/1000000	$(\pi A3^2 \times B3/10^6)$

The above formulas are correct for Excel. Quattro Pro and Lotus 123 use @ instead of = to introduce functions, and function names sometimes differ among the spreadsheet programs. However, the spreadsheet layout and the general form of equations is the same for all three spreadsheets noted above. Spreadsheet functions are extensive, typically at least a few hundred functions. They include logical, mathematical, statistical, financial, string, date/time, and other functions. You will find many of these functions to be very helpful in performing calculations required in later units of this text.

Spreadsheets also have excellent graphing capabilities. The graphs shown in Figure 1.01 are examples of spreadsheet graphs. Graphs can be created and edited with ease. All graphs shown in this chapter, and most graphs in later chapters, were produced using a spreadsheet. This graphing capability allows you to obtain rapid visual indication of results and trends. You can quickly plot data. You can also change spreadsheet data, and graphs already created will immediately change to reflect the updated data. Spreadsheets can be invaluable in solving numerical problems and analyzing experimental data.

The above comments cover some of the basic concepts of spreadsheets. As you use spreadsheets, you will find many additional features that are useful for specific applications. Some of these are as follows:

- Spreadsheets may have multiple pages, providing a 3-D effect.
- You can produce and play slide shows within spreadsheets.
- You can import text and numeric data from other files, if properly formatted, into spreadsheets. This is often useful in the analysis of experimental data.
- You can export spreadsheet tables, and graphs, to word processing documents.
- You can do simple regression analysis in spreadsheets.
- You can do limited database activities in spreadsheets.

Word processors and spreadsheets are probably the two most useful and widely used software packages for most scientists. Inability to use either of these packages leaves one at a considerable disadvantage.

For additional information regarding mathematical applications, consult Hartel et al., 1997. This is an excellent reference for applied problems in food engineering.

List of Symbols
(Units shown are preferred SI units for most applications)

A	area, m^2
C	circumference, m
C	concentration, $kmol/m^3$
D	diameter, m
D	diffusivity, m^2/s
E	voltage, volts
h	height or length, m
I	electrical current flow, amperes
J	diffusion rate, $kmol/(m^2\ s)$
k	thermal conductivity, W/(m K)
$\dot{q}$	heat transfer rate per unit area, W/m^2
r	radius, m
R	electrical resistance, ohms
R_T	total resistance to heat flow, $(m^2\ K)/W$
t	temperature, °C
V	volume, m^3

Note: Some texts use kg mole instead of kmol to indicate molar amounts.

References

1. Crew, Henry. 1928. *The Rise of Modern Physics*. The Williams & Wilkins Co., Baltimore.
2. Hartel, R. W., T. A. Howell, Jr., and D. B. Hyslop. 1997. *Math Concepts for Food Engineering*. Technomic Publishing Co., Lancaster, PA.
3. Huff, Darell. 1954. *How to Lie with Statistics*. W.W.Norton & Co., New York.
4. Petroski, Henry. 1995. Soft graphics. *American Scientist* 83(1): 17-20.
5. Selby, Samuel M., ed. 1968. *Standard Mathematical Tables*. CRC Press. Cleveland, OH.
6. Watson, Ernest L., and Harper, John C. 1988. *Elements of Food Engineering*, 2nd ed. Van Nostrand Reinhold Co. Inc. New York, NY.

Problems

1.1. How many significant digits are in each of the following numbers?

a.	24 705	f.	0.3003
b.	24 700	g.	3.000
c.	2.4700	h.	6
d.	0.0074	i.	3.760×10^6
e.	1.0074	j.	9.008×10

1.2. Using appropriate conversion factors, make the following conversions:

    a. 20 gal/min to liters/hr   d. 1 atmosphere to kPa

    b. 1497 ft lb$_f$ to KWH   e. 1 gram/cm^3 to kg/m^3

    c. 12 Btu/(hr ft^2 °R) to SI units

1.3. Milk ($\rho = 1030$ kg/m^3) flows at 0.08 m^3/min to a bottling machine. How many 1-liter bottles will be filled in a 10-hour work day?

1.4. A packing line handles 2 apples per second. If the apples average 4 ounces each, how many 4-pound packages can be filled in 4 hours?

1.5. A machine automatically fills cases of canned corn at the rate of one case (24 cans) in 15 seconds. If the cans are spaced 6" apart on the conveyor, what must by the conveyor speed in cm/sec to supply the machine?

1.6. If pork contains 75% water, how many kg of water are in 100 kg of pork?

1.7. If apples contain 87% water, how many kg of apples are needed to produce 17 kg of "dried" apples containing 25% moisture?

1.8. Find the logarithms of the following numbers (using tables—not calculators):

    a. log 10   g. log 0.25

    b. log 1   h. ln 1.75

    c. log 1000   i. ln 1

    d. log 67.2   j. ln 37.5

    e. log 0.1   k. ln 175

    f. log 3.75   l. ln 0.1

1.9. Perform the following operations using a calculator, then repeat using logarithms:

    a. 3.75 × e   e. $10^{3.75}$

    b. 175 × 0.15   f. $1.75^{2.5}$

    c. 5.45/375   g. $3.98^{-1.5}$

    d. 26/4.96   h. $577^{0.35}$

1.10. If x = 5, solve for y in each of the following equations:

    a. $y = ax + b$ $a = 48, b = 7$

    b. $x = by + d$ $b = 3.5, d = 17$

    c. $y = a \log x + b$ $a = 3, b = 0.5$

    d. $y = a \ln x + b$ $a = 3, b = 0.5$

    e. $y = ae^{bx}$ $a = 2, b = 0.1$

    f. $x = be^{ky}$ $b = 3, k = 0.7$

    g. $y = ax^b$ $a = 4, b = 2.5$

    h. $x = by^d$ $b = 1.5, d = 0.25$

1.11. Plot the following curves. Find the intercept and slope at the intercept.

    a. $A = 4.5W + 10.8$ (Cartesian)

    b. $\dfrac{Y + M}{Y + 1} = 0.5$ (Cartesian)

    c. $\text{Log } Q = 0.0436T + 0.904$ (Cartesian and semi-log)

    d. $S = 4.75W^{0.66}$ (Cartesian and log-log)

    e. $\text{Log } V = 0.604 \log \dfrac{dP}{dx} + 1.93$ (Cartesian and log-log)

1.12. The air flow through a porous medium is sometimes expressed as

$$u = A\left(\frac{dP}{dx}\right)^{B}$$ where u = average velocity, $\dfrac{dP}{dx}$ is the pressure gradient, and A

and B are constants. For snap beans, $A = 1.31$ and $B = 0.604$ when u is in m/min

and $\dfrac{dP}{dx}$ is in Pa/m.

    a. What is the velocity at a pressure gradient of 100 Pa/m?

    b. What pressure gradient is present for a velocity of 30 m/min?

    c. Convert the equation to a linear form.

1.13. Graph the equation given in Problem 1.12 using A and B values for snap beans. Follow the guidelines provided in this chapter.

1.14. Repeat problem 1.13, but graph the equation in the linear form noted for part c of problem 1.12.

1.15. A chocolate syrup is to be mixed with water and a semi-syrup to produce a sweeter syrup with less chocolate. The components and the finished syrup ingredients are as shown in the table below.

Component	% Chocolate	% Sugar	% Water	Kg in product
Choc. syrup (C)	10	10	80	_____
Semi-syrup (S)	0	60	40	_____
Water (W)	0	0	100	_____
Desired syrup	5	20	75	100

    a. How much of each component is needed to produce 100 kg of the syrup?

    b. Can these ingredients be used to produce a syrup that is 10% chocolate, 20% sugar and 70% water?

1.16. Repeat Example 1.2 with a "dry" leather output of 26.7 kg/h with a moisture content of 0.333 kg H_2O/kg dry leather. All other parameters are unchanged.

1.17. Repeat Example 1.2 for drying air entering with a moisture content of 0.015 kg H_2O/kg DA. All other parameters are unchanged.

Physical Properties of Food Materials

2

Abstract. *This chapter reviews selected physical properties of food and biological materials. The primary emphasis is upon mechanical and thermal properties, although electromagnetic properties are briefly reviewed.*

Keywords. *Electrical properties, equilibrium moisture content, mechanical properties, non-Newtonian fluids, optical properties, permeability, physical characteristics, thermal properties, viscosity, water activity.*

2.1 Introduction

Lord Kelvin once said, "When you can measure what you are speaking about, and can express it in numbers, you know something about it; and when you cannot measure it, when you cannot express it in numbers, your knowledge is of a meager and unsatisfactory kind; it may be the beginning of knowledge, but you have scarcely in your thoughts advanced to the stage of a science." This chapter covers the basic physical characteristics of foods and food products. Since the physical characteristics of plant and animal food materials affect how they are to be processed, handled, stored, and consumed, knowledge of these characteristics are important to engineers, processors and food scientists, plant and animal breeders, and other scientists. The following provides a list of various properties that will be discussed either in this or following chapters:

Physical Characteristics

1. Shape	5. Surface area	9. Appearance
2. Size	6. Density	10. Drag coefficient
3. Weight	7. Porosity	11. Center of gravity
4. Volume	8. Color	

Mechanical Properties

1. Hardness	7. Sliding coefficient of friction	11. Plasticity
2. Compressive strength	8. Static coefficient of friction	12. Bending strength
3. Tensile strength	9. Coefficient of expansion	13. Aerodynamic
4. Impact resistance	a. moisture	properties
5. Shear resistance	b. thermal	14. Hydrodynamic
6. Compressibility	10. Elasticity	properties

Thermal Properties

1. Specific heat	4. Thermal conductivity	7. Emmisivity
2. Thermal capacity	5. Surface conductance	8. Transmissivity
3. Thermal diffusivity	6. Absorptivity	

Electrical Properties
1. Conductance
2. Resistance
3. Capacitance

4. Dielectric properties
5. Reaction to electromagnetic radiation
6. Conductivity—ability of seeds to hold a surface charge

Optical Properties
1. Light transmittance
2. Light reflectance

3. Light absorptance
4. Color

5. Contrast
6. Intensity

2.2 Physical Properties Applications

The study of food engineering focuses on the analysis of equipment and systems used to process food on a commercial production scale. Engineering of systems for food materials can be more thorough if there is an understanding of the changes that occur in food as it is processed by the system. Raw food materials are biological in nature and as such have certain unique characteristics which distinguish them from other manufactured products. Because food materials are mainly of biological origin they have (a) irregular shapes commonly found in naturally occurring raw materials; (b) properties with a non-normal frequency distribution; (c) heterogeneous composition; (d) composition that varies with variety, growing conditions, maturity and other factors; and they are (e) affected by chemical changes, moisture, respiration, and enzymatic activity. Dealing with materials that have these unique characteristics requires additional consideration, mostly indirectly, in that there are additional sources or causes of variation. People unfamiliar with this natural variability of biological materials may overlook these factors or be frustrated by lack of control over the input parameters. The characteristics of a food material that are independent of the observer, measurable, can be quantified, and define the state of the material (but not how it attained that state) are considered as its physical properties. **Physical properties** describe the unique, characteristic way a food material responds to physical treatments involving mechanical, thermal, electrical, optical, sonic, and electromagnetic processes. A better understanding of the way food materials respond to physical and chemical treatments allows for optimum design of food equipment and processes to insure food quality and safety. Knowledge of a food's physical properties is necessary for:

- defining and quantifying a description of the food material,
- providing basic data for food engineering and unit operations, and
- predicting behavior of new food materials.

It is common for the physical properties of a food to change during processing operations. Not recognizing these changes can lead to potential processing failures. Physical properties are an important aspect of food quality and relate to food safety. They are the basis for instruments and sensors. A few examples of select physical properties of foods are presented in this unit.

2.3 Physical Characteristics

Physical characteristics of raw, unprocessed, as well as processed food materials include particle size and shape, particle and bulk density, porosity, and surface area. The size and shape of a raw food material can vary widely. The variation in shape of a product may require additional parameters to define its size. The size of spherical particles like peas or cantaloupes is easily defined by a single characteristic such as its diameter. The size of non-spherical objects like wheat kernels, bananas, pears, or potatoes may be described by multiple length measurements. The longest diameter (major) and shortest diameter (minor) will adequately describe the size of an ellipsoidal object such as grain kernel or potato. The two dimensions are usually measured perpendicular to one another. The size of pear-shaped objects such as pears, carrots, or beets can be expressed by diameter or circumference of the largest part and an overall length in the direction of the stem. The size of irregular-shaped materials like bananas, okra, or squash requires more extensive considerations.

Particle size is used in sieve separation of foreign materials or grading (i.e., grouping into size categories). Particle size is particularly important in grinding operations to determine the condition of the final product and determines the required power to reduce the particle's size. Small irregular-shaped objects can be sized with sieves by expressing particle size as the smallest sieve opening through which the particle passes. The size of larger objects may be expressed only in terms of its largest diameter or circumference. The size of a banana might be given only in overall length. Precise methods incorporating optical, light, or lasers in machine vision systems exist to define shape and size of irregular-shape objects. These systems are costly; their use is warranted in applications of high value materials more commonly found in highly processed, final products rather than raw, unprocessed materials.

Ultimate use will dictate which physical characteristic properly represents size. Size of a carrot may be expressed only in length or in diameter of its large end. Size may be indicated by weight since it is so easily determined by simply placing on a scale. Thus, the physical property *size* is actually related or correlated to the property *weight*. In practice, there is often a compromise between ease or cost of measurement and usefulness or value of that property in the market channel.

Shape affects the grade given to fresh fruit. To make the highest grade a fruit or vegetable must have the commonly recognized expected shape of that particular fruit/vegetable. Misshapen fruit and vegetables will be down-graded and may sell at a lower price in high volume markets.

The shape of an irregular object can be described by terms such as the following:

Shape	Description
Round	Approaching spheroid
Oblate	Flattened at the stem end and apex
Oblong	Vertical diameter greater than the horizontal diameter
Conic	Tapered toward the apex
Ovate	Egg-shaped and broad at the stem end
Oblate	Inverted oblate
Lopsided	Axis connecting stem and apex slanted
Elliptical	Approaching ellipsoid

Truncate	Having both ends squared or flattened
Unequal	One half larger than the other
Ribbed	In cross section, sides are more or less angular
Regular	Horizontal section approaches a circle
Irregular	Horizontal cross section departs materially from a circle

Various methods are used to measure or characterize the shape and size characteristics of foods and food products. In several cases, actual measurements are made to estimate the major dimensions and cross sections of the product. Tracings or projections are made to compare the shapes to listed standards. Mohsenin (1970) illustrates the use of standard charts in the describing and defining the shape of a product (Figure 2.01).

Various formulas and methods have been devised to estimate cross sections and other characteristics of the materials.

Roundness, as defined by Mohsenin (1970), "is a measure of the sharpness of the corners of the solid." Curray (1951) and Mohsenin (1970) provided the following equations for estimating roundness under different conditions of geometry and application:

$$Roundness = \frac{A_p}{A_c} \qquad (2.01)$$

where: A_p = largest projected area of object in natural rest position
A_c = area of smallest circumscribing circle

$$Roundness = \frac{\Sigma r}{NR} \qquad (2.02)$$

where: r = radius of curvature as defined in figure 2.01
R = radius of maximum inscribed circle
N = total number of corners summed in numerator

$$Roundness \ ratio = \frac{r}{R} \qquad (2.03)$$

where R in this case is the mean radius of the object and r is the radius of curvature of the sharpest corner. It should be noted that, in the last definition (2.03), the use of the radius of curvature of a single corner determines the roundness or flatness of an object. Roundness values will differ for each of the above methods. Thus, the method for roundness determination should always be noted.

Sphericity expresses the characteristic shape of a solid object relative to that of a sphere of the same volume (Mohsenin, 1970). Curray (1951) suggested the following equation for estimating the sphericity of an object:

$$Sphericity = \frac{D_i}{D_c} \qquad (2.04)$$

where: D_i = diameter of largest inscribed circle
D_c = diameter of smallest circumscribed circle

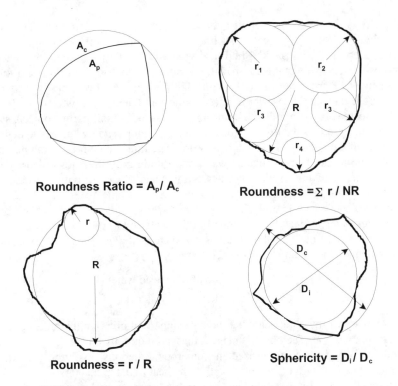

Roundness Ratio = A_p / A_c

Roundness = $\Sigma\, r\, /\, NR$

Roundness = $r\, /\, R$

Sphericity = D_i / D_c

Figure 2.01. Roundness and sphericity as defined by geologists to describe shape of grains and pebbles (Curray, 1951, and Mohsenin, 1970).

Density (ρ) of a material is the amount of that material occupying a certain space and is expressed in units of mass per unit volume. Materials consisting of particles or grains with interstitial air spaces have different values of particle density and bulk density. Materials without internal air spaces, such as fluids and solids, have equal particle and bulk density. **Particle density** is the mass divided by the volume of the particle alone. **Bulk density** is the mass of a group of individual particles divided by the space occupied by the entire mass, including the air space. Density of food materials is useful in mathematical conversion of mass to volume. The grain industry determines the amount of agricultural grains by converting the weight to volume (bushels). Even though grain marketing is done in terms of bushels, grain weight, not actual bushels, is the property measured. The density of processed products dictate the characteristics of its container or package. Product density influences the amount and strength of packaging material. Breakfast cereal boxes contain a required weight of cereal. More weight of material can be placed into a box if the cereal density is greater. Also, food density influences its texture or mouth feel. Processing can affect product density by introducing more air, such as is done in the manufacture of butter or ice cream. In products like whipped cream, which are primarily air, control of density is essential.

Porosity is the percentage of air between the particles compared to a unit volume of particles. Porosity allows gases, such as air, and liquids to flow through a mass of particles referred to as a **packed bed** in drying and distillation operations. Beds with low porosity (low percentage air space) are more resistant to fluid flow and thus are more difficult to dry, heat, or cool. With high porosity, air flows easily through the bed, drying is fast, and the power required by fans and pumps is low.

A frequently used method of measuring the **volume** of non-porous objects such as vegetables and fruits is the use of platform scales or a top loading balance to determine the volume of a displaced liquid such as water. The liquid volume is computed by determining the mass of the displaced water and dividing by the known density of the water. The mass of the displaced water is the scale's reading with the object submerged minus the mass of the container and water. For objects that float, it is necessary to force the object entirely into the water with a thin stiff rod. If the object is heavier than water, it must be suspended in the water by a rod or other support to insure that the added mass of the object is not measured. The following expression is used to calculate the volume of displaced water:

$$\text{Volume}\,(\text{m}^3) = \frac{\text{mass of displaced water (kg)}}{\text{density of water (kg/m}^3)} \tag{2.05}$$

The **density** of the object can then be determined by dividing the object's mass by the measured volume. The object's mass is measured directly on the scale. The density of foods and food products is used in numerous situations involving heat transfer. Several applications will be demonstrated in the heat transfer chapters.

The **specific gravity** is defined as the ratio of the mass of that product to the mass of an equal volume of water at 4°C, the temperature at which water density is greatest. A reference temperature other than 4°C may be used if that temperature is explicitly specified with the specific gravity value. Specific gravity may be calculated from the following expression:

$$\text{Specific gravity} = \frac{\text{mass in air} \times \text{specific gravity of water}}{\text{mass of displaced water}} \tag{2.06}$$

Another important physical characteristic, **surface area**, is related to size but also depends on particle shape. Surface area is difficult to measure for irregular-shaped objects and thus is often determined indirectly or computed by assuming a specific shape. Several methods have been developed to measure the surface area of items. Surface area is most easily measured for items that very closely resemble common geometric shapes. A frequently used method is the projection method, which uses photographs or projected images to obtain an outline of the object. Once the object outline is obtained, segments can be defined by drawing parallel lines and calculating the area enclosed in each segment. Another method involves tracing an object. The area enclosed in the tracing may be determined by the use of a planimeter, development of segments as defined above, or other methods.

Surface area is useful in estimating the amount of wax applied to fruit, amount of packaging film to wrap fruit, and rate of heating, cooling, freezing, and drying. For granular materials, porosity is closely related to surface area. Particle surface area is important in heating and cooling operations since heat transfer is proportional to surface area.

The physical characteristics of food materials are readily recognized and commonly utilized throughout the marketing channel. Variation in these properties for raw food materials requires the use of statistical measures such as the average or minimum percentage of a particular size. This variation may be affected by seasonal growing conditions.

2.4 Surface Activity

Many foods are a mixture of multi-phase materials (i.e., a mix of solid, liquid, and gas). The boundary between these phases, the interface, plays a significant role in the properties of the food. Examples of a **foam**, a gas in a liquid, are whipped creams and toppings. An **emulsion**, a liquid in a liquid, example is mayonnaise. A **solid foam** example is the meringue on pies. Both oil and water, which do not readily mix, exist in many foods. Milk and cream (oil-in-water) and butter and margarine (water-in-oil) are examples of emulsions. Uniform distribution of oil and water throughout a food material incorporates the use of surface properties. Surface properties are important in unit operations such as spray drying, aeration, hydrogenation, and fermentation. A knowledge of surface properties is also important in cleaning operations. Emulsifying agents and detergents clean because they reduce the surface tension to more readily remove solids (dirt). These liquids wet solid surfaces and dissolve water-soluble and fat-soluble components. Detergents reduce surface tension to break apart large particles and promote spreading over the surface. Detergents allow mechanical force such as sprays or bulk turbulent flow in cleaned-in-place systems to be more effective.

The forces acting on the surface of a liquid tending to minimize its area are known as **surface tension**. The surface tension of water is twice as high as for cooking oils. Thus, water tends to form spherical droplets on clean surfaces. Materials when mixed with water to reduce its surface tension are referred to as surface active, i.e., surfactants. The addition of low concentrations of surfactants decreases the surface tension of water significantly. Wetability and solubility of powders affect their mixing with liquids. The liquid's surface properties control the rate of wetting and dissolution of the powder's particles. Wetting properties of milk powder during spray drying are affected by particle size, surface tension, presence of wetting agents, and the form and location of fat molecules. Although data on the surface properties of food materials are not quantified as extensively as other properties, it is no less important; and empirical, qualitative data are often used as the only information available.

2.5 Moisture in Foods

Foods are composed of nothing in greater amount than water. Fresh fruit, vegetables, and milk contain over 80% water. The amount of water in a food is denoted by its **moisture content**. A food's storability is directly related to moisture content, along with temperature and oxygen availability. High amounts of available moisture lead to mold growth and microbial activity. Fruit must be dried below 30% and agricultural grains below 12% for good long-term storage.

Moisture is present in foods in either solid form (ice), liquid (water), or vapor (humidity in air). The properties of water in each of these forms are significantly different. For example, the dielectric constant of water is 25 times higher than that of ice. Microwave heating is highly affected by a material's dielectric constant. Thus, heating of a frozen food in a microwave takes place significantly more slowly than heating of the same unfrozen food. The change in form or phase of water is accompanied by an exchange in energy. Thus, externally produced thermal energy is required to add sufficient heat to change the form from solid to liquid or liquid to vapor. Similarly, as water turns into ice heat energy is released by the food. These phase changes affect the other food constituents and properties such as density and thermal conductivity. Moisture affects many other physical properties. Since the physical properties of water differ from the other constituents and since water is a major constituent of food, it therefore has a major influence on a food's properties. Moisture content will be considered in more detail in the chapter on drying and dehydration.

Foods, being biological materials, have an affinity for moisture. This interaction of food with water is known as its hygroscopic nature. The moisture content of a hygroscopic material such as food is in direct relation to the humidity of the surrounding air. A hygroscopic material left sufficiently long will eventually reach a unique moisture content known as the **equilibrium moisture content** (*EMC*) for that relative humidity (*rh*) and temperature condition. The *rh-EMC* relationship is non-linear; it is a sigmoid shaped curve. At air relative humidities below 10% and above 90% there is a large change in *EMC* for small relative humidity changes. Each biological material has a unique and different *rh-EMC* relationship. The *EMC* is important in predicting the drying potential of air or storage potential of grain. Materials with moisture contents below their *EMC* will tend to increase in moisture if there is adequate air flow. Materials with moisture contents above their *EMC* will tend to decrease in moisture. The term *EMC* is commonly used in dealing with lower moisture materials, i.e., below 30%, such as agricultural grains and seeds. Agricultural grains, seeds, and nuts need to be kept at low moisture, below 12%, if they are to be stored for long periods in warm temperatures. More details on *EMC* will be given in the drying and dehydration chapter (Chapter 10).

For higher moisture materials such as most food products, the commonly used moisture related property is **water activity** (commonly identified by the symbol a_w), which is the relative humidity of the surrounding air in equilibrium with the moisture in the product. Water activity is a term indicating the amount of free water in a biological material. The free water is the moisture available for microbial and enzymatic activity and for chemical reaction. With water activity above 0.8 there is sufficient water to promote mold growth (Figure 2.02) and water activity above 0.9 allows bacterial growth. Susceptibility to spoilage can be controlled by lowering water activity. Thus, water activity influences a food's storability.

Water activity indicates a product's tendency to dehydrate. Figure 2.03 shows the typical sigmoid shape relationship between water activity and equilibrium moisture content. The curve on the graph shows the lowest moisture content a product can be dried to for a given water activity and temperature. Raising the temperature reduces the equilibrium moisture content, thus allowing for more drying.

The moisture in food has a direct influence on its weight, and weight of material is related to its value in dollars. If the weight of fruit in a packing house decreases by 5% due to moisture lost to the air, the owner has lost 5% of his product, which is 5% of gross income. Moisture in fruit has significant monetary value. Moisture in any food has the same value as the going unit price of the food. For example, if apples are selling for $2.00 per kg and part of the weight is lost in storage due to low humidity air, the lost water has the value of $2.00 per kg! For every 1,000 kg of $2.00/kg product shipped having 5% moisture loss, the owner will be paid $100 less than the cost of the product that was placed into storage. Minimizing weight loss is important in maintaining amount of product as well as its quality.

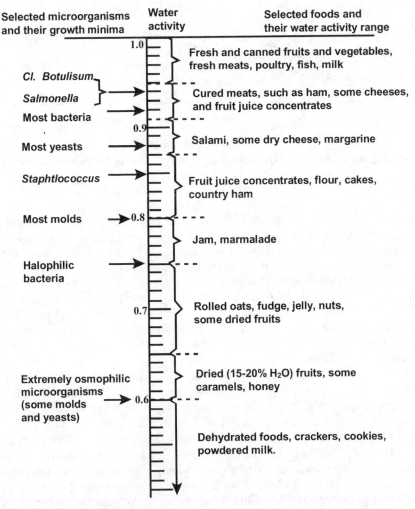

Figure 2.02. Water activities required for growth of organisms.
(Based upon Labuza, 1984, and Beuchat, 1981.)

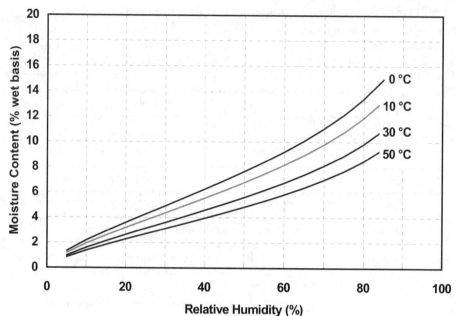

Figure 2.03. Equilibrium moisture content curves for peanut kernels.

Moisture has a tendency to move from a location of higher concentration to a region of lower concentration. More specifically, moisture in the air at a high vapor pressure will go towards a location of lower vapor pressure. This movement of moisture is a natural phenomenon, commonly occurring in foods, and has numerous ramifications. Fruit left open to room air will quickly dry, lose moisture, and eventually become inedible. Preventing or restricting the movement of moisture is a major objective of the wrapping materials business. Foods are wrapped with plastics to prevent the exchange of moisture. Foods are covered with plastic wraps before being heated in the oven to retain moisture in the food. The availability and variety of packaging materials has grown significantly since the 1980's. Materials, primarily plastics, have been developed with unique moisture and gas transmitting properties to meet the defined food requirements (Fellows, 1988).

Permeability (P) is defined as $P = [(\text{volume of gas or vapor}) \times (\text{material thickness})]/[(\text{area}) \times (\text{time}) \times (\text{pressure difference across the materials})]$. Wrapping materials have permeability properties unique for each gas or vapor as shown in Table 2.01. Cellophane has an oxygen permeability of 0.0021×10^{10} compared to 2.88×10^{10} cm^3 cm cm^{-2} s^{-1} cm Hg^{-1} for 0.914 gm/cm^3 density polyethylene, while water permeabilities are 1900×10^{10} and 90×10^{10}, respectively. That is, cellophane allows water through faster and oxygen slower than polyethylene. Saran® wrap is 3800 times less permeable to water vapor than cellophane. Plastics are now available to minimize the loss of moisture from fresh fruit while allowing gases like oxygen and carbon dioxide to pass through without accumulating to high levels inside the bag. Without the provision for

Table 2.01. Permeability coefficients and diffusion constants of polymers.[a]

Polymer	Permeant	T (°C)	$P \times 10^{10}$	$D \times 10^6$
Poly(ethylene) (density 0.914)	O_2	25	2.88	0.46
	CO_2	25	12.6	0.37
	N_2	25	0.969	0.32
	H_2O	25	90	
Poly(ethylene) (density 0.964)	O_2	25	0.403	0.17
	CO_2	25	1.69	0.116
	CO	25	0.193	0.096
	N_2	25	0.143	0.093
	H_2O	25	12	
Poly(propylene)	H_2	20	41	2.12
	N_2	30	0.44	
	O_2	30	2.3	
	CO_2	30	9.2	
	H_2O	25	51	
Cellulose acetate	N_2	30	0.28	
	O_2	30	0.78	
	CO_2	30	22.7	
	H_2O	25	5500	
Cellulose (Cellophane)	N_2	25	0.003	
	O_2	25	0.002	
	CO_2	25	0.005	
	H_2O	25	1900	
Poly(vinyl acetate)	O_2	30	0.5	0.055
Poly(vinyl alcohol)	H_2	25	0.009	
	N_2	14[b]	<0.001	
	N_2	14	0.33	0.045
	O_2	25	0.009	
	CO_2	25	0.012	
		23[c]	0.001	
		23[d]	11.9	0.0476
	ethylene oxide	0	0.002	
Poly(vinyl chloride)	H_2	25	1.7	0.5
	N_2	25	0.0118	0.004
	O_2	25	0.0453	0.0118
	CO_2	25	0.157	0.003
	H_2O	25	275	0.0238
Poly(vinylidene chloride) (Saran)	N_2	30	0.00094	
	O_2	30	0.0053	
	CO_2	30	0.03	
	H_2O	25	0.50	

Source: Yasuda and Stannett (1989).
[a] Units used are as follows: P in [cm^3 (STP) cm cm^{-2} s^{-1} (cm Hg)$^{-1}$] and D in [cm^2 s^{-1}]
[b] Relative humidity 0%   [c] Relative humidity 90%   [d] Relative humidity 94%

gaseous exchange, the respiring fresh fruit would eventually produce unacceptable levels of oxygen or carbon dioxide in the surrounding environment. The quality of fresh fruit, and even cut fruit, can now be maintained in refrigerated, modified atmosphere packages for 2-5 times longer than unwrapped products. Oranges and apples have long had wax applied to reduce the loss of moisture and thereby lengthen storage life. The latest moisture reducing materials include newly developed edible films, coatings which reduce moisture loss and are edible, thus eliminating the need for disposal. Edible films are being developed to uniquely match the product's respiration rate to its market requirements.

Moisture in the air affects the food's physical properties and determines the potential for the air to be used in drying operations. Humid air properties are known as the psychometric properties of the air. Psychrometric properties are important in food storage, drying, and adsorption as well as human comfort. Moisture properties are of great economic importance to the food industry. Air with low relative humidity has a greater tendency to withdraw moisture from food materials. Foods in high humidity air will have less tendency to lose moisture to the air. Extremely high humidity, however, can lead to condensation and mold growth. Fruits are solar dried in areas with abundant sunshine and low humidity. At higher humidities, drying occurs at a slower rate. Crop and food dryer design and operation must account for input air temperature and humidity. Operating efficiency, time, and cost depend on the air's moisture and energy content. Air psychometrics will be explained further in the chapter on psychrometrics.

Human comfort is affected primarily by the air temperature but humidity is also a factor. Relative humidities of 30% to 50% are ideal for workers while humidities over 70% add to the discomfort at temperatures above 30°C. To improve comfort in hot weather, air can be cooled with refrigerated air or by evaporative cooling, a low-cost process that lowers temperature but raises humidity.

2.6 Solid-Fluid Behavior

2.6.1 Introduction

Materials exist in either a solid, liquid, or gaseous state. An additional word, *fluid*, is used to include both gases and liquids, although most fluids involved in food processing are liquids. Food materials, as we know them, commonly exist as some intermediate state, mixture, or composite with gas contained within either the solid or fluid. The usual approach taken by food scientists is to consider foods as one of the two extremes, either solid or liquid, and modify previously developed theories to explain the behavior of one of these two ideal-state materials. Solid-fluid behavior is utilized in food engineering in some of the following:

- design of pumps, mixers, extruders, and piping systems,
- design of instruments and sensors for use in process control,
- determining force to cut or shear, or energy to mill or grind,
- determining strength to withstand puncture, cracking, or failure forces,
- defining tenderness of meat products for quality control, and
- correlating texture measurement with sensory information.

Liquids are defined as materials that flow to take the shape of the container. They commonly are pumped or flow due to gravity. The physical property describing the flowability of a liquid is its viscosity. Ideal fluid flow behavior is Newtonian, i.e., shear stress is proportional to shear rate. "Thicker" fluids have higher viscosity. As viscosity is increased there is a tendency for the flow behavior to become less ideal as it is affected by other parameters. This is described as non-Newtonian flow where shear stress changes with shear rate according to some non-linear relationship. Fluid-like behavior is most often utilized during manufacturing of continuous flow processing. Thus plant engineers and processing operations personnel use fluid properties of foods, usually in bulk or large volumes. Fluid flow characteristics are further discussed in the next section.

Solid-like materials tend to maintain their shape with relatively minor changes so they are recognized as such at later times and after undergoing external loads or stresses. The stress-strain relationship of ideal solids is represented by elasticity theory and described by its elastic modulus. The theory has been extensively developed to explain elastic behavior of non-biological materials, which food engineers can use as a starting point in describing food response to mechanical loads. Non-elastic behavior of solids is exhibited by non-linear stress vs. strain associated with large deformations or variations with time. Solid-like material considerations are often more important to quality control personnel in food plants and then to the consumer. They usually are concerned with individual, sometimes small, pieces of food. Solid-like behavior of foods will be considered further in the texture chapter. **Rheology** is the study of the deformation and flow of materials, either fluid- or solid-like. Rheology is interrelated to other properties such as viscosity, density, porosity, and moisture content. Rheological and these other physical properties are used to quantify texture of foods.

2.6.2 Newtonian and Non-Newtonian Fluids

Solids and fluids differ greatly in their reaction to shearing. (Since the following paragraphs apply to both liquids and gases, the term *fluid* is used here.) Shearing occurs when a material is held between two parallel plates, one of which is moving with respect to the other as shown in Figure 2.04. Under this condition, a solid will deform only a certain amount depending upon the material. If this amount is exceeded, the solid will permanently deform and may even break. If this limit is not exceeded, the solid will return to its original condition when the shearing force is removed—just as a rubber band contracts upon release from stretching.

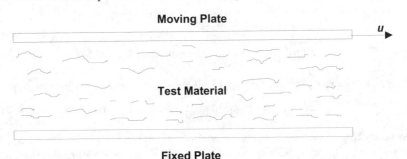

Moving Plate

u

Test Material

Fixed Plate

Figure 2.04. Example of shearing.

In contrast to the solid, a fluid deforms continuously with time when exposed to shear. The exact action of fluids under deformation is somewhat complicated; however, certain flow models have been established that describe the actions of the fluid sufficiently for most applications. Before discussing models of interest to us, it is desirable to review certain additional definitions:

Specific weight (w)—Weight of material occupying a unit volume. $w = \rho g$ where g is the gravitation acceleration. Under standard conditions, ρ and w may have the same *numerical* value but different units, i.e., w has units of weight (force) per unit volume (lb_f/ft^3).

Viscosity (μ)—A measure of the resistance of adjacent fluid layers to shearing motion. It has units of $\dfrac{\text{force} \times \text{time}}{\text{length}^2}$ with common units being $\dfrac{N\ s}{m^2}, \dfrac{dyne}{cm^2}$, and $\dfrac{lb_f\ s}{ft^2}$. Viscosities of both liquids and gases vary significantly with temperature.

Kinematic viscosity $\left(\nu = \dfrac{\mu}{\rho} \right)$—The form of viscosity commonly used in fluid flow because of the frequent occurrence of the ratio $\dfrac{\mu}{\rho}$. It commonly has units of $\dfrac{cm^2}{s}$ (stoke), $\dfrac{m^2}{s}$, or $\dfrac{ft^2}{s}$.

Shear rate $\left(\dfrac{du}{dy} \right)$—Velocity gradient normal to the flow direction, i.e., $\dfrac{cm/s}{cm} = -\dfrac{}{s}$ or $\dfrac{ft/s}{ft} = -\dfrac{}{s}$. See Figure 2.05.

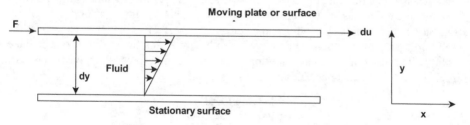

Figure 2.05. Shear rate for a viscous fluid.

Shear stress (τ)—Friction force per unit area on the surfaces restraining the fluid, i.e., $\dfrac{dynes}{cm^2}, \dfrac{lb_f}{ft^2}$, or $\dfrac{N}{m^2}$. For flow through a pipe (or other closed channel), the shear stress is directly related to the pressure gradient in the pipe. The shearing stress on the pipe walls tends to resist flow and must exactly balance the pressure drop in the pipe which tends to cause flow, thus keeping the forces inside the pipe equalized.

   Ideal fluid—A fluid model that assumes no viscosity for a fluid and thus no friction effects. It is used widely in aerodynamics for the study of flow over certain body shapes (i.e., aircraft) but it is not suitable for most pipe flow calculations.

   Newtonian fluid—Fluids for which the viscosity is not affected by changes in velocity. Water, air, and many other commonly used fluids are Newtonian under almost all conditions.

   Non-Newtonian fluids—Fluids for which the viscosity is not constant but changes with velocity and/or pressure gradient. Many food products fall into this category (i.e., applesauce, banana puree, and other materials that contain suspended solids in a liquid).

   To examine the relationship between shearing stress (τ), shear rate $\left(\dfrac{du}{dy}\right)$, and viscosity ($\mu$), we will make use of Figure 2.06. (Remember that you can read shear rate as velocity gradient and shearing stress as friction force per unit area.)

   In equation form, viscosity is defined by the equation:

$$\tau = \mu\left(\frac{du}{dy}\right) \tag{2.07}$$

for laminar flow in one direction only. Thus:

$$\mu = \frac{\tau}{\dfrac{du}{dy}} \tag{2.08}$$

and the viscosity of any fluid under given conditions of τ and $\left(\dfrac{du}{dy}\right)$ is represented by the slope of a curve on a plot such as Figure 2.06. Thus, a Newtonian fluid produces a straight line going through the origin. Non-Newtonian fluids produce a curved line, or do not go through the origin, or both. It has been found that many of these fluids, including some food products, can be represented by a model where the shear stress is described as:

$$\tau = b\left(\frac{du}{dy}\right)^{n} + c \tag{2.09}$$

   This relationship has been widely used in the study of non-Newtonian fluids. Equation 2.09 is called the "power law" equation. Materials which can be described by this equation are called power law fluids. Several food materials obey the power law equation quite well. Some of these are given in Table 2.02.

Example 2.1

A simple method of measuring viscosity is to record the time required for a given amount of fluid to flow through a tube of a given size. Tube systems designed for this purpose are called viscometers. If a food grade oil requires 225 seconds to flow through a viscometer having a constant of 0.035 cSt/s, determine the kinematic (v) and dynamic (μ) viscosities of the fluid. (The fluid has a density of 875 kg/m³.)

Solution:

Solve first for the kinematic viscosity, v, converting from centistokes to m²/s.

$$v = \left(0.035\,\frac{\text{cSt}}{\text{s}}\right) \times (225\,\text{s}) = (7.875\,\text{cSt}) = (0.07875\,\text{St}) \times \frac{1\frac{\text{m}^2}{\text{s}}}{10^4\,\text{St}} = \left(7.875 \times 10^{-6}\,\frac{\text{m}^2}{\text{s}}\right)$$

Then solve for $\mu = \rho v$.

$$\mu = \rho v = \frac{875\,\frac{\text{kg}}{\text{m}^3} \times 7.875 \times 10^{-6}\,\frac{\text{m}^2}{\text{s}}}{1\frac{\text{kg m}}{\text{N s}^2}} = 6.891 \times 10^{-3}\,\frac{\text{N s}}{\text{m}^2} \qquad \textbf{ANSWER}$$

Table 2.02. Flow constants for various materials.[a]

Material	Temperature (°C)	$b, \left(\frac{N}{m^2}\right)s^n$	n	$c, \left(\frac{N}{m^2}\right)$
Applesauce A	24	0.500	0.645	0
Applesauce B	24	0.660	0.408	0
Banana puree A	24	6.50	0.458	0
Banana puree B	24	10.7	0.333	0
Banana puree C	22	107.3	0.283	0
Honey A	24	5.60	1.00	0
Honey B	24	6.18	1.00	0
Minced fish paste	3 - 6	8.55	0.91	1600
Olive Oil	10	0.138	1.00	0
	70	0.0124	1.00	0
Orange juice	0	1.80	0.68	0.7
Tomato paste		15.0	0.475	36.1

[a] Based on data from Charm (1971) and Steffe (1992).

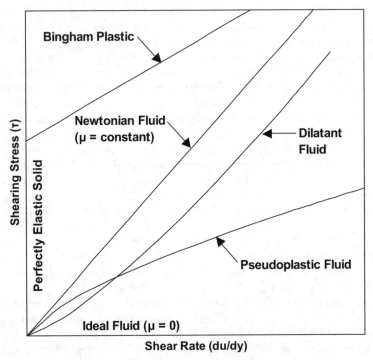

Figure 2.06. Flow characteristics of certain fluids.

2.7 Thermal Properties

Food materials often experience the movement of heat around and through them in various forms and degrees during growth, harvest, handling, processing, transport, storage, and preparation for consumption. Only a few foods such as fresh fruit and some vegetables go from field to the table without any thermal processing. Most foods are thermally processed to extend their shelf life and maintain high quality. Foods are exposed to heat transfer numerous times during heating, cooling, freezing, frying, and/or baking. Thermal operations are also used to insure safe food products for extended periods. A classic example is the pasteurization of milk, a heating process that eliminates bacteria. Pasteurization, followed by proper cooling, provides a safe milk product for weeks. Canned foods, which are good for years, are sterilized with heat processes. Juice, having been heated and aseptically packaged in boxes, is shelf stable without refrigeration for months.

Heat transfer occurs by conduction, convection, and radiation. These mechanisms can occur individually or simultaneously. In food processing, heat transfer is usually a combination of conduction and convection. Conduction is principally involved during heat transfer within solid-like materials, i.e., solids or static liquids. Convection is the transfer between solids (walls of pipes, vats, rooms) and fluids (food materials). In other cases, the food may be the solid and the fluid might be air or water. Radiant heat transfer is less frequently used but is becoming more common in microwave and infra-red heating. Having an understanding of the mechanisms of heat transfer allows the food engineer to better design equipment and processes.

The movement of heat to and through a food material depends primarily on the existence of a temperature difference and on physical characteristics such as size, shape, density, and thermal properties. The thermal properties are unique for each food. Each mechanism of heat transfer has an associated thermal property. **Specific heat** (c_p) or heat capacity is the heat required to increase the temperature of one unit of mass by one degree. The subscript (p) is included because specific heat of solids and liquids is determined at constant pressure. In steady state conduction through a solid-like material the important thermal property is **thermal conductivity** (k). Thermal conductivity is a measure of the ease with which heat flows through a material. Heat is conducted quickly through a metal like copper, hence its thermal conductivity value is high. Heat flows more slowly through materials like wood or fiberglass insulation; their thermal conductivity is low. The thermal conductivity of most food materials is in a relatively narrow range between 0.2 and 0.5 W/m K. Values of specific heat and thermal conductivity for many food materials are published in food engineering textbooks and handbooks (Mohsenin, 1980; Singh and Heldman, 1993; Heldman and Lund, 1992; ASHRAE, 1993; Rao and Rizvi, 1995).

Thermal properties are strongly influenced by a material's water content and to a lesser degree by temperature and pressure. Lacking measured data, thermal properties can be computed from equations using only the material's water content. Siebel's formulas, first proposed over 100 years ago (Siebel, 1892) have been widely used to estimate specific heat values above and below freezing. These formulas, converted to SI units, are:

$$c_P = 3.35X_W + 0.84 \quad \text{(above freezing)} \tag{2.10}$$

$$c_P = 1.26X_W + 0.84 \quad \text{(below freezing)} \tag{2.11}$$

where c_p is specific heat and X_w is the mass ratio of water. These equations assume constant specific heat values of 4.2 and 2.1 kJ/(kg K) for water and ice respectively. Remember, these are only approximations—especially for conditions below freezing, where c_p varies significantly with temperature.

Another relationship for a variety of products above freezing (see figure 2.07) is:

$$c_P = 1.67 + 2.51X_W \tag{2.12}$$

As shown in figure 2.07, this relationship provides an excellent correlation for a variety or products over a wide range of moisture contents.

While water has the greatest effect upon specific heat, other constituents, especially fat content, can also be a factor. Product composition for a variety of products is given in Agriculture Handbook No. 8 (Gebhardt et al., 1982; Haytowitz and Matthews, 1984). Selected values from these publications are shown in Appendix Tables A.6 and A.7. Using these values we can compute c_p using the equation (Heldman and Singh, 1981):

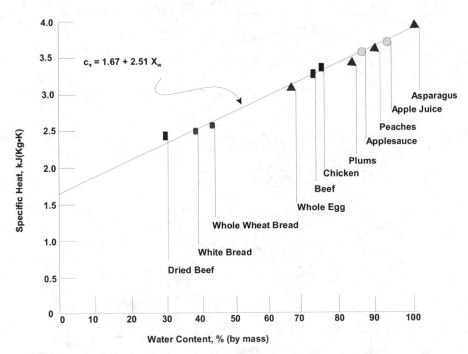

Figure 2.07. Specific heat of food products (at 0° to 20°C for meats, 4° to 32°C all others). Based upon ASHRAE data. (Courtesy of the American Society of Heating, Refrigeration and Air-Conditioning Engineers, 1989.)

$$c_P = 1.42X_c + 1.549X_p + 1.675X_f + 0.837X_a + 4.187X_W \qquad (2.13)$$

where X represents the mass fraction of each constituent: carbohydrate (c); protein (p); fat (f); ash (a); and water (w).

Many equations have been proposed for estimating thermal conductivities of food products. Only a few representative equations are shown here. For fruits and vegetables with water content greater than 60%, thermal conductivity can be computed by the equation (Sweat, 1974):

$$k = 0.148 + 0.493X_w \qquad (2.14)$$

where: k = thermal conductivity, W/(m K)
         X_w = mass fraction of water

For meat products of 60% to 80% water content, Sweat (1974) suggests:

$$k = 0.08 + 0.52X_w \qquad (2.15)$$

An alternate approach is to use an equation based upon the overall food composition to estimate thermal conductivity (Sweat, 1995):

$$k = 0.25X_c + 0.155X_p + 0.16X_f + 0.135X_a + 0.58X_W \qquad (2.16)$$

where the parameters of the equations are as defined for equation 2.13.

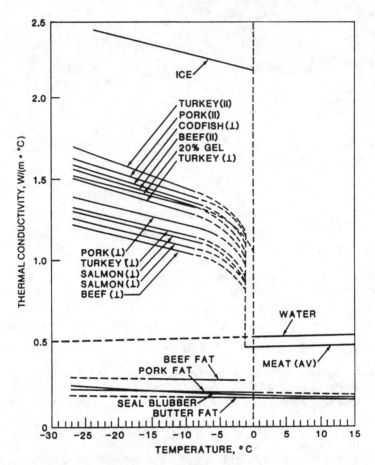

|| indicates heat flow parallel to fiber structure
⊥ indicates heat flow perpendicular to fiber structure

Figure 2.08. Effect of freezing upon thermal conductivity of selected products. (Courtesy of the American Society of Heating, Refrigerating and Air-Conditioning Engineers.)

These equations typically predict thermal conductivity to within 15% of measured values. Greater errors commonly occur at low moisture content. Figure 2.08 shows the variation of thermal conductivity with temperature above and below freezing for a variety of products. Note especially the change of thermal conductivity with temperature below 0°C. Only the high fat products, near the bottom of the chart, show little change below 0°C. For other products, thermal conductivity is at least doubled after freezing. A major contributor to this change is the increased thermal conductivity of ice over that of liquid water.

In transient heat transfer, where temperature varies with time and location, the relevant thermal property is thermal diffusivity. **Thermal diffusivity (α)** is a combination of three basic thermal properties, defined as thermal conductivity/(density × specific heat) or $\alpha = k/\rho c_p$. When these three basic properties are known, the diffusivity can be readily computed. Values of thermal diffusivity for food products range from 1×10^{-7} to 2×10^{-7} m^2/s. In the absence of experimental data, Riedel's equation (Riedel, 1969) can be used:

$$\alpha = 0.088 \times 10^{-6} + (\alpha_W - 0.088 \times 10^{-6})X_W \qquad (\alpha \text{ in } m^2/s) \qquad (2.17)$$

where α is thermal diffusivity, α_w is thermal diffusivity of water, and X_w is mass fraction water.

The use of equations to estimate thermal properties is valuable in the absence if experimental data. Rahman (1995) provides additional data and reference equation for thermal properties.

The thermal property associated with convective heat transfer is the **convective heat transfer coefficient** (h); it also goes by the names *surface heat transfer coefficient*, *local heat transfer coefficient*, or *film coefficient*. Unlike thermal conductivity, which depends only upon the particular material, the convective heat transfer coefficient depends upon fluid velocity, fluid properties, surface characteristics of the solid, and the geometry of each situation. Because the convective heat transfer coefficient is affected by these numerous factors, tables are not available to list values for all foods and situations. The convective heat transfer coefficient varies widely from about 3 W/m² °C for still air next to a flat surface to 100,000 W/m² °C for steam condensing on a metal pipe. Selecting a proper convective heat transfer coefficient to use in a particular application requires a certain degree of experience.

Heat transfer may involve either sensible energy or latent energy. If the temperature of an object is changed due to the heat transfer, then the heat transfer involves a transfer of sensible heat. The exchange of energy that occurs during a change in phase is called the latent heat. **Latent heat** involves heat exchange without a temperature change. The heat exchange during the phase change from liquid to solid is the **heat of fusion** (h_{sf}) or heat of solidification. Freezing water into ice or the opposite, thawing, is a common example of heat of fusion. The energy to change a liquid to vapor is the latent heat of vaporization. **Latent heat of vaporization** (h_{fg}) is useful in applications involving drying or evaporation where a liquid is vaporized for ease of separation from the mixture. Vaporizing water is commonly done to dry food materials. Drying is a fast method to remove moisture but is more energy intensive than mechanical methods. The heat of vaporization is about seven times more than the heat of fusion, which is five times more than raising the temperature (sensible heating) by 100°C.

Pure water freezes at 0°C, while food products freeze at lower temperatures. This lower freezing temperature phenomenon is called the **freezing point depression**. The freezing point is lowered due to the presence of solutes, solids, in the water. The change in the freezing point temperature is primarily dependent on the concentration or amount of solids. Knowing the exact freezing point temperature is useful in operations involving freezing and thawing. Similarly, the boiling point is elevated by the presence of solute in the liquid phase as found in most foods. The boiling point is useful in evaporation and drying operations. Examples would be the depression of the freezing point for high salt products i.e., processed meats, and the boiling point rise with sugar content in candy making.

Fruit and vegetable products are living organisms. To maintain their life processes, they must consume energy. They do this by a "combustion" process that "burns" sugar to produce CO_2 and heat. The heat produced by this process is commonly called the **heat of respiration** (Q_R). While small for any single item such as an apple or an ear of sweet corn, the heat of respiration can become a significant source of heat when large quantities of material are present. High respiration rates also cause rapid deterioration in food quality. Heats of respiration vary greatly among products and increase exponentially with temperature. Appendix Table A.8 lists heats of respiration of selected products at different temperatures. The following equations provide approximate values for heats of respiration for sweet corn with husk and apples. They are based upon data from Hardenburg et al. (1986).

$$\text{Log}_{10} \, Q_R = 0.0379 \, t + 1.028 \quad \text{(Sweet corn with husk)} \tag{2.18}$$

$$\text{Log}_{10} \, Q_R = 0.0456 \, t - 0.047 \quad \text{(Apples)} \tag{2.19}$$

where: Q_R = heat of respiration, kJ/kg day
t = temperature in °C

Heats of respiration are also affected by maturity and storage time. Information regarding changes with storage time for a limited number of products is provided by ASHRAE (1998). The data show that heats of respiration can change greatly with storage time. This change may be either an increase or a decrease, depending upon the product and the storage temperature. For example, broccoli stored at 5°C showed a decrease from 217 mW/kg to 98 mW/kg over eight days of storage. Plums, on the other hand, showed an increase from 12 to 27 mW/kg over 18 days of storage at the same temperature. Strawberries stored for 5 days showed a decrease in respiration at 0°C while respiration increased when strawberries were stored at 5°C for 5 days.

These are the primary thermal properties that, together with other physical properties, are involved during thermal processing of food materials. These thermal properties are not constant but vary with moisture content, temperature, and food constituents. Choosing the best value of the thermal property is important to predicting and describing thermal operations.

2.8 Electromagnetic Properties

Electromagnetic radiation encompasses a wide variety of phenomena as represented by the various regions along its broad spectrum (Figure 2.09). Utilizing selective parts of the electromagnetic spectrum is the basis for our modern electrical power distribution system and the many forms of transmitted communication including radar, radio, television, and satellite. Short wavelength energy is used for medical purposes including X-rays and radiography. The intermediate range includes the infrared, visible, and ultraviolet portions of the spectrum. Only a few specialized, narrow regions are utilized in food applications. These include light, infrared, and microwave frequencies.

   The interaction of visible light and matter is referred to as color. The color of an object is affected by the surrounding lighting intensity and wavelength. Thus, the color one perceives of an object can be influenced by changing the ambient light. The color of a food material is therefore not only dependent on its own characteristic properties but also is affected by the surrounding light. For this reason optical properties of food materials are considered as they interact with light. The human perception of color is important in marketing most products including foods. Color printing and television advertising regularly use color to deliver their message. The visible portion of the electromagnetic spectrum is that part which lies approximately in the wavelength range of 4 to 8 ×10^{-7} m. Light energy in this range incident on biological materials is either transmitted, absorbed, or reflected. Most foods are opaque: they do not allow energy to be transmitted through them, thus most energy is absorbed or reflected. Energy is reflected at various wavelengths each representing a different color to the human eye (Table 2.03). Electromagnetic energy in the 622-780 nm range is recognized as red while the 492-577 nm range is green, etc. Color is the basis of optical sensors used in high speed sorting machines to separate and grade raw nuts, fresh fruit, processed vegetables, etc. Optical sensors are extremely fast and allow sorting decisions to be made in less than 0.1 sec. Color sorting machines are able to sense and remove off-color objects to provide a similar colored acceptable product that is clear of foreign matter. The capability of color sorting equipment has improved in the last 30 years with more intense, consistent light sources, narrower wavelength filters, and faster

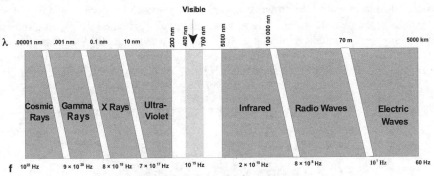

λ = wavelength   f = frequency
$f \times \lambda = c$ (speed of light = 3.00 × 10^{8} m/s)

Figure 2.09. Electromagnetic spectrum.

Table 2.03. Wavelengths and frequencies of colors in the visible spectrum.

Color	Wavelength, nm	Frequency, 10^{14} Hz
Violet	390 - 455	7.69 - 6.59
Blue	455 - 492	6.59 - 6.10
Green	492 - 577	6.10 - 5.20
Yellow	577 - 597	5.20 - 5.03
Orange	597 - 622	5.03 - 4.82
Red	622 - 780	4.82 - 3.84

signal processing components. Machine vision has advanced from the use of non-color, i.e., grey- level, to use of three-component RGB color. The combination of optical sensors, machine vision, high-speed signal processing, and decision making with fuzzy logic provide opportunities for new applications in the food industry.

The electrical properties of biological materials have long been utilized for rapid, non-destructive measurement of moisture content. The moisture in agricultural grains is routinely sampled for making decisions about drying, storing, and marketing. Moisture content can be measured rapidly, with low cost electronic sensors, as food products flow through processing operations. For these reasons, moisture is the primary quality factor used in the agricultural grain trade. Electrical conductance and resistance of water differs significantly from dry matter so that property can be utilized in determining moisture in food materials (Figure 2.10). Knowledge of these properties provides for rapid assessment of current quality and storage potential in a modern marketing system.

Dielectric properties of food materials are utilized in microwave heating. Home microwave ovens became so popular in the 1980s that now most U.S. homes use them for thawing, heating, and cooking food. Home microwave ovens use the 2450 MHZ frequency. Industrial usage of microwave ovens has not been as widespread. Microwave heating results from absorption of electromagnetic waves. Absorption of microwave energy depends primarily on the composition of the material. Water and high moisture foods are excellent absorbers of microwave energy while dry materials and ice are poor absorbers. Microwave heating, therefore, works best to heat unfrozen foods of high moisture. Microwave differs from convection heating where heat must move from the outside inward. Microwave energy can penetrate deeply into the product, although the intensity of this energy decreases with depth. For example, when heating raw potatoes at 2450 MHz, half the total energy is absorbed by the first 0.93 cm of depth (Table 2.04). Despite this depletion of energy, heating occurs rapidly at

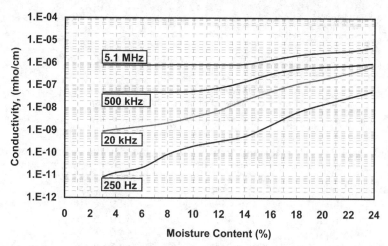

Figure 2.10. Example of the dependence of dielectric properties upon moisture content. Based on data of Nelson and Stetson (1976).

Table 2.04. Dielectric properties of foods and materials at 2450 MHz.[a]

	Dielectric Constant ϵ'	Loss Factor ϵ''	Penetration Depth d_p (cm)
Water, distilled	77.4	9.2	1.7
Water + 5% NaCl	67.5	71.1	0.25
Ice	3.2	0.003	1162
Potatoes, raw	62.0	16.7	0.93
Banana	61.8	16.7	0.93
Beef, raw	50.8	16.0	0.87
Beef, cooked	32.1	10.6	1.10
Ham	57.4	33.2	0.46
Bread	4.0	2.0	2.00
Glass ceramic	6.0	0.03	160
Paper	3 - 4	0.05 - 0.10	50

[a]Selected data from Buffler (1993).

all locations in a product exposed to microwave energy. This heating may not be uniform throughout due to spatial variation in material properties and in the microwave radiation. The interaction of the food material and the microwave heat source makes it even more important to know the dielectric properties of the food. Table 2.04 lists dielectric properties of selected food products and related materials.

Near infrared properties of foods are utilized in component analysis, particularly moisture, protein, and oil. Laboratory instruments based on near infrared wavelengths of 1 to 10×10^{-7} m are available to determine composition of samples in a few minutes. These instruments are considerably more expensive ($15,000 - $30,000) than dielectric-based moisture meters. As researchers find the unique wavelengths for a particular food constituent, new instruments will be developed for laboratory analysis of off-line samples, lower-cost portable units, and as on-line sensors in production control systems.

High energy radiation, very short wavelengths such as 10^{-11} to 10^{-12} m, can be utilized in sterilization of foods. The exposure of foods to gamma or X-rays has produced products that can be stored for long periods without refrigeration or other processing methods. Irradiated foods are more available in European stores than in the U.S. where irradiated fruit is currently found only at a few locations. Research continues to investigate the safe processing, handling, and consumption of irradiated foods.

Food materials react to and interact with electromagnetic radiation in ways which depend on their unique properties. Having an awareness of their existence and knowledge of these effects provide scientists and engineers with powerful alternatives to process food materials.

2.9 Sources of Physical Properties Data

Physical properties have been identified for various food materials and in many processing applications. The recognition and importance of these properties leads to the need for physical properties data for specific food materials. Physical properties data have been obtained over the years and are currently being collected at an increasing rate with advances in instrumentation and data acquisition. The number of food materials for which physical properties data are determined increases daily, but the number of unknown products is also increasing. New foods are constantly being formulated and raw materials are changing over the years as new varieties are developed and growing conditions change.

When the need arises, how can one obtain physical properties data? Data can be obtained directly from published sources, such as textbooks and handbooks, for certain materials, computed by formula for unknown but similar materials, or measured experimentally. Data listed in tables in published sources must be used with caution. Take note of any limitations or conditions for which the values may or may not apply. Publishers usually do not have sufficient space to give the entire explanation of conditions under which the data were obtained. If the exact food material is not given in a published table, a formula from a food engineering textbook or other source can be used to compute some physical properties, i.e., thermal properties, based on the constituents. These mixture formulae are based on the linear combination of the constituent components. Another approach is to interpolate or extrapolate a "best guess" number from values listed for similar materials. This is often the quickest way for an immediate answer. The best approach seems to be to actually measure the physical property of the exact material in question. This is the most costly and time consuming and may not be the most accurate if measured values are obtained incorrectly. A byproduct of making your own measurements is that you develop an appreciation for the technique of determining physical properties and thereby can better use published values. Unless the economics dictates the need for a property value with high accuracy or for a substantially different material, using published values wisely may be the most efficient use of resources.

List of Symbols

a_w	water activity, dimensionless ratio
A	area, m^2
b	coefficient in power law equation. If fluid is Newtonian, $b = \mu$.
c	intercept term for power law equation
c	speed of light, m/s
c_p	specific heat capacity at constant pressure, J/(kg K) or KJ/(kg K)
d_p	penetration depth (microwave energy), cm
D	diameter, m
D	diffusivity, m^2/s
EMC	equilibrium moisture content, decimal or percent
f	frequency, Hz
h	convective (surface) heat transfer coefficient, W/(m^2 K)
h_{fg}	$(h_g - h_f)$, latent heat of vaporization, kJ/kg
h_{sf}	$(h_f - h_s)$, latent heat of fusion, kJ/kg
k	thermal conductivity, W/(m K)
P	permeability, cm^3 (STP) cm cm^{-2} s^{-1} (cm Hg)$^{-1}$
Q_R	heat of respiration, kJ/kg day
r	radius, m
t	temperature, °C
u	velocity, m/s
w	specific weight , force/unit volume
X	mass ratio (mass fraction) of a specified material
α	thermal diffusivity, m^2/s
ϵ'	dielectric constant
ϵ''	dielectric loss factor
λ	wavelength, m
μ	dynamic (or absolute) viscosity, Pa s or (N s)/m^2
ρ	density, kg/m^3
τ	shear stress, N/m^2 or Pa
ν	kinematic viscosity (μ/ρ), m^2/s

Subscripts

a	ash
c	carbohydrates
f	fat
p	protein
w	water

Superscript

n	exponent in power law equation

References

1. ASHRAE. 1993. *Handbook of Fundamentals*, Chapter 30: Thermal properties of foods. ASHRAE, Atlanta, GA.
2. ASHRAE. 1998. *Handbook of Refrigeration*. Chapter 8: Thermal properties of foods. ASHRAE, Atlanta, GA.
3. Batty, J. C., and S. L. Folkman. 1983. *Food Engineering Fundamentals*. John Wiley & Sons, New York, NY.
4. Beuchat, L. R. 1981. Microbial stability as affected by water activity. *Cereal Foods World* 26(7): 345-349.
5. Buffler, C. R. 1993. *Microwave Cooking and Processing*. AVI, Van Nostrand Reinhold, New York, NY.
6. Charm, S. E. 1971.*The Fundamentals of Food Engineering*. AVI, Westport, CT.
7. Curray, J. K. 1951. *Analysis of Sphericity and Roundness of Quartz Grains*. M. S. Thesis in Mineralogy. The Pennsylvania State University, University Park, PA.
8. Fellows, P. 1988. *Food Processing Technology, Principles and Practice*. Ellis Horwood, Ltd., Chichester, England.
9. Gebhardt, S. E., R. Cutrufelli, and R. H. Matthews. 1982. *Composition of Foods: Fruits and Fruit Juices*. Agricultural Handbook Number 8-9. USDA, Washington, DC.
10. Hardenburg, R. E., A. E. Watada, and C. Y. Wang. 1986. *The Commercial Storage of Fruits, Vegetables and Nursery Stocks*. USDA Handbook Number 66. USDA-ARS, Washington, DC.
11. Haytowitz, D. B., and R. H. Matthews. 1984. *Composition of Foods: Vegetables and Vegetable Products*. Agricultural Handbook Number 8-11. USDA, Washington, DC.
12. Heldman, D. R., and R. P. Singh. 1981. *Food Process Engineering*, 2nd ed. AVI, Westport, CT.
13. Heldman, D. R., and D. B. Lund. 1992. *Handbook of Food Engineering*. Marcel Dekker, Inc., New York, NY.
14. Labuza, T. P. 1984. *Moisture Sorption: Practical Aspects of Isotherm Measurement and Use*. American Association of Cereal Chemists, St. Paul, MN.
15. Mohsenin, N. N. 1970. *Physical Properties of Plant and Animal Materials*. Gordon and Breach Science Publishers, New York, NY.
16. Mohsenin, N. N. 1980. *Thermal Properties of Foods and Agricultural Materials*. Gordon and Breach Science Publishers, New York, NY.
17. Mohsenin, N. N. 1984. *Electromagnetic Radiation Properties of Foods and Agricultural Products*. Gordon and Breach Science Publishers, New York, NY.
18. Nelson, S. O., and L. E. Stetson. 1976. Frequency and moisture dependence of the dielectric properties of hard red wheat. *Journal of Agricultural Engineering Research* 21: 181-192.
19. Rahman, Shafiur. 1995. *Food Properties Handbook*. CRC Press, Boca Raton, FL.
20. Rao, M. A., and S. S. H. Rizvi. 1995. *Engineering Properties of Foods*. 2nd ed. Dekker, New York, NY

21. Riedel, L. 1969. Measurement of thermal diffusivity in foodstuffs rich in water. *Kaltechnik-Klimatisierung* 21 11): 315.
22. Siebel, J. E. 1892. Specific heat of various products. *Ice and Refrigeration* April: 256.
23. Singh, R. P., and D. R.Heldman. 1993. *Introduction to Food Engineering.* Academic Press, San Diego, CA.
24. Steffe, J. F. 1992. *Rheological Methods in Food Process Engineering.* Freeman Press, East Lansing, MI.
25. Sweat, V. E. 1974. Experimental values of thermal conductivity of selected fruits and vegetables. *Journal of Food Science* 39(6): 1080.
26. Sweat, V. E. 1995. Thermal properties of foods. In *Engineering Properties of Foods*, M. A. Rao and S. S. H. Risvi, eds. Marcel Dekker, Inc., New York, NY.
27. Yasuda, H., and V. Stannett. 1989. Permeability coefficients. In *Polymer Handbook,* 3rd ed. John Wiley & Sons, New York, NY.

Problems

2.1. Write a definition of physical properties.

2.2. Why are physical properties important to food processing handlers?

2.3. List some of the terms used to describe the different shapes of fruits and vegetables.

2.4. How is "roundness" determined?

2.5. Write the equation for determining "roundness."

2.6. How is the "sphericity" of a food product determined?

2.7. Write the equation for determining "sphericity."

2.8. List two ways to determine roundness as suggested by Curry and Mohsenin.

2.9. Show the calculating formula for each answer to the previous problem.

2.10. Many foods are weighed by water displacement. Explain this weighing method.

2.11. Express the water displacement method in an equation.

2.12. Can volume be determined by the same water displacement method?

2.13. How is weight density measured?

2.14. How is specific gravity measured?

2.15. Write the equation for measuring specific gravity.

2.16. Explain the term "porosity."

2.17. Explain the importance for determining porosity in the storage of food products.

2.18. List two methods of determining surface area of a food product.

2.19. An apple has a mass of 0.14 kg and a volume of 2×10^{-4} m^3. What is its density?

2.20. An experimental study has shown that the surface area of apples can be approximated by:

$$S = 43.35 + 0.832 \, W$$

where S is in cm^2 and W is in grams. Plot the surface area of apples for mass ranging from 0.05 kg to 0.25 kg. Use increments of 0.05 kg.

2.21. The surface area of an egg may be approximated by:

$$S = 4.75 W^{0.66}$$

where S is in cm^2 and W is in gm. What is the surface area of a 50-gm egg?

2.22. The heat of respiration of summer squash may be approximated as:

$$\log_{10} Q_R = 0.0436 \, T + 0.904$$

where T is in °C and Q_R is in kJ per kg per day. How many kJ would be produced by 1000 kg of squash at 10°C? At 30°C?

2.23. Apples have a specific heat of 3.60 kJ/kg K. How many kJ of heat must be removed to cool 10 kg of apples from 30°C to 4°C?

2.24. Compare the heat of respiration values for sweet corn and strawberries at 25°C and at 15°C.

2.25. How many kg of ice are needed to cool 1000 kg of apples from 20°C to 0°C if only the latent heat of fusion is available for cooling?

2.26. Compare the computed specific heat values at +10°C (above freezing) and −10°C (below freezing) for a food product that is 86% water.

2.27. Compare the computed specific heat values for raw apples using equations 2.10, 2.12, and 2.13.

2.28. Compare the computed thermal conductivity of bananas using equations 2.14 and 2.16.

2.29. Compute the shear stress of orange juice at 0°C
   a. for a shear rate of 10 s^{-1}
   b. for a shear rate of 20 s^{-1}
   c. How does a twofold increase in shear rate affect the shear stress?

2.30. Compute the shear stress of olive oil for a shear rate of 5 s^{-1}
   a. for a temperature of 10°C
   b. for a temperature of 20°C

2.31. What is the viscosity of olive oil at 10°C? At 70°C?

Texture of Food Materials

3

Abstract. *This chapter provides a brief coverage of selected food texture parameters. Emphasis is placed upon instrumental measurements.*

Keywords. *Bending, compression, sensory, shear, stress, strain, tension, texture instruments.*

3.1 Introduction to Texture

Texture of food materials plays a key role in consumer acceptance and market value. Texture characteristics are important factors for raw products and for processing, preparation, and consumption. Texture features are also important considerations in quality assurance, including hazard analysis critical control program (HACCP) and food safety issues. Additionally, flavor, juiciness, color, and other appearance characteristics are important factors in food selection and contribute to texture.

Some of the descriptive terms utilized to characterize food properties include toughness vs. tenderness, hard vs. soft, dry vs. moist, brittle vs. elastic, roughness vs. smoothness, crispness vs. sogginess, firmness, stickiness, ripeness, springiness, blandness, flakiness, grittiness, aroma, etc. Many of the methods utilized by food scientists and engineers to classify characteristics of food products represent attempts to develop techniques that will reasonably predict how consumers will perceive the item and, therefore, purchase it.

The two main methods for evaluation of texture characteristics are instrumental and sensory (Bourne, 1982; Rosenthal, 1999). Humans are especially sensitive at identifying differences between two samples, whereas instruments can quickly provide a quantitative measurement on an absolute scale.

3.2 Sensory or Subjective Measurements

Sensory measurements can be classified into two general categories. Consumer acceptance taste tests are frequently conducted in shopping malls, supermarkets, and other areas having large numbers of consumers. The purpose of these tests is to obtain a general profile of consumer acceptance or rejection of the product. Since the consumers are not trained panelists, the results of the tests are essentially qualitative. The information gathered provides consumer reaction, which includes numerous characteristics of which texture is but one factor. The test results are not normally very helpful in identifying methods to improve the product.

The second category of measurements includes those tests conducted by professionals with experience in sensory evaluation techniques. The panelists are trained to detect, with a high degree of replication, specific food characteristics such as tenderness/toughness, flavor, juiciness, brittleness/softness, sponginess, odor, etc. In highly controlled sensory evaluation laboratories, the panelists are periodically blind tested to evaluate scientific standards. A sensory panel commonly consists of 6 to 12 people who can evaluate up to 10 characteristics on a 1 to 10 scale in one session of 1 to 3 hours. There is a wide variation between people in their ability to detect individual food characteristics. Results from the sensory evaluation tests are often correlated with those obtained from instrumental or objective measurement methods as a means to determine the use of the non-sensory tests.

3.3 Instrumental or Objective Measurement Methods

Various instruments have been developed and tested for measuring selected characteristics of raw and manufactured food products. Here we present only a sampling of the instrumental methods. Instrumental measurements are conducted with equipment that provides precise control of all important conditions that may affect the results. In many cases, data gathered from tests conducted with instruments are compared with sensory evaluation results.

3.3.1 Fundamental Concepts and Definitions

Mechanical properties are those characteristics having to do with the change in shape and size of a material when forces are applied (Mohsenin, 1986). Mechanical properties are expressed in terms of force, deformation, and modulus of elasticity. Rheology is the study of deformation and flow of materials having a consistency intermediate between solid and liquid. Examples of rheological properties are time-dependent stress and strain, creep, and stress relaxation.

The terms *mechanical* and *rheological* properties are sometimes used inter-changeably in cases involving force vs. deformation or stress vs. strain when time effects are considered.

Mechanical properties of materials have a strong scientific base for which engineers have agreed upon commonly used terms. Some of that terminology is appropriately used in the application to foods. For a more extensive list of terms see a standard strength of materials textbook. Refer to Figure 3.01 for diagrams of the loading types discussed in the following definitions.

Stress (σ) is the applied force per unit area and may be expressed as Newtons per square meter (Pascals), pounds force per square inch, kilograms force per square meter, etc. The force may produce tension, shear, or compression within the sample. Bending involves both tension and compression. Torque involves only shear forces.

Tensile stress is a stress resulting from forces directed away from the sample. Stretching a rubber band produces tensile stress in the band.

Compressive stress is a stress resulting from forces directed at the sample and acting to push on, or compress, it.

Shear stress is the stress that is tangential to the plane on which the forces act tending to change the sample's shape. Shear stress is produced like a tensile (or compressive) stress but the two pulling (or pushing) forces are offset from each other.

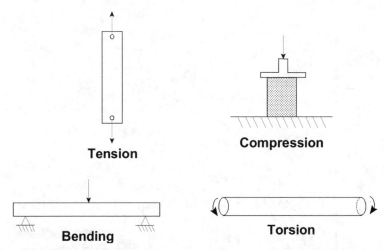

Figure 3.01. Examples of tension, compression, bending, and torsion loading.

Torsional stress is that shear stress exerted on the sample resulting from a twisting action.

Strain ($\in$) is the change, due to the applied force, in the size or shape of a body referred to its original size or shape. Strain is a dimensionless quantity, but it is frequently expressed in meters per meter, inches per inch, or percent. Strain in most objects is relatively small, but strain in a rubber band can be quite large.

Modulus of elasticity (E) is calculated as the ratio of the stress to the corresponding strain in the linear portion of the stress vs. strain or force vs. deformation curve (Figure 3.02). In cases where the stress vs. strain relation is not linear (the case with many biological materials), various apparent moduli are computed for use in select conditions.

Poisson's ratio is the ratio of transverse strain to the corresponding axial strain. It provides a measure of the change in length vs. change in width of the sample during loading.

Tensile strength is the maximum stress a material is capable of sustaining without failure. The tensional strength is calculated utilizing the maximum load during a tension test and is based on the sample's original cross-sectional area.

Bioyield point is the first stress in a material, less than the maximum attainable stress, at which an increase in strain occurs without an increase in stress. The bioyield point is typically identified by a dip in the stress-strain curve as shown in Figure 3.02. Materials exhibiting a bioyield point commonly are composites made of more than one uniform homogeneous substance. This is common in whole fruit and vegetables having a stronger outer layer.

Plasticity is the capacity of a material to take permanent, nonrecoverable deformation.

Viscoelasticity describes the combined solid-like and liquid-like behavior in which the stress-strain relationship is time dependent. Analysis of viscoelastic materials is very complex and will not be considered here.

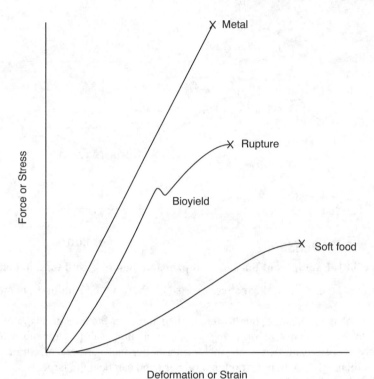

Figure 3.02. Stress-strain relationships for metal, curvilinear,
and bioyield materials.

3.3.2 Stress-Strain Behavior

Mechanical properties of agricultural and food products can be measured by uniaxial compression, uniaxial tension, shear, and bending. Various instruments used in these tests will be illustrated and discussed. The type of loading, preparation of the specimen, loading rate, strain (deformation) rate, and other factors are dependent upon the material and desired use of the data. The value of the modulus of elasticity is usually calculated and utilized for comparison with known and desired properties.

3.3.2.1 Uniaxial Compression

One of the very important requirements for uniaxial compression tests of biological materials is that of applying a true axial load in a manner to ensure that the force is applied uniformly over the cross section of the specimen. Specimens having large length-to-diameter ratios, i.e., slender specimens, will buckle or bend when sufficiently loaded, rather than compress axially. This buckling condition occurs before and instead of uniaxial compression. To prevent buckling and insure uniaxial compression, specimen length should be less than five times the diameter, or equivalent if noncircular in cross-section. The length-to-diameter ratio of the specimen must be selected to prevent buckling during loading. A special device is frequently utilized to cut a cylindrical core sample from the material being tested. The device minimizes irregularities in the specimen and permits proper preparation of the ends, which will come in contact with the loading and support plates. The diameter of the cored specimen is measured prior to loading and recorded for later computations of stress and strain.

One of the major properties calculated is the modulus of elasticity (E) according to the following formula:

$$E = \frac{F / A}{\Delta L / L} \qquad (3.01)$$

where: F = force in Newton, N
A = cross-sectional area of the specimen, m^2
ΔL = change in length due to application of the force F, m
L = initial length of the specimen, m

Example 3.1

Compute the modulus of elasticity when a 50 mm long by 20 mm (0.020 m) diameter sample compresses 0.50 mm upon loading by a 20 N force.

Solution:
The modulus of elasticity (E) is defined as stress/strain. Thus:

$$\text{Stress} = \text{Force / area} = 20 \text{ N}/[3.14 \times (0.020)^2/4] \text{ m}^2 = 0.06366 \times 10^6 \text{ N/m}^2$$

$$\text{Strain} = \Delta L/L = 0.50 \text{ mm}/50 \text{ mm} = 0.01$$

$$E = \frac{\text{stress}}{\text{strain}} = \frac{0.06366 \times 10^6 \text{ (N/m}^2)}{0.01} = 6.366 \times 10^6 \frac{\text{N}}{\text{m}^2} = 6366 \text{ kPa} \quad \textbf{ANSWER}$$

Not all compression tests require a coring device to obtain a test specimen. In many cases, it is desirable to measure the rheological properties of the entire material where the shape is such that other techniques must be used. For example, many food materials are convex in shape. Materials and methods for compression tests of food materials of convex shape are described in ASAE Standard S368.

3.3.2.2 Uniaxial Tension

Uniaxial tensile testing is easy to perform for hard materials like metal, concrete, and plastic. Soft biological tissues can be especially difficult to test in tension if the gripping device deforms the specimen to the degree that failure is caused by stress concentration at the grip. High-moisture specimens can cause slippage by the grips that would normally be compensated by increased grip pressure but in this case just accentuates the problem of holding the specimen. A solution for long flexible specimens has been to have an unusually large area of contact with the grip. Specialized grips have been developed to minimize the effect of overstressing the biological tissues by the clamping action during the pulling load. Various glues have also been tried to facilitate the holding of the material during the application of the tensile forces. However, several problems make this technique unworkable for soft, wet, and/or small samples. Tensile testing is reasonable for some applications but not feasible for most soft food materials. For example, try applying tension to a short length of peeled banana without damaging the ends where you are holding the banana.

A special device, a hamburger patty tension tester, was developed to hold specimens to conduct tension tests to measure the textural and binding properties of ground beef patties (Suter et al., 1976) (Figure 3.03). Measurement of binding strength allows determination of the effect on texture of constituents such as meat substitutes, fat content, moisture content, and other ingredients.

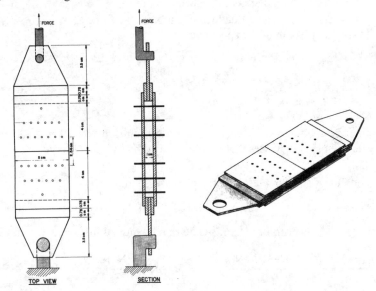

Figure 3.03. Apparatus for holding beef patty during tension loading.

3.3.2.3 Shear

The operation of particle size reduction requires applied forces that exceed the localized strength of the tissue. Breaking the tissue is done partially by shearing. Shearing can be done by a mechanism or in the human mouth as food is chewed for digestion. Thus, people use terms like toughness, tenderness, crispness, etc., to describe a material's shear strength. In most shearing tests of biological materials, true shearing does not occur but rather there is cutting of the tissues. Shear stresses act parallel to the shearing plane rather than normal to the plane as is the case in uniaxial compression and uniaxial tension. One of the oldest applications of this principle with biological materials is the Warner-Bratzler shearing device.

The Warner-Bratzler shear device consists of a blade and two fixed shear bars. The sample is inserted into a triangular hole in the blade (Figure 3.04). Formed meat products, such as frankfurters, and vegetables with long pieces such as string beans, carrots, and broccoli stalks, are commonly tested with this device.

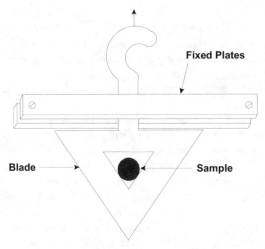

Figure 3.04. Illustration of Warner-Bratzler shearing device.

Another widely used device is the Kramer shear press (Figure 3.05). This device has multiple blades that are forced into the food material, which is held in a box. The Kramer press is best suited for foods consisting of many small uniform particles or materials that are not rigid enough to hold their own shape, i.e., more fluid-like. Examples of its use include ground meat and vegetables such as peas and corn.

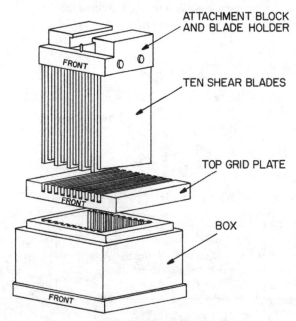

Figure 3.05. The Kramer shear press.
(Courtesy of Food Technology Corporation, Sterling, Virginia.)

3.3.2.4 Bending

Bending tests are often used when it is desirable to measure the stiffness of individual specimens or the resistance to breakage. For example, breakage of chicken legs during the handling or processing operations causes a significant economic loss. Varying the feed ration is one of the most common practices to prevent breakage of the leg. A three-point bending test device is used to determine the mechanical properties of animal bones such as the ultimate shear strength, ultimate bending strength, apparent modulus of elasticity, and fracture energy. Strength tests of animal bones provide an objective method for evaluating the effects of nutrition, age, sex, and environment on the physical condition of the animal (ASAE Standard S459). To ensure that the legs are sufficiently elastic and not too brittle, simple breaking tests are conducted using a device similar to that shown in Figure 3.06.

Although bending tests have been utilized primarily on biological materials that are hard and/or brittle, some applications have been developed for soft and/or flexible products. Suter et al. (1976) developed a device to obtain stress-strain data utilizing a three-point loading concept. The device was utilized to measure the "pop" of meat frankfurters. Many consumers expected to sense a sudden shearing of the meat when they bit into the frankfurter. When they would apply sufficient force with their teeth to cut or shear the frankfurter, the mouth feel would be similar to that experienced with rubber (elastic behavior), but a sudden shearing of the meat would often produce a "pop" sound and sensation. This type of mouth feel would be very different from that when the frankfurter would simply display elastic behavior and a "mushy sensation" until the final shearing takes place coincident with the biting through the skin. During the cooking phase of the meat emulsion utilized to form the frankfurter, the protein is denatured and becomes more firm and less rubbery.

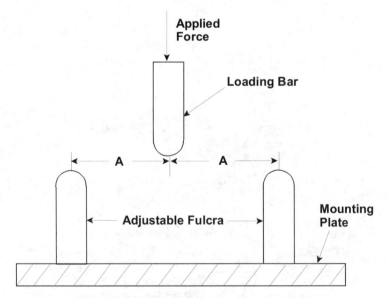

Figure 3.06. Three-point bending test fixture.

3.4 Compression Test of Food Materials of Convex Shape

It is not always feasible to obtain a sample having an ideal simple shape such as a cube, sphere, or cylinder. Test methods are needed for materials in their original condition regardless of their shape. A method has been developed to determine the mechanical attributes of convex shapes, such as fruits, vegetables, seeds, grains, and manufactured food materials in their unaltered, original condition (ASAE Standard S368.2).

Various types of compression tools with smooth surfaces are used for applying the load to the sample. The type of the compression tool used for each test depends on the size and shape of the sample, the nature of the test, and the amount of information expected from the specific test. Examples of compression tools for "solid like" food materials with convex or flat surfaces are illustrated in Figure 3.07. In certain cases, the test specimen will require a special holding apparatus. For fruits such as pears or apples, the specimen can be cut in half. The deformation of the flat bottom plate will be negligible because the area of contact between the flat surface of the fruit and supporting plate will be many times greater than the area of contact between the compression tool and the fruit.

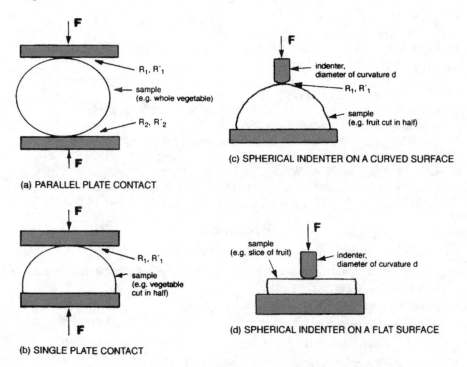

**Figure 3.07. Examples of compression tools with spherical ends.
ASAE Standard 368.3, 1997 (courtesy of ASAE).**

3.5 Conclusion

Food texture is a complex phenomenon; its measurement is not an exact science. Many approaches have been taken to indicate some aspect of texture. Each method is best suited to specific kinds of food materials. Few if any methods are applicable to all foods and so the search continues for better techniques and instruments for measurement of food texture.

List of Symbols

A	area, m^2
D	deformation, m
E	modulus of elasticity, N/ m^2 or Pa
F	force, N
L	initial length, m
$\in$	strain = D/L, m/m, or similar dimensionless ratio
σ	stress = F/A, N/ m^2 or Pa

References

1. ASAE. 1997. *ASAE Standard* S368.2: Compression test of food materials of convex shape. ASAE, St. Joseph, MI.
2. ASAE. 1997. *ASAE Standard* S459: Shear and three-point bending test of animal bone. ASAE, St. Joseph, MI.
3. Bourne, M. C. 1982. *Food Texture and Viscosity: Concept and Measurement.* Academic Press, New York, NY.
4. Mohsenin, N. N. 1986. *Physical Properties of Plant and Animal Materials.* Gordon and Breach Science Publishers, New York, NY.
5. Rosenthal, A. J. 1999. *Food Texture: Measurement and Perception.* Aspen Publishers, Gaithersburg, MD.
6. Suter, D. A., E. Sustek, C. W. Dill, W. H. Marshall, and Z. L. Carpenter. 1976. A method for measurement of the effect of blood protein concentrates on the binding forces in cooked ground beef patties. *Journal of Food Science* 41:1428-1432.

Problems

3.1. Name the two main methods of evaluating food texture.

3.2. Name two categories of sensory measurements with their relative advantages and disadvantages.

3.3. Explain the difference between stress and strain.

3.4. How is force related to stress?

3.5. How is deformation related to strain?

3.6. Explain why metals do not display a bioyield point.

3.7. Why does viscoelasticity explain the stress vs. strain behavior of fresh fruit better than dry cereal grains?

3.8. Why is a cylindrical core sample cut out of a whole fruit for compression testing?

3.9. Tensile testing does not work well for fruit for what reasons?

3.10. Name at least one advantage of three point bending test over compression and tensile loading.

3.11. The Warner–Bratzler shear device is best used with what food products?

3.12. The Kramer shear press is best used with what food products?

3.13. Describe the shape of the tip of a compression tool which is used to compress whole food products.

3.14. Name at least three characteristics that contribute to a food's texture.

Fluid Flow

4

Abstract. *This chapter provides basic coverage of fluid statics and fluid flow parameters relative to processing applications. The emphasis is upon Newtonian liquids, although a brief coverage of fan performance is included.*

Keywords. *Bernoulli Equation, conservation equations, density, fans, flow measurement, friction, pressure, pump performance, pumps, system curves, viscosity.*

4.1 Characteristics of Fluids

Both gases and liquids are fluids and obey the same general laws of fluid mechanics. However, there are some very distinct differences between liquids and gases. These differences can best be observed by looking at some important fluid properties.

Density (mass per unit volume, ρ) is perhaps the most important fluid property. The SI units for density are kg/m^3. Other units still commonly used are lb$_m$/ft^3 and gm/cc. Since the density of gases is usually quite small, the inverse of density—or specific volume (v)—is often used for gases such as air. Density of gases varies greatly with both temperature and pressure. Variations of liquid density with pressure can usually be ignored but variation with temperature may be significant. A secondary property, specific weight (w), is derived from the density. It has units of force per unit volume (i.e., lb$_f$/ft^3) and may be taken as numerically equal to the density in equivalent mass units. Specific weight is used primarily in equations involving US (customary) units.

Compressibility refers to the change in density of a fluid due to a change in temperature or pressure. This property is especially important for gases but can usually be ignored for liquids. When compressibility effects are not significant, the governing laws of fluid mechanics can be greatly simplified.

Viscosity is the tendency of a fluid to resist any motion within the fluid. The underlying mechanisms of viscosity are very complex and will not be discussed here. For many common liquids, such as water, viscosity varies with temperature. For some fluids, the viscous effect cannot be evaluated in terms of a numerical value for viscosity. These fluids are called non-Newtonian fluids and will not be discussed in this chapter. Newtonian fluids include water, air, aqueous solutions, and honey. Some non-Newtonian fluids are fruit and vegetable purees, paint, tomato paste, and orange juice concentrate. Fluids with a high concentration of suspended solids are likely to exhibit non-Newtonian characteristics.

The remainder of this chapter will be concerned primarily with liquids. Water will be the primary liquid discussed, although applications to other liquids will be presented. While water is used to illustrate physical phenomena involved, relationships provided are equally applicable to other Newtonian liquids. Because of compressibility effects, some relationships must be modified for use with gases.

4.2 Pressure vs. Depth

When we speak of pressure we must explain whether we mean absolute pressure or gage pressure. **Gage pressure** is the pressure that would be indicated by gages such as those used to measure tire pressure and water pressure. Atmospheric pressure is the reference pressure for these measurements. Therefore, these gages are actually measuring the difference between pressure at the point of measurement and atmospheric pressure. Thus, gage pressure measurements indicate a vacuum if pressure is below atmospheric and a positive pressure for pressure above atmospheric. **Absolute pressure,** on the other hand, indicates a pressure measurement referenced to a perfect vacuum. Thus, atmospheric pressure has a numeric value of 101.325 kPa or 14.696 psi absolute. Absolute pressure is then the sum of gage pressure and atmospheric pressure. An air tank pressurized to a gage pressure of 500 kPa would have an absolute pressure of 601.3 kPa. Most pressure measurements are given in terms of gage pressure. For this reason, absolute pressure measurements should always be clearly identified.

Pressure below a fluid surface is closely related to the depth below that surface. We are aware that pressure well below the surface of an ocean is much greater than pressure slightly below the surface. We can use Figure 4.01 to show why this is true. The leftmost tank contains 1 m^3 of water with a mass of 1000 kg (1 m^3 × 1000 kg/m^3). This mass exerts a uniform force on the bottom of the container. We find this force by using Newton's Second Law ($F = ma$ or $F = mg$ for gravitational force). *(Here we assume that there are no significant deviations from the Earth's gravitational attraction. If g ≠ 9.807 m/s² (32.2 ft/s²), then the force exerted by a given mass of fluid must be adjusted for the different gravitational force. This distinction, though technically important, is not significant for the conditions with which we are concerned.)* Thus:

$$F = 1000 \text{ kg} \times 9.807\,\frac{m}{s^2} = 9807\,\frac{\text{kg m}}{s^2} = 9807 \text{ N}$$

Note: We use $g_c = 1\,\dfrac{\text{kg m}}{\text{N s}^2}$ to obtain units of Newtons for force.

The force computed above is applied to the entire bottom of the tank—an area of 1 m^2. Thus the pressure (force/area) on the tank bottom is 9807 N/m^2, or 9807 Pa, or 9.807 kPa. If the depth of water is doubled, as shown in the second tank, the total mass becomes 2000 kg, the force is 19 614 N and the pressure is 19.614 kPa. Similarly, a depth of 10 m would produce a pressure of 98.07 kPa. (In normal use, we would usually round the value of g to 9.81 m/s², giving slightly different results from those shown above.)

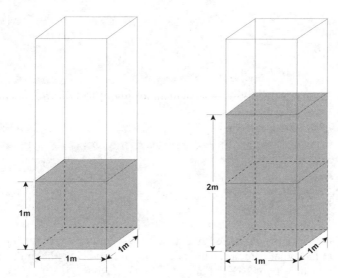

Figure 4.01. Illustration to demonstrate the relationship between pressure and depth.

Our analysis used a tank of uniform size (1 m × 1 m) from bottom to top. The results we found are equally valid for any tank regardless of shape. Only the depth of fluid affects the pressure on the tank bottom. We can follow a similar analysis using US units. The depth in US units is commonly referred to as 'head" and is expressed in feet or inches. This can be confusing since "head" is expressed in units of length, but "head" as used here represents pressure. It is important to remember that "head" actually represents the depth of fluid that produces a corresponding pressure.

We have used water for our analysis. The same procedure can be followed for any liquid. We simply use the density for that liquid instead of the 1000 kg/m^3 value for water. We also assumed that the tank was unpressurized—the pressure at the water surface was atmospheric. If the tank is pressurized, the pressure at the tank bottom is the sum of the pressure at the water surface and the pressure due to the water depth. In equation form, this may be expressed as:

$$P_d = P_s + Kd \qquad\qquad (4.01)$$

where: P_d = pressure at any depth d below the liquid surface
         P_s = pressure at the liquid surface
         d = depth below the surface
         K = appropriate constant depending upon the liquid density and the units of P and d. If P is in kPa and d is in m, then K = 9.807 kPa/m for water, or if P is in psi and d in feet, then K = 0.4333 psi/ft for standard gravity conditions.

Example 4.1.

What is the pressure, in kiloPascals, 10 m below the surface of a lake?
Solution:
$P = Kd = 9.807$ kPa/m $\times$ 10 m = <u>98.07 kPa</u>   **ANSWER**

Example 4.2.

A milk storage tank is pressurized such that the air pressure above the liquid surface is 100 kPa. What is the pressure at a depth of 2 m below the milk surface? The milk has a density of 1032 kg/m^3.

Solution:
We can apply Equation 4.01 to solve this problem. Since the density of milk is greater than that of water by a factor of 1.032, K becomes 9.807×1.032.
Thus: $P_d = 100$ kPa + (9.807×1.032) kPa/m $\times$ 2 m = <u>120.2 kPa</u>   **ANSWER**

4.3 Conservation Equations

A conservation equation is an accounting process. Just as checkbook reconciliation accounts for every penny in the account, a conservation equation must account for all components being "conserved." The two conservation equations significant to our consideration of flowing liquids are the Conservation of Mass and the Conservation of Energy. These equations are also referred to as mass and energy balance equations. When a fluid is incompressible, the conservation of mass can be simplified to a simple volumetric analysis. We will use that approach in this unit.

4.3.1 Continuity Equation (Conservation of Mass)

The Continuity Equation simply states that we must account for all material. Every kilogram of fluid added to a system must be stored or removed from the system. Since liquids are essentially incompressible, the equation is usually written in terms of volume rather than mass. We will consider application of this volumetric analysis to three different physical arrangements: (1) flow in a single channel with area change; (2) flow into a channel with more than one exit; and (3) flow with accumulation. The basic principles applied to these three conditions can be readily expanded to more complex arrangements. The key relationship for the volumetric flow analysis is that the flow rate $\dot{Q}$ (m^3/s) is equal to the average velocity in the channel or pipe, u (m/s), multiplied by the channel area A (m^2). This relationship, $\dot{Q} = uA$, can then be applied to the physical arrangements noted above and shown in Figure 4.02.

a. Area change only

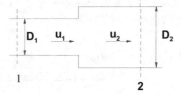

b. Area change and flow division

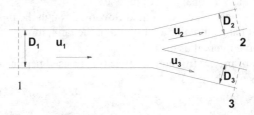

C. Area change and storage

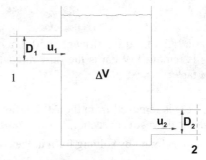

Figure 4.02. Three common flow conditions for application of the continuity equation.

In Figure 4.02a, the conservation of mass requires that flow across plane 1 be equal to the flow across plane 2:

$$\dot{Q}_1 = \dot{Q}_2 \quad \text{or} \quad A_1 u_1 = A_2 u_2 \tag{4.02}$$

A relationship between velocity and pipe diameter can readily be obtained from Equation 4.02:

$$\frac{u_1}{u_2} = \left(\frac{A_2}{A_1}\right) = \left(\frac{d_2}{d_1}\right)^2$$

For Figure 4.02b, output flow is divided between two exits:

$$\dot{Q}_1 = \dot{Q}_2 + \dot{Q}_3 \quad \text{or} \quad A_1 u_1 = A_2 u_2 + A_3 u_3 \tag{4.03}$$

For Figure 4.02c, we have input, output, and accumulation. Remember that accumulation may be positive or negative.

$$\dot{Q}_1 = \frac{\Delta V}{\theta} + \dot{Q}_2 \quad \text{or} \quad A_1 u_1 = \frac{\Delta V}{\theta} + A_2 u_2 \quad \text{or} \quad \left(\dot{Q}_1 - \dot{Q}_2\right)\theta = \Delta V \quad (4.04)$$

where: $\dot{Q}$ = volumetric flow rate, m^3/s
A = cross sectional area of pipe, m^2
u = average velocity of liquid flowing through the pipe, m/s
ΔV = change in volume of liquid in the tank, m^3
θ = time interval used, s

Although units of meters (m) and seconds (s) are used herein, any other dimensionally consistent units may be used.

Example 4.3

Milk flows at a rate of 2.0 L/s through a 50-mm diameter pipe. At a tap in the pipe, 0.7 L/s is removed. What is the flow rate and velocity of the milk downstream of the tap?

Solution
(1) Since 0.7 L/s is removed from the 2.0 L/s flowing in the pipe, 1.3 L/s must flow through the downstream section.

(2) The velocity is found by solving for u in the continuity relationship:

$$\dot{Q} = A \times u.$$

The cross-sectional area of a 50 mm pipe is:

$$A = \frac{\pi D^2}{4} = \frac{\pi(0.05)^2}{4} = \frac{\pi}{4}\left(2.5 \times 10^{-3}\right) = 1.965 \times 10^{-3} \ m^2$$

The flow rate, converted to m^3/s, is:

$$\dot{Q} = 1.3 \ L/s \times \left(1 \times 10^{-3}\right) \ m^3/L = 1.3 \times 10^{-3} \ m^3/s$$

Thus: $$u = \frac{\dot{Q}}{A} = \frac{1.3 \times 10^{-3} \ m^3/s}{1.96 \times 10^{-3} m^2} = 0.662 \ m/s \qquad \textbf{ANSWER}$$

Example 4.4

Water flows in a 0.1 m diameter pipe at a velocity of 1.0 m/s. Near the pipe exit the diameter is reduced to 0.03 m. What is the exit velocity of the water?

Solution:

From the continuity equation, we know that $A_1 u_1 = A_2 u_2$. Thus:

$$u_2 = u_1 \left(\frac{A_1}{A_2} \right) = u_1 \left(\frac{d_1}{d_2} \right)^2 = 1 \times \left(\frac{0.1}{0.03} \right)^2 = \underline{11.11 \text{ m/s}} \qquad \textbf{ANSWER}$$

4.3.2 Conservation of Energy

Before discussing the conservation of energy we must first identify the types of energy with which we will be concerned. We first observe that a liquid may possess energy in three forms. If the liquid is moving, it has kinetic energy that may be used to do work. If it is elevated, it has potential energy that may also be used to do work. If it is under pressure, this pressure can be used to do work. Thermal energy is not a factor in our analysis of fluid flow since we assume there is very little change in temperature. In addition to the energy possessed by the liquid, we must also consider the energy added and removed in a flow system. Normally the only source of added energy is a pump, and the only energy removed is that lost due to friction. Referring to Figure 4.03, we may now write a general equation for the conservation of energy as follows:

$$E_1 + E_p - E_f = E_2 \qquad (4.05)$$

or energy present at the entrance (location 1) plus energy added by the pump minus energy lost due to friction must equal energy remaining at the exit (location 2). This is simply an accounting process, similar to balancing a checkbook at the end of the month.

To write this equation in a useful form, we must decide upon a consistent set of units to be used, and we must define each of the terms in the equation. The terms E_1 and E_2 include kinetic, potential and pressure energies—each of which are normally expressed in different units. Any consistent set of units can be used for the energy equation. The most useful equation for use with SI units is written such that all terms have units of energy per unit mass of flowing fluid (Equation 4.06). Note that the "Ground Level" shown in Figure 4.03 is not a factor in the problem solution. Only the elevation difference between z_1 and z_2 affects the energy analysis. Equation 4.06 is commonly called the **Bernoulli Equation**.

$$\frac{P_1}{\rho} + \frac{g z_1}{g_c} + \frac{u_1^2}{2 g_c} + E_p - \frac{\Delta P_f}{\rho} = \frac{P_2}{\rho} + \frac{g z_2}{g_c} + \frac{u_2^2}{2 g_c} \qquad (4.06)$$

where: E_p = energy input from pump, J/kg
          g = gravitational acceleration, 9.81 m/s²

g_c = gravitational constant, $1\dfrac{\text{kg m}}{\text{N s}^2}$

P_1, P_2 = pressure at inlet and outlet, respectively, N/m²
ΔP_f = pressure loss due to friction, N/m²

u_1, u_2 = velocities at inlet and outlet, respectively, m/s
z_1, z_2 = elevation at inlet and outlet, respectively, m
ρ = fluid density, kg/m³

The first three terms and the last three terms of Equation 4.06 represent respectively total energy entering and leaving the system. This total energy consists of a pressure term $\left(\dfrac{P}{\rho}\right)$, an elevation term $\left(\dfrac{gz}{g_c}\right)$, and a kinetic energy term $\left(\dfrac{u^2}{2g_c}\right)$. The units of each term of the equation are J/kg. Magnitudes of these individual terms vary greatly depending upon flow conditions. However, except for extremely high velocity flows, the kinetic energy term is usually small compared to pressure and elevation differences.

As noted above, we have an equation relating the energy balance in terms of energy per unit mass of flowing fluid. If we multiply each term of Equation 4.06 by density (ρ), the resulting equation is now expressed in units of pressure. While valid in these units, the Bernoulli Equation is not normally written in units of pressure.

When US units are used, the equation is commonly expressed in terms of elevation or "head," typically in units of feet. In this form, the equation becomes:

$$H_1 + H_p - H_f = H_2 \tag{4.07}$$

where: H_1 =   total head at inlet = $\left(\dfrac{P_1}{w} + \dfrac{u_1^2}{2g} + z_1\right)$ $\tag{4.08}$

H_2 = total head at exit = $\left(\dfrac{P_2}{w} + \dfrac{u_2^2}{2g} + z_2\right)$ $\tag{4.09}$

          H_p = head added by the pump, ft
          H_f = head loss due to friction, ft
and g = gravitational acceleration, ft/s²
          P = pressure, lb$_f$ /ft²
          u = velocity, ft/s
          w = specific weight ($\rho g/g_c$), lb$_f$ /ft³
          z = elevation above any selected reference level, ft

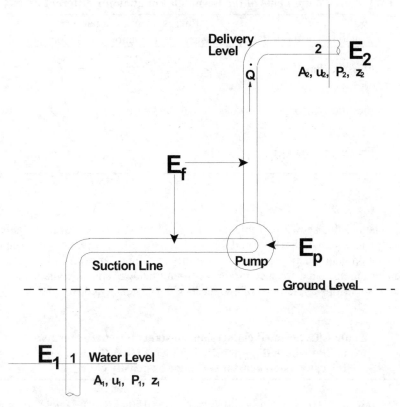

Figure 4.03. Sketch of pump flow system showing notation used.

A review of g and g_c: While the symbols g and g_c differ only in the subscript, they represent two very different parameters. The acceleration of gravity, g, is commonly taken as 9.81 m/s^2 at the Earth's surface, even though the actual value does vary slightly. g_c, however, is simply a unit conversion factor based upon Newton's Second Law. It permits conversion between units of force and mass. The numeric value of g_c is unity for SI units.

Since the different forms of energy used in the Bernoulli Equation often appear confusing to students new to the concept, we will pause here for a quick review. First, energy may be in the form of kinetic energy, elevation energy, or pressure energy. Second, these energy terms may be expressed in a number of different units. For example, the Bernoulli Equation could easily be written in units of pressure (Pa), length (m), or energy per unit mass of flowing fluid (J/kg); however, the first option is not normally used. Table 4.01 shows how each of the energy forms (pressure, elevation, and velocity) are expressed in these different units.

Table 4.01. Components of the Bernoulli Equation for different units.

Equation Form (Units)	Energy Term in Equation		
	Pressure	Elevation	Velocity
Pressure (Pa)	P	$\dfrac{\rho g z}{g_c}$	$\dfrac{\rho u^2}{2 g_c}$
Elevation (m, or ft)	$\dfrac{P g_c}{\rho g}$	z	$\dfrac{u^2}{2g}$
Energy/mass (J/kg)	$\dfrac{P}{\rho}$	$\dfrac{g z}{g_c}$	$\dfrac{u^2}{2 g_c}$

The relationships shown in Table 4.01 are valid for any system of units (although only SI units are shown for most) and for any fluid. Specific conversions relating pressure, elevation, and kinetic energy for three different fluids are shown in Table 4.02. Conversions in this table are specific for the SI units shown, and all components in the general relationships of the first column must be dimensionally consistent.

Table 4.02. Selected conversion constants for energy terms.
Note that where fluid density is a factor (first three rows),
the conversion constants change as density changes.

General	SI Units	Syrup ($\rho=1100$ kg/m³)	Water ($\rho=1000$ kg/m³)	Oil ($\rho=860$ kg/m³)
$P = \dfrac{\rho g z}{g_c}$	Pa	$P = 10\,790\,z$	$P = 9810\,z$	$P = 8436\,z$
$P = \dfrac{\rho u^2}{2 g_c}$	Pa	$P = 550\,u^2$	$P = 500\,u^2$	$P = 430\,u^2$
$P = \rho\left(\dfrac{P}{\rho}\right)$	Pa	$P = 1100\left(\dfrac{P}{\rho}\right)$	$P = 1000\left(\dfrac{P}{\rho}\right)$	$P = 860\left(\dfrac{P}{\rho}\right)$
$\dfrac{P}{\rho} = \dfrac{g z}{g_c}$	J/kg	$\dfrac{P}{\rho} = 9.81\,z$	$\dfrac{P}{\rho} = 9.81\,z$	$\dfrac{P}{\rho} = 9.81\,z$
$\dfrac{P}{\rho} = \dfrac{u^2}{2 g_c}$	J/kg	$\dfrac{P}{\rho} = \dfrac{u^2}{2 g_c}$	$\dfrac{P}{\rho} = \dfrac{u^2}{2 g_c}$	$\dfrac{P}{\rho} = \dfrac{u^2}{2 g_c}$
$z = \dfrac{u^2}{2g}$	M	$z = \dfrac{u^2}{19.62}$	$z = \dfrac{u^2}{19.62}$	$z = \dfrac{u^2}{19.62}$

Example 4.5a

What is the total energy per unit mass (E_2) at a pipe outlet where the pressure is 140 kPa, the outlet is at ground level and water is flowing at 14 L/s in a 76-mm pipe?

Solution:

(1) We may select any reference elevation we desire. Therefore, if we choose the outlet level as the reference elevation, the elevation term in the expression becomes zero. We need only calculate the pressure and kinetic energy terms.

(2) To find the velocity, we must first solve the continuity equation for velocity (u):

$$u = \frac{\dot{Q}}{A} = \frac{14 \text{ L/s} \times 1 \text{ m}^3/1000\text{L}}{\frac{\pi}{4} \times (0.076)^2 \text{ m}^2} = \frac{0.014 \text{ m/s}}{0.00454} = 3.09 \text{ m/s}$$

then:

$$E_2 = \frac{P_2}{\rho} + \frac{gz_2}{g_c} + \frac{u_2^2}{2g_c} = \frac{140,000 \text{ N/m}^2}{1000 \text{ kg/m}^3} + \frac{9.81 \text{ m/s}^2 (0 \text{ m})}{1\frac{\text{kg m}}{\text{N s}^2}} + \frac{(3.09)^2 \text{ m}^2/\text{s}^2}{2 \times 1\frac{\text{kg m}}{\text{N s}^2}}$$

$$E_2 = 140\frac{\text{N m}}{\text{kg}} + 0 + 4.77 \frac{\text{N m}}{\text{kg}} = 145 \frac{\text{N m}}{\text{kg}}$$

$$\underline{E_2 = 145 \text{ J/kg}}$$ **ANSWER**

Example 4.5b

What is the total head at a pipe outlet where the pressure is 20 psi, the outlet is at ground level, and water is flowing at 30 cfm in a 3-inch pipe? (These values are roughly equivalent to those in Example 4.5a.)

Solution:

(1) Following the steps outlined in Example 4.5a:

$$u = \frac{30\dfrac{ft^3}{min}}{\dfrac{\pi}{4}\left(\dfrac{3}{12}\right)^2 ft^2} \times \frac{1\,min}{60\,s} = \frac{0.5}{0.0419}\frac{ft}{s} = 10.2\frac{ft}{s}$$

(2) Substituting into the expression for total head:

$$H_2 = \frac{20\,lb/in.^2 \times 144\,in.^2/ft^2}{62.4\,lb/ft^3} + \frac{(10.2)^2\,ft^2/s^2}{2\,(32.2)\,ft/s^2} + 0\,ft$$

$$= 46.2\,ft + 1.6\,ft = 47.8\,ft \qquad\qquad \textbf{ANSWER}$$

The pressure energy could have been calculated using the conversion constant of 0.4333 psi/ft discussed earlier. Note also that the kinetic energy term contributes only a small amount to the total head. In most applications the kinetic energy term will be low since velocities are kept low to avoid high friction losses.

4.4 Fluid Friction

We know that a pressure difference is required to produce flow of fluid in a pipe. Thus any flow of fluids in a pipe must have a pressure drop. This pressure drop, commonly called friction loss, is often significant and must be considered in any flow analysis.

4.4.1 Factors Affecting Friction Losses

The major factors affecting friction loss in pipe flow of any fluid are: (1) the fluid properties, (2) the fluid velocity, and (3) type and size of the pipe. To develop relationships that are valid for a wide variety of flow conditions, it is necessary to consider these factors in a dimensionless form. For example, the type of pipe influences friction because of the roughness of pipe walls. This roughness ($\in$) is presented in terms of a ratio called relative roughness ($\in/D$), where the roughness and pipe diameter are in the same units to give a dimensionless ratio. Values of roughness have been determined and tabulated for common types of pipe so that relative roughness is easily determined. Table 4.03 lists these values for common materials.

A second dimensionless ratio used in determining friction loss is the Reynolds number (Re). The Reynolds number is expressed as:

$$Re = \frac{uD\rho}{\mu} = \frac{uD}{v} \qquad \text{where} \qquad \left(v = \frac{\mu}{\rho}\right) \qquad\qquad (4.10)$$

The Reynolds number is a very important parameter in fluid flow. If the Reynolds number is small (low velocity, high viscosity, or both), flow is laminar. Laminar flow occurs when all particles of fluid are moving along parallel paths. Low velocity flows of heavy syrups are typical of laminar flow. If the Reynolds number is large, flow is turbulent with particles "bouncing" about as they move in the general direction of

Table 4.03. Absolute roughness values for pipe surfaces.

Material[a]	Absolute Roughness (ϵ)	
	(ft)	(m)
Smooth pipe (theoretical)	0	0
Asphalted cast iron	0.005	1.5×10^{-3}
Cast iron	0.00085	260×10^{-6}
Concrete (average)	0.003	910×10^{-6}
Drawn tubing	0.000005	1.5×10^{-6}
Galvanized steel	0.0005	150×10^{-6}
Riveted steel (average)	0.01	3.0×10^{-3}
Stainless steel	<0.000 004	1.2×10^{-6}
Steel or wrought iron pipe	0.00015	46×10^{-6}

[a] All values are for new material. Additional information can be found in references such as Avallone and Baumeister (1986) and Perry and Green (1984).

flow. Water flow is turbulent under most common applications that we see. There is no exact value of Reynolds number for transition from laminar to turbulent flow. Flow is usually laminar for Reynolds numbers below 2000 to 2300. At and slightly above this range, flow may be either laminar or turbulent—or it may alternate between the two. At higher values, flow becomes turbulent.

The third dimensionless parameter is called the friction factor (f). It is defined by the expression:

$$f_f = \frac{D}{L}\left(\frac{\frac{\Delta P_f}{2\rho u^2}}{g_c}\right) \qquad \text{Fanning } f \qquad (4.11)$$

$$f_d = \frac{D}{L}\left(\frac{\frac{\Delta P_f}{\rho u^2}}{2g_c}\right) \qquad \text{Darcy } f \qquad (4.12)$$

Note that the two friction factors, Fanning and Darcy, differ by a factor of 4 ($f_d = 4f_f$). Note also that, with consistent units, the above equations are valid for either US or SI units. Both friction factors are widely used. In using any reference containing friction factor information, you should check to determine which f is used. Regardless of the friction factor used, the resulting computed friction loss should be the same. We will use the Fanning f exclusively to avoid confusion.

We can rearrange Equation 4.11 to solve for the pressure drop due to friction:

$$\Delta P_f = f_f \frac{L}{D}\frac{2\rho u^2}{g_c} \qquad \text{Fanning } f \qquad (4.13)$$

This equation can also be expressed in another common form that is useful for calculating friction energy losses:

$$\frac{\Delta P_f}{\rho} = f_f \frac{L}{D} \frac{2u^2}{g_c} \qquad \text{Fanning } f \qquad (4.14)$$

4.4.2 Calculation of Friction Losses

The three dimensionless parameters: relative roughness, Reynolds number, and friction factor, are related as shown in Figure 4.04. To determine the pressure drop for a given flow condition (Re and ϵ/D), it is only necessary to read f from the chart and calculate pressure drop using Equation 4.13 or Equation 4.14 above.

As an alternative to using the chart, equations are available for calculating f under different flow conditions. The equation for laminar flow is quite simple, a function only of the Reynolds number:

$$f = \frac{16}{Re} \qquad (4.15)$$

For turbulent flow, the general equation is:

$$\frac{1}{\sqrt{f_f}} = -4\,log\left(\frac{\epsilon}{3.7D} + \frac{1.256}{Re\sqrt{f_f}}\right) \qquad (4.16)$$

For rough pipes, at sufficiently high Reynolds numbers, the relationship of Equation 4.16 becomes a function only of relative roughness:

$$\frac{1}{\sqrt{f_f}} = -4\,log\left(\frac{\epsilon}{3.7D}\right) \quad \text{or} \quad f_f = \left(\frac{1}{-4\,log\frac{\epsilon}{3.7D}}\right)^2 \qquad (4.17)$$

For smooth pipes, Equation 4.16 simplifies to:

$$\frac{1}{\sqrt{f_f}} = -4\,log\left(\frac{1.256}{Re\sqrt{f_f}}\right) \qquad (4.18)$$

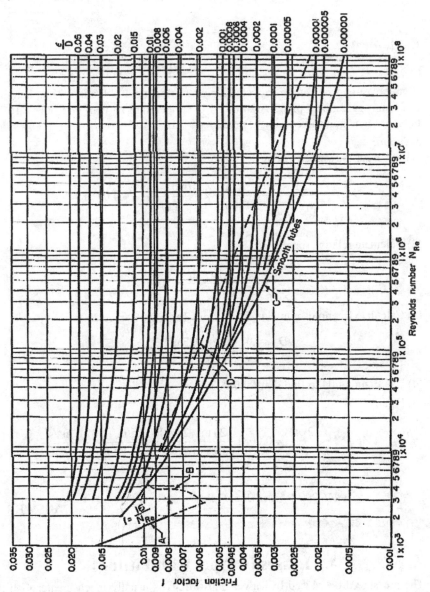

Figure 4.04. Relationship between Fanning friction factor (f) and Reynolds number. (Perry et al. 1973. *Perry's Chemical Engineering Handbook,* McGraw Hill. Reproduced with permission of McGraw Hill Companies.)

Example 4.6

What pressure drop can be expected for water flowing at 2 L/s in a 23-m length of 25-mm galvanized pipe? Assume 20°C temperature so that $v=1.006 \times 10^{-6}$ m²/s. For new galvanized pipe, $\in = 152 \times 10^{-6}$ m.

Solution:
(1) Solve for the velocity in m/s:

$$u = \frac{2 \text{ L/s}}{\frac{\pi}{4}(25)^2 \text{ mm}^2} \times \frac{1 \text{ m}^3}{1000 \text{ L}} \times \frac{(1000)^2 \text{ mm}^2}{1 \text{ m}^2} = 4.07 \text{ m/s}$$

(2) Calculate relative roughness:

$$\frac{\in}{D} = \frac{152 \times 10^{-6} \text{ m}}{0.025} = 0.006$$

(3) Calculate Reynolds number (find v from Table 9.05, page 252):

$$Re = \frac{uD}{v} = \frac{4.07 \text{ m/s} (0.025 \text{ m})}{1.006 \times 10^{-6} \text{ m}^2/\text{s}} = 1.01 \times 10^5$$

(4) Use Figure 4.04 to find that $f = 0.0081$.
(5) Finally:

$$\Delta P = f \frac{L}{D} \frac{2\rho u^2}{g_c} = 0.0081 \frac{23 \text{ m}}{0.025 \text{ m}} \frac{2 \times 1000 \text{ kg/m}^3 (4.07)^2 \text{ m}^2/\text{s}^2}{1 \frac{\text{kg m}}{\text{N s}^2}}$$

$$= 246\,900 \text{ N/m}^2 = 246.9 \text{ kPa}$$

ANSWER

4.5 Losses in Pipes with Fittings

The pressure drop caused by valves and fittings is usually much greater than the loss through an equal length of straight pipe. Because of this, valve and fitting losses must be considered in the analysis of any distribution system. To analyze these losses, it is usually most convenient to replace (in theory—not physically) each fitting by a length of straight pipe that results in the same pressure loss as that caused by the fitting. We can then find the pressure loss for the total length of pipe, including the hypothetical sections added to replace the fittings. Nomographs and tables to convert fittings to equivalent lengths of pipe are available.

Table 4.04. Constants for use in computing friction losses in fittings.[a]

Fitting	L_e/D[b]	K[b]
Elbow, 90°, standard	32	0.74
Elbow, 90°, medium sweep	26	0.50
Elbow, 90°, long sweep	20	0.25
Elbow, 45°, standard	15	0.35
Tee, used as elbow	70	1.50
Tee, used as coupling, branch plugged	20	0.4
Gate valve, open	7	0.16
Gate valve, half open	200	4.5
Globe valve, open	300	6.0
Globe valve, 1/4 open	1000	24.0
Coupling or union	2	0.4

[a] See Perry & Green (1984) and Avallone and Baumeister (1986)
for additional information.
[b] Values presented here are typical. Actual magnitudes vary with
conditions, and published values vary for many fittings.

The equivalent length approach determines an equivalent length by expressing the fitting loss as a function of the fitting type and pipe size. This is accomplished by noting that the equivalent length of straight pipe is a function of the fitting type and the pipe diameter. Thus, the equivalent length (L_e) for a particular fitting can be approximately expressed as a constant (for that fitting) multiplied by the pipe diameter. Constants for several fittings are given in Table 4.04. To find the equivalent length (L_e), simply multiply the value of L_e/D by the pipe diameter ($L_e = L_e/D \times D$). The "equivalent length" values may be used with either the Fanning or Darcy friction factors. We will use this equivalent length method for our analyses.

An alternate method of estimating fitting losses is through the use of a dimensionless loss coefficient (K), where $K = f L_e/D$. For this approach, the loss for any fitting is simply the value of K for that fitting multiplied by $2u^2/g_c$. Thus the energy loss through any fitting can be expressed as $\dfrac{\Delta P_f}{\rho} = K \dfrac{2u^2}{g_c}$. Note that the loss coefficient values given here are specific to the Fanning friction factor. Also note that K and L_e are both estimates of losses due to fittings, not exact computations.

Example 4.7

Find the head loss (m) and energy loss (J/kg) for 30 m of 25-mm diameter galvanized pipe carrying 0.60 L/s if the pipe has one globe valve and two 90° elbows. The water temperature is 20°C.

Solution:

(1) Find the equivalent pipe length for the valve and fittings (use Table 4.04):

Fitting	Equivalent Length	
globe valve	300×0.025	$= 7.50$ m
90° elbows	$2 \times 32 \times 0.025$	$= \underline{1.60}$ m
	TOTAL	9.10 m

This value of 9.10 m is the length of straight pipe that would result in the same energy loss as the fittings.

(2) The total equivalent length is $L = 30$ m $+ 9.10$ m $= 39.1$ m.

(3) Solve for the velocity:

$$u = \frac{0.6 \text{ L/s}}{(\pi/4) \times (25)^2 \text{ mm}^2} \times \frac{(1000)^2 \text{ mm}^2}{1 \text{ m}^2} \times \frac{1 \text{ m}^3}{1000 \text{ L}} = 1.222 \text{ m/s}$$

(4) Compute the Reynolds number:

$$Re = \frac{uD}{v} = \frac{1.222 \text{ m/s} (0.025 \text{m})}{1.006 \times 10^{-6} \text{m}^2/\text{s}} = 3.04 \times 10^4$$

(5) Noting that the relative roughness is 0.006 (see Example 4.6), we can use Figure 4.04 to find $f = 0.009$.

(6) We can now compute the friction loss in terms of head loss, pressure drop, or energy loss per unit mass of flowing fluid.

Head loss: $H_f = \dfrac{\Delta P_f}{\rho} \dfrac{g_c}{g} = f \dfrac{L}{D} \dfrac{2u^2}{g}$

$$= 0.009 \times \frac{39.1 \text{ m}}{0.025 \text{ m}} \times \frac{2 \times (1.222)^2 \text{ m}^2/\text{s}^2}{9.81 \text{ m/s}^2}$$

$$= 0.009 \times 1564 \times 0.304 = \underline{4.29 \text{ m}}$$ **ANSWER**

Pressure drop: $\Delta P_f = \dfrac{\Delta P}{\rho} \rho = f \dfrac{L}{D} \dfrac{2\rho u^2}{g_c}$

$$= 0.009 \times \frac{39.1}{0.025} \times \frac{2 \times 1000 \text{ kg/m}^3 (1.222)^2 \text{ m}^2/\text{s}^2}{1 \dfrac{\text{kg m}}{\text{N s}^2}}$$

$$= 0.009 \times 1564 \times 2976 \times 41900 \text{ N/m}^2 = \underline{41.9 \text{ kPa}}$$ **ANSWER**

Energy loss: $\left(\dfrac{\Delta P_f}{\rho} \right) = f \dfrac{L}{D} \dfrac{2u^2}{g_c}$

$$= 0.009 \times \frac{39.1}{0.025} \times \frac{2 \times (1.222)^2 \, m^2/s^2}{1 \frac{kg \, m}{N \, s^2}}$$

$$= 41.9 \frac{N \, m}{kg} = 41.9 \, J/kg \qquad\qquad \textbf{ANSWER}$$

4.6 Selecting the Correct Pipe Size

The selection of correct pipe sizes involves a considerable amount of judgment. For some applications, a smaller pipe—with its higher pressure losses—may be used in place of a larger, more expensive pipe. For other applications, the power requirements associated with higher energy losses may justify the greater initial cost of larger pipe. As a general guide, pipe sizes that result in a pressure drop per unit length of between 100 and 1000 Pa/m would probably be suitable for flow of water and similar liquids. However, systems with friction losses near the upper end of this range should be used only for very short distances due to the high energy losses.

4.7 Power Requirements for Pumping

The pump power requirements for a liquid flow system may be determined by using the energy conservation equation (Equation 4.06 for SI units or Equation 4.07 for US units.) The total energy that the pump must supply is given by Equation 4.06 as:

$$E_p = E_2 + E_f - E_1$$

The pump power is the product of the energy input of the pump (E_p) and the mass flow rate $\left(\dot{m} \right)$:

$$P_w = E_p(J/kg) \times \dot{m}(kg/s) \qquad (J/s \text{ or } W) \qquad (4.19)$$

This equation can also be written in terms of flow rate and total pressure difference:

$$P_w(W) = P_t(Pa) \times \dot{Q} \ (m^3/s),$$

where: $P_t = E_p(J/kg) \times \rho(kg/m^3)$ (Units note: $J/m^3 = N \, m/m^3 = N/m^2 = Pa$)

The power calculated above represents the power that must be imparted to the water. Since the pump is never 100% efficient, the power to the pump shaft (P_p) must be greater than P_w. In addition, drive motors have inefficiencies that must be considered. When these factors are included, the pump motor input power (P_m) is given by:

$$P_m = \frac{E_p \, \dot{m}}{\eta_m \eta_p} \qquad\qquad (4.20)$$

where: η_m = the motor efficiency in decimal form

         η_p = the pump efficiency in decimal form

Computation of pump power in US units is slightly more complicated. From Equation 4.07, the total head which a pump must overcome is given by:

$$H_p = H_2 + H_f - H_1 \qquad (4.21)$$

The power is then found by multiplying the pump head by the flow rate:

$$P_w = \dot{w}\left(\frac{1b}{min}\right) \times H_p(\text{ft}) \qquad \left(\frac{\text{ft } 1b}{min}\right) \qquad (4.22)$$

or, in terms of horsepower:

$$P_w = \frac{\dot{w}\,H_p}{33\,000} = \frac{\dot{Q}\,w\,H_p}{33\,000} \qquad (4.23)$$

where: H_p = total pump head, ft,

        P_w = power in horsepower,

        $\dot{Q}$ = volumetric flow rate, cfm,

        w = specific weight, $1b_f/ft^3$,

        $\dot{w}$ = the product of $\dot{Q}$ and w with units of $1b/min$, and the number 33 000
           converts the units from ft-lb/min to horsepower.

Considering pump and motor efficiencies, the motor input horsepower then becomes:

$$P_m = \frac{\dot{Q}\,w\,H_p}{\left(\eta_m \eta_p\right) \times 33000} \qquad (4.24)$$

Example 4.8

A pump (see the sketch below) supplies 40 L/min of water through 30 m of 2.54 cm (1 in.) galvanized pipe. The pipe has one globe valve and two 90° elbows. Water is delivered at 140 kPa to a tank located 15 m above the pump intake. What is the pump motor power requirement if the combined pump and motor efficiency is 0.70?

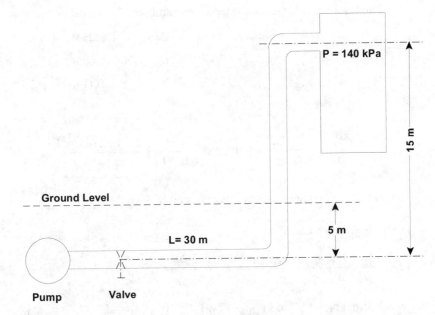

Solution:

We must first solve for E_p using Equation 4.06 and then solve for the power.

(1) Solve for velocity and Reynolds number:

$$u = \frac{\dot{Q}}{A}$$

$$\dot{Q} = 40\frac{L}{min} \times \frac{1\,min}{60\,s} \times \frac{1\,m^3}{1000\,L} = 6.667 \times 10^{-4}\,m^3/s$$

$$A = \frac{\pi}{4}\left(2.54\,cm \times \frac{1\,m}{100\,cm}\right)^2 = 5.067 \times 10^{-4}\,m^2$$

$$u = \frac{6.667 \times 10^{-4}\,m^3/s}{5.067 \times 10^{-4}\,m^2} = 1.32\,\frac{m}{s}$$

$$Re = \frac{uD}{\nu} = \frac{1.32\,m/s \times 0.0254\,m}{1.006 \times 10^{-6}\,m^2/s} = 33330$$

(Viscosity at 20°C was used to find Re.)

(2) Find the friction factor:

From Figure 4.04 at $Re = 33\,330$ and $\frac{\epsilon}{D} = \frac{152 \times 10^{-6}}{2.54 \times 10^{-2}} = 0.005\,98$

We find $f = 0.0089$.

(3) Find the equivalent length of the pipe with fittings and the friction loss:

For 90° elbow: $L_e/D = 32$ $L_e = 2(32)(0.0254) = 1.63$

Globe valve: $L_e/D = 300$ $L_e = 1(300)(0.0254) = \underline{7.62}$

$$\text{TOTAL} \quad 9.25$$

$$L_e = 30 + 9.25 = 39.25 \text{ m}$$

$$\frac{\Delta P_f}{\rho} = f \frac{L_e}{D} \frac{2u^2}{g_c} = 0.0089 \times \left(\frac{39.25}{0.0254}\right) \times \frac{2 \times (1.32)^2 \, \text{m}^2/\text{s}^2}{1\dfrac{\text{kg m}}{\text{N s}^2}}$$

$$= 0.0089 \times 1545 \times 3.4848 = 47.9 \text{ N m/kg}$$

(4) Solve Equation 4.06:

$$E_p = \frac{P_2}{\rho} - \frac{P_1}{\rho} + \frac{gz_2}{g_c} - \frac{gz_1}{g_c} + \frac{u_2^2}{2g_c} - \frac{u_1^2}{2g_c} + \frac{\Delta P_f}{\rho}$$

$$= \frac{140 \text{ kPa}}{1000 \text{ kg/m}^3} - 0 + \frac{9.81 \text{ m/s}^2 (15 \text{ m})}{1\dfrac{\text{kg m}}{\text{N s}^2}} - 0 + \frac{(1.32)^2 \text{m}^2/\text{s}^2}{2\dfrac{\text{kgm}}{\text{N s}^2}} - 0 + 47.9 \frac{\text{N m}}{\text{kg}}$$

$$= \frac{140\ 000 \text{ N/m}^2}{1000 \text{ kg/m}^3} + 147 \frac{\text{N m}}{\text{kg}} + 0.87 \frac{\text{N m}}{\text{kg}} + 47.9 \frac{\text{N m}}{\text{kg}}$$

$$E_p = (140 + 147 + 0 + 87 + 47.9)\frac{\text{N m}}{\text{kg}} = 336 \frac{\text{J}}{\text{kg}}$$

$$P_m = \frac{E_P\left(\dfrac{\text{J}}{\text{kg}}\right) \times \dot{m}\left(\dfrac{\text{kg}}{\text{s}}\right)}{\eta}$$

$$P_m = \frac{336 \text{ J/kg} \times \left(6.667 \times 10^{-4} \text{m}^3/\text{s} \times 1000 \text{ kg/m}^3\right)}{0.7}$$

$$= \underline{320 \text{ W}} \qquad\qquad \textbf{ANSWER}$$

Example 4.9

Repeat Example 4.8 for a range of flow rates between 0 and 500 L/min. Plot E_p as a function of flow rate for this range.

Solution:
For each flow rate we must calculate the velocity (u), Reynolds number (Re), friction factor (f), friction loss $(\Delta P_f/\rho)$, and pump energy input (E_p). We follow the steps of Example 4.8, using different flow rates for each calculation. The results are summarized in the following table, and E_p is plotted in the accompanying graph. The curve produced is commonly called a **system curve**.

Note that the pump energy (E_p) increases rapidly as flow rate increases. That is due to the friction loss increase, from 14% of E_p at 40 L/min to 96% at 500 L/min. The friction loss increases approximately as the square of the velocity. (This is not an exact relationship since the friction factor decreases slightly as velocity increases.) This increase in $\Delta P_f/\rho$ clearly shows the need to maintain relatively low flow rates to keep friction losses low.

(L/min)	u (m/s)	Re	f_f	$\Delta P_f/\rho$ (J/kg)	E_p (J/kg)
0	0	0	0.01600	0	288
40	1.32	33 300	0.00890	48	336
100	3.29	83 050	0.00860	288	575
150	4.93	124 600	0.00840	632	920
200	6.58	166 100	0.00830	1110	1398
250	8.22	207 600	0.00820	1714	2002
300	9.87	249 100	0.00815	2453	2740
400	13.16	332 200	0.00815	4360	4648
500	16.45	415 200	0.00810	6771	7059

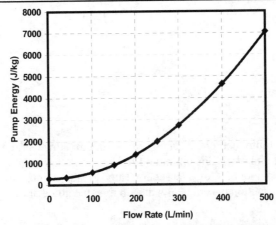

4.8 Pump Types and Characteristics

4.8.1 Introduction

A wide range of pump types is available to meet the many needs of individual water supply systems and special fluids handling systems. To be knowledgeable concerning these many pump types, one must understand the meaning of terms such as centrifugal, positive displacement, peristaltic, turbine, gear, deep well, shallow well, jet, etc., as they apply to pumps. This section presents a brief survey of pumps and discusses some of the more common types.

4.8.2 Suction Pumps

In an earlier section, we observed the relationship between pressure and depth (or head). Consider the sketch below where a piston draws water up inside a pipe until the absolute pressure (P_s) between the water surface and the piston is exactly zero. Atmospheric pressure will force water up into the pipe to that height—and no further. The height must be equivalent to atmospheric pressure, 101.325 kPa (101 325 Pa) or:

$$z = \frac{g_c \Delta P}{g \rho} = \frac{1\dfrac{\text{kg m}}{\text{N s}^2} \times 101\,325 \text{ N/m}^2}{9.81\dfrac{\text{m}}{\text{s}^2} \times 1000\dfrac{\text{kg}}{\text{m}^3}} = \underline{10.3 \text{ m}}$$

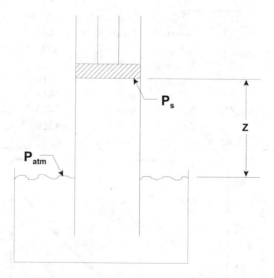

Thus the maximum theoretical suction lift is 10.3 m. However, no pump can maintain a perfect seal and reach this optimum lift. This and other factors reduce the maximum suction lift to about 7.6 m. The suction (intake) side of pumps must operate such that the maximum suction is kept below the 7.6 m value noted above.

4.8.3 Positive Displacement Pumps

Positive displacement pumps use a piston, gear, screw, or similar device to force fluids through the pump. This feature causes positive displacement pumps to have the following unique characteristics:

- constant capacity (if pump speed is constant) regardless of pump head (or pressure difference across the pump);
- constant efficiency;
- power requirement that varies linearly with pressure difference across pump; and
- discharge pressure that is limited only by power input and pump construction.

The **piston pump** operates in the same manner as the hand pumps (Figure 4.05) common many years ago. Although hand pumps are now relatively rare, piston pumps operated by electric motors are still in use. Except for limited applications, however, the piston pump has been replaced by the centrifugal pump in distribution systems for water and other fluids.

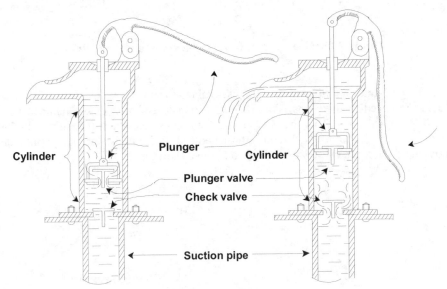

Cylinder   Plunger   Cylinder

Plunger valve

Check valve

Suction pipe

Figure 4.05. Hand operated piston pump.

The **gear pump** uses rotating gears to force the pumped fluid through the pump. Figure 4.06 shows one design for this type of pump. Several variations in design are possible. Close tolerances and associated high wear rates are a characteristic of these pumps. They are more appropriately used for special fluids handling applications than for water systems.

The **screw pump** is a refinement of the Archimedes Screw developed centuries ago. It is essentially a rotating screw mounted inside a tube. As the screw turns, material is forced up through the tube. High pressures can be attained in this type of pump. The screw pump is commonly used in the food industry. It can be used to "pump" dough-like materials that cannot be handled by many pumps.

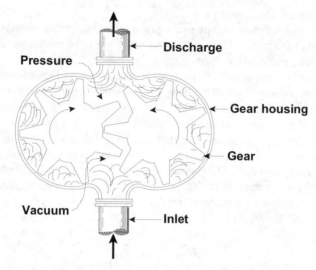

Figure 4.06. Gear pump. Rotating gears "pump" the fluid.

The **peristaltic pump** (Figure 4.07) uses rollers to squeeze fluids along a length of tubing mounted in the pump. This permits complete isolation of the pumped fluid from the pump body. This may be an important consideration if the fluid is highly corrosive. Specially designed tubing must be used in the peristaltic pump since the constant flexing can cause some tubing to fail in a short time.

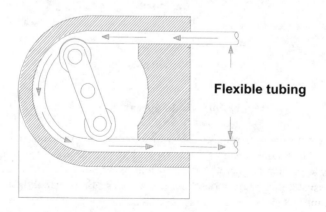

Figure 4.07. Peristaltic pump.
Rollers on a rotating shaft squeeze fluid through the tube.

4.8.4 Centrifugal Pumps

If you fill a bucket with water, punch a small hole in the bottom and then hold the bucket in front of you as you turn around rapidly, what happens? If you are lucky (don't become dizzy and drop the bucket on your toes), a stream of water will be propelled out the hole due to the centrifugal force produced by the rotation. This is the principle used in the operation of centrifugal pumps (Figure 4.08). The fluid enters at the center and is propelled outward by the pump impeller, which is rotating with sufficient speed to produce significant centrifugal force. The operating characteristics of centrifugal pumps are significantly different from those of positive displacement pumps:

- Capacity decreases as pump head (pressure difference) increases.
- Efficiency decreases as pump head (pressure difference) increases.
- Power requirement increases with flow rate.
- Pumps can be readily installed in series.

With these characteristics, centrifugal pumps are well suited for water handling as well as many other fluids-handling systems. Centrifugal pumps with several impeller stages in series can produce high pressure differences. At the other extreme, high capacity, low pressure difference centrifugal pumps also are widely used.

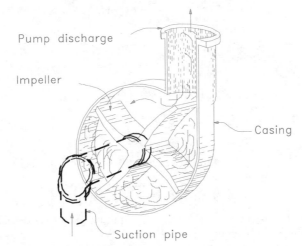

Figure 4.08. Centrifugal pump. Flow enters at the center and is forced outward by centrifugal force.

The **jet** (or ejector) pump refers not to the pump but to a jet-like mechanism (Figure 4.09) usually placed at the bottom of the pump intake. The jet is used with a centrifugal pump which recycles a certain amount of the flow to the jet where the high pressure is converted to a high velocity stream flowing through a small opening. Since energy is conserved, pressure energy is converted to velocity (kinetic energy).

This high velocity stream flows into the throat of a venturi where it draws in water from the area surrounding the jet. The recycled water and the "new" water then flow upward through the lift pipe to the pump impeller inlet. Jet pumps may be used for either shallow or deep wells. As the well depth increases, the pump efficiency decreases since more water must be recycled through the jet. For depths of over 100 m, the efficiency of a jet pump is quite low. The jet pump principle is used in a variety of low flow specialty applications (e.g., the device for emptying waterbeds contains a jet that uses water from a faucet to draw water from the bed).

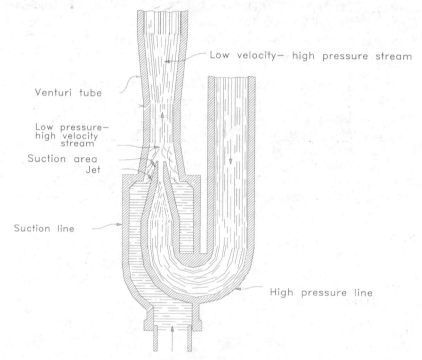

Figure 4.09. Jet or ejector mechanism.

4.9 Selecting a Pump

Pump selection is based upon (1) capacity required, (2) pressure difference (sometimes called pump head) required, and (3) other special factors such as fluid to be pumped, sanitary requirements, space limitations, noise restrictions, etc.

If a positive displacement pump is to be used, pump pressure difference is usually not a factor. It is only necessary to select a pump of the proper capacity that also meets any applicable special requirements. Size of the pump motor is a function of the pump pressure difference and may be determined using Equation 4.20.

For a centrifugal pump, other factors must be considered. Depending upon the type and number of impeller stages, a given pump will develop a certain pressure difference. Thus, if a greater pressure difference is necessary, a different pump must be selected. This situation is demonstrated by Figure 4.10.

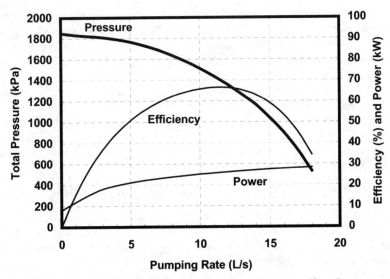

Figure 4.10. Typical performance curves for a centrifugal pump.

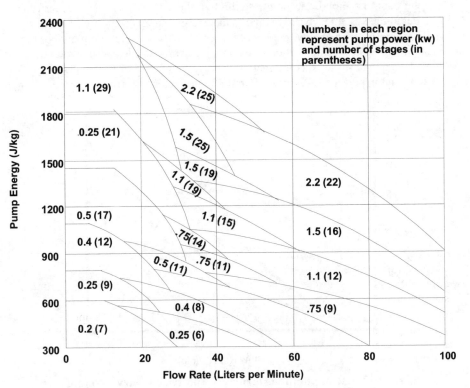

Figure 4.11. Operating ranges for different centrifugal pumps.

The typical centrifugal pump develops maximum pressure difference at zero flow, as flow increases the pressure difference produced by the pump decreases. This curve, which may be expressed in units of pressure, is called the pump **performance curve**. While not always possible, the preferred operating condition is near the maximum efficiency for the pump. Each pump manufacturer will usually have a line of pumps which will cover a wide range of flow rates and pump heads. By referring to a summary graph such as Figure 4.11, a pump can be selected to meet any particular need. This graph displays data regarding a family of pumps. A specific model is selected by determining the flow rate and pump energy requirements. For example, a flow rate of 60 L/s and a pump energy requirement of 1500 J/kg would require a 2.2 kW pump with 22 impellers, the 2.2(22) range shown on the chart.

4.10 Pump Performance vs. System Curves

Other than our calculations in Example 4.9, we have assumed a fixed velocity for the analysis of any fluid flow system. In this section we will examine the interaction between a given pump and a given flow system (given pipe type, size, length, fittings, elevation difference, etc.). If we connect a centrifugal pump to the system of Example 4.9, the resulting flow rate is controlled by the interaction between the pump performance curve and the system curve.

Once the pump is started, the flow rate through the system will increase until the energy input to the system is exactly equal to the energy output capability of the pump at that flow rate. In other words, the operating point for a specific pump and system combination will be at the intersection of the pump performance and system curves.

Figure 4.12 demonstrates this interaction. The system curve of Example 4.9 (System A) and a pump performance curve (Pump A) intersect at point 1. This intersection

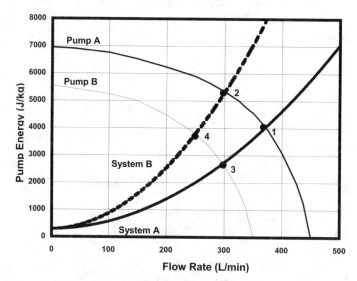

Figure 4.12. Use of pump performance and system curves to find operating points.

identifies the operating point for the pump and system combination. Addition of valves, fittings, or more pipe to a system would produce a new system curve (System B). The operating point for the new system is at intersection 2. If pump A is replaced by a different pump (B), with a different pump performance curve, operating conditions for systems A and B would move to locations 3 and 4 respectively. Whatever the pump performance-system curve combination, the operating point is always at the intersection of the two curves.

4.11 Fans

4.11.1 Introduction

Fans are pumps that move gases, usually air, at high flow rate but low pressure differences. Fans are classified based upon the pattern of flow through the fan impeller. Types of possible flow are axial flow, radial flow, mixed flow, and cross flow.

The most common type of axial flow fan is the common propeller fan such as the exhaust fan used in many homes and the radiator cooling fan on automobiles. This fan type can develop only a very small pressure difference. This difference can be slightly increased by enclosing the fan in a shroud as is done on many automobiles. Two other axial flow fans, tube-axial and vane-axial fans, are mounted inside tubes such that they develop higher pressures and are more efficient. Henderson et al. (1997) provide additional information regarding these fans.

For higher pressure differences, radial flow (centrifugal) fans may be used. These fans have the same general operating characteristics as centrifugal pumps. Air enters the impeller along the axis, is accelerated outward by the blades, and is discharged radially. Specific performance characteristics depend upon blade design. The three general blade designs are: forward curved, backward curved, and radial. Typical examples of each blade type are shown in Figure 4.13. Fans with forward curved blades, also known as "squirrel cage" fans, have many short curved blades. They operate at relatively low speeds and pressures, are relatively quiet, and suitable only for clean air. Radial (straight or curved) blade fans can handle dirty air and develop higher pressures.

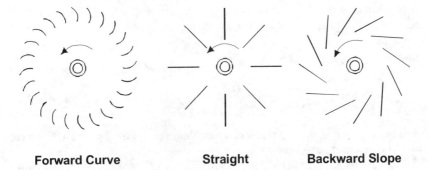

Forward Curve   **Straight**   **Backward Slope**

Figure 4.13. Examples of the three major types of centrifugal fan blades.

Backward sloped and backward curved blades can also develop relatively high pressures. They also have one very important characteristic. When operated at constant speed, the motor cannot be overloaded regardless of the amount of static pressure or flow rate of the fan. Obviously the static pressure and flow rate are interrelated and cannot be varied independently with a given fan. Any change in one will produce a change in the other so that no overload can occur. Centrifugal fan performance curves are similar in appearance to those of centrifugal pumps (Figure 4.10). Typical performance curves for several fan types are given by ASHRAE, 1996.

4.11.2 Fan Power Requirements

As with liquid pumps, fan power requirements are a function of the air flow rate, the pressure across the fan, and efficiencies of the system. Two pressure terms are used with fan operation. Static pressure (P_s) is simply the measured pressure difference across the fan. Fan total pressure (P_t) is the sum of the static pressure and the velocity pressure. The general equation for fan power can be written as:

$$P_f(\text{W}) = \frac{\dot{Q}(\text{m}^3/\text{s}) \times P_t(\text{Pa})}{\eta_f \eta_m} \tag{4.25}$$

where: P_f = fan power input required, W
P_t = fan total pressure, Pa

$\dot{Q}$ = air flow rate, m^3/s

η_f = fan efficiency, decimal
η_m = fan motor efficiency, decimal

Example 4.10

A fan provides 10,000 L/s of air at a total pressure (static pressure plus velocity pressure) of 200 Pa. What is the fan output power? If the fan efficiency is 70% and the motor efficiency is 90%, what is the fan input power?

Solution:
Using the fan power equation:

$$P_{f(out)} = 10,000 \frac{\text{L}}{\text{s}} \times \frac{1 \, \text{m}^3}{1000 \, \text{L}} \times 200 \frac{\text{N}}{\text{m}^3} = 2000 \frac{\text{N m}}{\text{s}} = 2000 \, \text{W} = \underline{2 \, \text{kW}} \; \textbf{ANSWER}$$

The output power is the input power times the overall efficiency. Thus, we can calculate the input power as:

$$P_{f(in)} = \frac{P_{f(out)}}{\eta_f \eta_m} = \frac{2 \, \text{kW}}{0.7 \times 0.9} = \frac{2 \, \text{kW}}{0.63} = \underline{3.17 \, \text{kW}} \qquad\qquad \textbf{ANSWER}$$

4.11.3 Fan Laws

Relationships commonly identified as "fan laws" can be used to relate flow rate, pressure difference, and power required for geometrically similar fans. These relationships can be used to determine the effect of a change in speed for a given fan or to compare fans of the same design but different sizes. The fan law relationships are:

$$\frac{\dot{Q}_1}{\dot{Q}_2} = \frac{N_1}{N_2}\left(\frac{D_1}{D_2}\right)^3 \tag{4.26}$$

$$\frac{P_{t1}}{P_{t2}} = \left(\frac{N_1}{N_2}\right)^2\left(\frac{D_1}{D_2}\right)^2\frac{P_1}{P_2} \tag{4.27}$$

$$\frac{P_{f1}}{P_{f2}} = \left(\frac{N_1}{N_2}\right)^3\left(\frac{D_1}{D_2}\right)^5\frac{\rho_1}{\rho_2} \tag{4.28}$$

where:　subscripts 1 and 2 refer to the two fans

　　　　P_f, P_t, $\dot{Q}$ are as defined in the previous section

　　　　N = impeller rotational speed

　　　　D = impeller diameter

　　　　ρ = density of the air, kg/m^3

The fan laws as stated above ignore the compressibility factor (K). This is not a problem for typical fan operations, since pressure differences are usually small and the value of K can be taken as 1 with little error. In most instances, density changes are small and can also be ignored. See Henderson et al. (1997), Avallone and Baumeister (1986), or Jorgensen (1999) for additional information regarding use of the fan laws. The fan laws above also apply for centrifugal pumps. When used for pumps, the density ratio can be deleted from the equations.

In addition to fan comparisons, the fan laws indicate other important relationships that are useful in analyzing fan operations. Key relationships are as follows: air flow ($\dot{Q}$) is proportional to fan speed (N); pressure is proportional to the speed squared (N^2); and power is proportional to the speed cubed (N^3). The effect of size is even more significant. If all other factors are constant, doubling the fan size will increase air flow by a factor of six; pressure difference by a factor of four; and required power by a factor of 32.

Example 4.11

The fan of the previous example is delivering more air than needed. The owner wants to reduce air flow to 8,000 L/s. What fan speed would be needed to produce this flow rate assuming an original fan speed of 600 rpm? How much (as a percent) would the fan power requirement be changed?

Solution:

Using the fan law equation relating flow and fan speed (Equation 4.26), and noting that fan size is unchanged, we can solve for the new fan speed:

$$N_2 = N_1 \frac{\dot{Q}_2}{\dot{Q}_1} = 600 \frac{8000}{10000} = \underline{480 \quad \text{rpm}} \qquad \textbf{ANSWER}$$

To compute the power change, we use the fan law for power (Equation 4.28), noting that fan size is unchanged and that density changes are insignificant:

$$\frac{P_{f2}}{P_{f1}} = \left(\frac{N_2}{N_1}\right)^3 = \left(\frac{8000}{10000}\right)^3 = 0.512$$

The new power requirement is <u>51.2%</u> of the original.   **ANSWER**

4.12 Flow Measurement

4.12.1 Introduction

There are many different types of flow measurement equipment. Some are very simple and easy to use, while others are complex and delicate instruments requiring great care in their use. In this section, we will look at some of the more common methods of flow measurement. The methods using more complex equipment will be mentioned only briefly.

4.12.2 Collection Methods

For many liquids, one of the easiest flow measurement methods is to measure the amount collected during a specified period of time. Since most liquids change little in density, the measurement may be either a volume measurement or a mass measurement. This method of measurement gives only an average value for the flow rate during the specified period. If the flow is not constant, other methods should be used. The time interval used for collection must be sufficiently long to permit accurate measurements. Depending upon the application, time periods of less than 30 to 60 seconds may produce unsatisfactory results due to difficulty in accurately measuring lapsed time.

Example 4.12

A stopwatch is used to measure the time required to collect 100 kg of water in a continuously weighed container. The time required is measured as 38 s. What is the flow rate in L/s, assuming a density of 1000 kg/m³? If the time measurement has a potential error of 1 second (it can be anywhere between 37 and 39 s) what is the potential range of flow rate?

Solution:
The mass flow rate is 100 kg/38 s = 2.63 kg/s. For the standard density of 1000 kg/m³, the flow rate is:

$$\dot{Q} = \frac{2.63\dfrac{kg}{s}}{1000\dfrac{kg}{m^3}} \times 1000\frac{L}{m^3} = 2.63\frac{L}{s} \qquad \textbf{ANSWER}$$

Following a similar procedure for the possible maximum and minimum times, the range in flow rates is 2.56 to 2.70 L/s. The difference between these two rates is approximately 5%. This potential error could have been reduced by collecting a greater amount of water over a longer measurement period.

4.12.3 Positive Displacement Meters

Positive displacement meters measure flow rate by using the flowing fluid to displace the sensing portion of the meter. In many cases positive displacement meters are very similar to pumps. Because of the direct relationship between flow rate and pump speed, many positive displacement pumps may be used as flow meters.

4.12.4 Obstruction Meters

Referring to Equation 4.13, we see that if the type, size, and length of pipe are fixed, we can solve for velocity (and thus flow rate) as a function of pressure drop in the pipe. This principle is the basis of several restriction type flow meters. These devices are usually permanently installed and are generally unsuitable for portable use. The governing equations for three common restriction meters (orifice, venturi, and flow nozzle) can be simplified to:

$$\dot{Q} = K\sqrt{\Delta P} \qquad (4.29)$$

where K is a function of the type of liquid, the type and size of the meter, and the units of $\dot{Q}$ and P.

The **orifice meter** is one of the most common types of restriction meters. It is simply a thin plate placed in the pipe. The plate contains a hole significantly smaller than the inside diameter of the pipe (Figure 4.14). Pressure measurements on each side of the orifice can then be used to determine the flow rate. Since the pressure varies with distance on each side of the orifice, location of the orifice meter pressure taps is important. Three different "standard" installations are possible:

1. flange taps, located in the flanges on each side of the orifice (a common arrangement);
2. diameter taps, located one pipe diameter upstream and half a pipe diameter downstream; and
3. vena contracta taps, located one pipe diameter upstream and downstream at the vena contracta.

The value of K in Equation 4.29 is a function of the pressure tap location in addition to the other factors already mentioned.

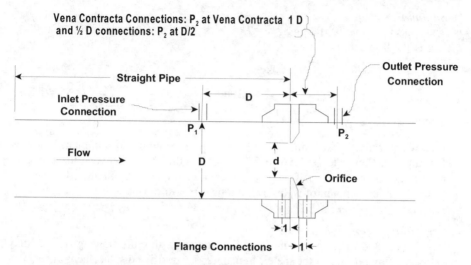

Vena Contracta Connections: P_2 at Vena Contracta 1 D
and ½ D connections: P_2 at D/2

Figure 4.14. Orifice installation. Pressure connections may be flange, vena contracta, or 1D and 0.5D taps.

Example 4.13

An orifice meter is used to measure air flow. It measures an orifice pressure difference of 800 kPa at an air flow rate of 80 L/s. What is the air flow rate at a pressure difference of 600 kPa?

Solution:
Using Equation 4.29, we can solve for the orifice coefficient, K:

$$K = \frac{\dot{Q}}{\sqrt{\Delta P}} = \frac{80}{\sqrt{800}} = 2.828$$

We can use this coefficient in the equation and solve for the flow rate at a new pressure. (Note that the coefficient includes unit conversions, and we must use the same sets of units in any application of the coefficient.)

$$\dot{Q} = K\sqrt{\Delta P} = 2.828\sqrt{600} = 69.3 \text{ L/s} \qquad \textbf{ANSWER}$$

When more precision in flow measurement is needed, the **venturi meter** (Figure 4.15) may be used. In addition to being one of the more accurate restriction meters, it has the advantage of low pressure loss through the meter. It is considerably more expensive than the orifice meter.

A third type of restriction meter is the **flow nozzle** (Figure 4.16). Except for the pressure tap location, its use is very similar to that of the orifice meter.

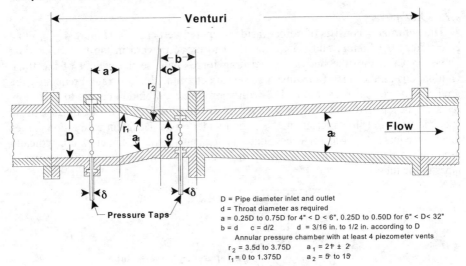

Venturi

D = Pipe diameter inlet and outlet
d = Throat diameter as required
a = 0.25D to 0.75D for 4" < D < 6", 0.25D to 0.50D for 6" < D< 32"
b = d   c = d/2   d = 3/16 in. to 1/2 in. according to D
   Annular pressure chamber with at least 4 piezometer vents
   r_2 = 3.5d to 3.75D a_1 = 21° ± 2°
   r_1 = 0 to 1.375D a_2 = 5° to 15°

Figure 4.15. Details of a venturi meter.

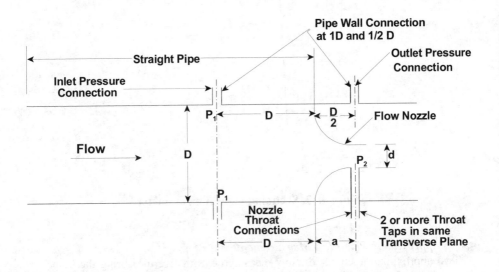

Figure 4.16. Flow nozzle. P_2 may be measured at pipe taps (top)
or a throat tap (bottom).

4.12.5 Rotameters

The **rotameter** consists of a float inside a tapered vertical tube (Figure 4.17). Flow enters from the bottom and causes the float to move upward in the tube. The float moves upward until the buoyancy and drag forces balance the weight of the float. Graduations on the side of the tube are used to determine the flow rate. Frequently the graduations are scaled from 0 to 100 with appropriate calibration curves to give flow rates in the desired units. Many rotameters are designed so that the floats can be changed to permit flow measurements over a wider range. Different calibration curves must, of course, be used for each float and for each fluid. Rotameters are typically used only for low flow rates. Accuracy depends upon tube length and the amount of taper in the tube.

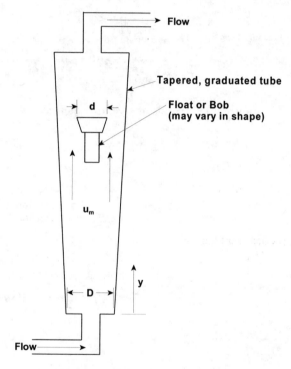

Figure 4.17. Sectional view of a rotameter.

4.12.6 Approximate Pipe Flow Measurements

Two approximate methods of flow measurement involve measuring the trajectory of the fluid after it leaves the pipe exit. Intuitively, we know that as the velocity changes, the trajectory will change. Figure 4.18 shows how this can be used to determine approximate flow rates for vertical or horizontal pipes of known diameter.

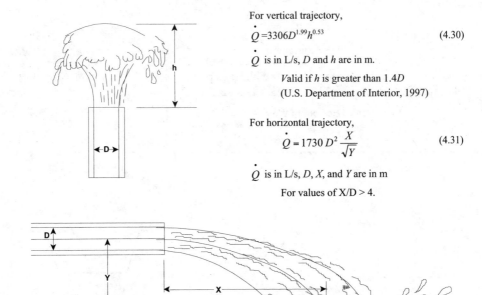

For vertical trajectory,

$$\dot{Q} = 3306 D^{1.99} h^{0.53} \qquad (4.30)$$

$\dot{Q}$ is in L/s, D and h are in m.

Valid if h is greater than $1.4D$
(U.S. Department of Interior, 1997)

For horizontal trajectory,

$$\dot{Q} = 1730\, D^2 \frac{X}{\sqrt{Y}} \qquad (4.31)$$

$\dot{Q}$ is in L/s, D, X, and Y are in m

For values of $X/D > 4$.

Figure 4.18. Approximate pipe flow measurements using the trajectory method.

4.12.7 Open Channel Flow

Flow in open channels is often measured by a **weir** or a **flume**. These are both restriction type measuring devices. The several types of weirs are comparable to the orifice meter while the flume is comparable to the venturi. As the fluid flows over a weir, the flow rate varies essentially with the fluid height (h) above the bottom of the weir (Figure 4.19). The general formula for flow over a weir may be written as:

$$\dot{Q} = C_w h^n \qquad (4.32)$$

where C_w and n are constants for a given weir. For a triangular weir with $\theta = 90°$, the above equation becomes:

$$\dot{Q} = 1.375\, h^{5/2} \qquad (4.33)$$

where $\dot{Q}$ is in cubic meters per second and h is in meters.

Flumes, such as the Parshall flume, are quite simple in use. However, they must be designed for specific ranges of flow rate. Computations for flow are complex and are usually performed using charts for specific flume sizes. See U.S. Department of Interior (1997) for additional information.

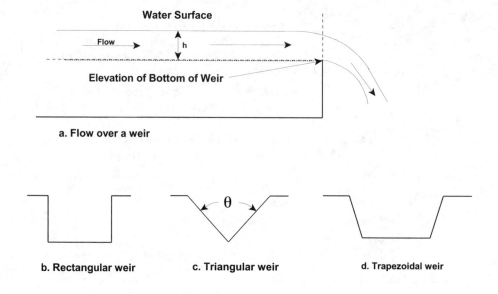

a. Flow over a weir

b. Rectangular weir   c. Triangular weir   d. Trapezoidal weir

Figure 4.19. Weirs used for flow measurement.

4.12.8 Velocity Measurement

The devices discussed to this point are primarily used to determine flow rate directly without calculating velocity. It is sometimes more convenient to measure the velocity of the moving fluid and use the continuity equation to determine the flow rate. The pitot tube (Figure 4.20) discussed below may be used for measurements of this type. It measures velocity head $\left(\dfrac{\rho\, u^2}{2g} \right)$ and is not accurate at low velocities.

The **pitot tube** is an L-shaped tube with an opening in its tip and other openings around the tube perimeter. When the tip is pointed directly into the flow, the opening at the tip measures the total pressure (including velocity head) of the fluid. The perimeter openings measure static pressure only and lead to a separate pressure connection. By using a manometer or other differential pressure meter, the difference between the two pressures, or velocity pressure, is found. Thus:

$$\frac{\rho\, u^2}{2\, g_c} = \Delta P \tag{4.34}$$

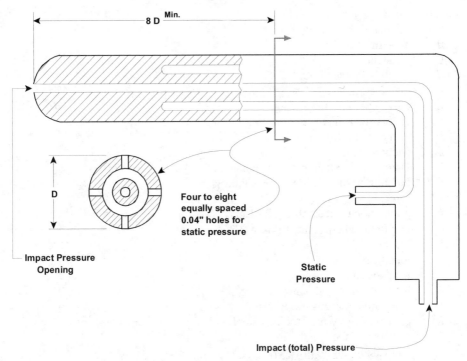

**Figure 4.20. The pitot tube measures velocity pressure,
the difference between total and static pressures.**

Solving for the velocity, we find:

$$u = \sqrt{\frac{2\,g_c\,\Delta P}{\rho}} = 1.41\sqrt{\frac{\Delta P}{\rho}} \qquad (4.35)$$

where: P = pressure, Pa
$\quad\quad\;\; u$ = velocity, m/s
$\quad\quad\;\; \rho$ = density, kg/m^3

The pitot tube may be used for either liquids or gases. For gases, such as air, temperature and pressure effects must be considered since they may change the density.

4.12.9 Other Methods

There are many other frequently used methods of flow (or velocity) measurement. Devices such as laser anemometers and hot wire anemometers are used in many applications where fluctuating flows must be measured. They provide highly accurate velocity measurements when properly calibrated. Turbine meters, magnetic flowmeters and various visualization techniques are also used for certain applications. Use of such flow measurement devices is quite complex and will not be covered here.

List of Symbols

a	acceleration, m/s^2
A	area, m^2
C	constant
d	depth below the liquid surface, m
D	diameter, m
E	energy per unit mass, J/kg
E_f	energy loss due to friction, J/kg
E_p	energy input from pump, J/kg
f	friction factor
f_d	Darcy friction factor, dimensionless, ($f_d = 4f_f$)
f_f	Fanning friction factor, dimensionless
F	force, N
g	gravitational acceleration, 9.81 m/s^2
g_c	gravitational constant, 1 (kg m)/(N s^2)
h	height, m
H	total head, ft or m
H_f	head loss due to friction, ft or m
H_p	head added by the pump, ft or m
K	constant in various equations
K	compressibility factor, dimensionless
L	a characteristic length, m
L_e	equivalent length, m
m	mass, kg
$\dot{m}$	mass flow rate, kg/s
n	constant
N	rotational speed, rpm
P	pressure, Pa
P_d	pressure at any depth (d) below the fluid surface, Pa
P_f	fan power, W
P_m	pump motor input power, W
P_s	pressure at a liquid surface, Pa
P_w	pump output power, W
ΔP	pressure drop, Pa
ΔP_f	pressure loss due to friction, Pa
$\dot{Q}$	volumetric flow rate, m^3/s
Re	Reynolds number, dimensionless
u	velocity, m/s
ΔV	volume change, m^2
w	specific weight, force/unit volume
x,y,z	coordinate direction
X	horizontal distance, m
Y	vertical distance, m
z	elevation above any selected reference level, m

$\in$ equivalent height of pipe roughness, m
η_f fan efficiency in decimal form
η_m motor efficiency in decimal form
η_p pump efficiency in decimal form
θ time, s
μ dynamic (or absolute) viscosity, Pa s or $(N \ s)/m^2$
ρ density, kg/m^3
ν kinematic viscosity (μ/ρ), m^2/s

Subscripts
1,2   position identification
d   depth
f   friction
p   pump
s   surface

References

1. American Society of Mechanical Engineers. 1961. *Flowmeter Computation Handbook.* ASME, New York, NY.
2. ASHRAE. 1996. *Handbook of HVAC Systems and Equipment,* Chapter 3: Fans. ASHRAE, Inc., Atlanta, GA.
3. Avallone, E. A., and T. Baumeister, III, ed. 1986. *Mark's Standard Handbook for Mechanical Engineers*, 9th ed. McGraw Hill, New York, NY.
4. Charm, S. E. 1971. *The Fundamentals of Food Engineering.* AVI, Westport, CT.
5. Henderson, S. M., R. L. Perry, and J. H. Young. 1997. *Principles of Process Engineering*, 4th ed. ASAE, St. Joseph, MI.
6. Jorgensen, R. 1999. *Fan Engineering: An Engineer's Handbook on Fans and Their Applications.* Howden Buffalo, Inc., Buffalo, NY.
7. Olsen, Lief O. 1974. *Introduction to Liquid Flow Metering and Calibration of Liquid Flowmeters.* NBS Technical Note 831. Government Printing Office, Washington, DC.
8. Perry, R. H., and D. W. Green, 1984. *Perry's Chemical Engineer's Handbook,* 6th ed. McGraw Hill, New York, NY.
9. Streeter, V. L., ed. 1961. *Handbook of Fluid Dynamics.* Section 1: Fluid Properties; Section 7: Flow of Non-Newtonian Fluids; Section 14: Flow Measurement; Section 15: Dimensional Analysis. McGraw-Hill, New York, NY.
10. U. S. Department of Interior. 1997. *Water Measurement Manual,* 2nd ed. USDI, Bureau of Reclamation, Denver, CO.

Problems

4.1. Determine conversion constants relating pressure (kPa and psi), head (for water) (m and ft), velocity squared (ft^2/sec), and energy (kJ/kg).

4.2. Complete the following table relating depth and pressure. Surface pressure in the fourth column of the table refers to pressure above the fluid surface.

Item No.	Product	Density (kg/m^3)	Surface pressure (kPa)	Depth (m)	Pressure (kPa)
A	Water	1000	0	10	
B	Water	1000	200		249
C	Milk	1032	0	1	
D	Mercury	13 546	0	1	
E	Oil	826	0		40.5
F	Syrup	1275	0		37.5
G	Syrup	1275	0	2	

4.3. Milk flows through a 50-mm pipe at a volumetric flow rate of 28 L/s. What is its average velocity?

4.4. If the pipe of problem 4.3 goes through a reduction to 25 mm diameter, what is the flow rate? The velocity?

4.5. Milk flows through a 4" pipe at a velocity of 10 ft/sec and empties into a tank. If milk is flowing out of the tank at 10 ft/sec through a 2" pipe, how many gallons of milk are added to the tank in 1 hour?

4.6. Water is flowing through a 50-mm fire hose at a rate of 2 L/s. The nozzle of the hose has an inside diameter of 25 mm. What is the flow rate through the noz-zle? What is the velocity of water in the hose? In the nozzle?

4.7. For the condition of problem 4.6, how high can the water be sprayed due to the velocity head?

4.8. A large storage tank contains 500 000 L of milk. Milk enters the tank through a 0.05-m diameter pipe at a velocity of 3 m/s. Milk is also being removed at a velocity of 2.5 m/s through a 0.06-m diameter drain. How much milk is in the tank after one hour?

4.9. Determine the pump power required for a pump to supply 1.5 L/s of 20°C water under the following conditions:
   • The submerged pump intake is a 6-m length of 50-mm diameter galvanized pipe.
   • The pump output is through 35 m of 25-mm diameter galvanized pipe.
   • Delivery is at 140 kPa, 35 m above the water supply level.
   • There are no fittings or bends.
   • The combined pump and motor efficiency is 70%.

4.10. Repeat problem 9 with the following changes:
   • The pump output is through 40-mm diameter galvanized pipe.
   • Delivery is 25 m above the water supply level.
   • Fittings are: 2 globe valves and 3 standard 90° elbows in the 40-mm line.

4.11. Thirty liters/second are to be pumped through 10 m of 100-mm diameter stainless steel pipe. The elevation difference is 5 m. Pressure difference is 70 kPa and there is one 90° elbow. What energy must the pump provide for the flowing fluid (milk)? ($\nu = 2 \times 10^{-6}$ m^2/s, $\rho = 1025$ kg/m^3)

4.12. A 60% sucrose solution has properties as given in the following table.

Temperature (°C)	Viscosity (m^2/s)	Density (kg/m^3)
0	182×10^{-6}	1294.7
25	34.3×10^{-6}	1283.0
50	11.1×10^{-6}	1269.6

Compare energy requirements for pumping at the three temperatures in the table if the system is as described in Problem 4.9. (i.e., solve Problem 4.9 for a 60% sucrose solution at temperatures of 0°, 25°, and 50°C.)

4.13. A farmer has a water tank on a hill above his home. A pump maintains the tank water level at the same point regardless of the rate of use. The distance from the tank to the farmer's house is exactly one mile. The tank is not pressurized and its water level is exactly 500 feet above the delivery point at the house. Plot a curve of flow rate in GPM as a function of pipe sizes from ½" to 10" if the delivery pressure is 20 psi. Assume a continuous pipe without valves and fittings. Ignore velocity head.

4.14. A plumber has a choice of installing 15 m of 25-mm pipe with three 90° elbows or 6 m of the same pipe with nine 90° elbows. Which installation would cause the lowest head loss? What if 50-mm pipe is used?

4.15. An elevated storage tank is 3 m deep and has a diameter of 4 m. The tank bottom is 30 m above the ground. The tank supplies water through a 25-mm line to a point on the ground 8 m from the tower. The total pipe length is 38 m. One elbow and a gate valve are installed in the system. The delivery pressure is 15 kPa.

a. How many liters of water will the tank hold?

b. If the tank is full and the gate valve is accidentally left fully open, what will be the flow rate through the line from an initially full tank? Note: this is a trial and error (iterative) solution.

c. Assuming constant flow, how long will it take to empty the tank?

4.16. An irrigation pump operating at 65% efficiency is driven by an electric motor with an efficiency of 80%. The total lift is 21 m and the delivery pressure is 345 kPa. Friction pressure drop is 120 kPa. The pipe diameter is 0.10 m and the flow rate is 16 L/s. What is the power requirement of the motor?

4.17. A pump supplies 20 L/s of water $\rho = 1000$ kg/m^3) at a pump pressure difference of 300 kPa. What is the pump power output?

4.18. A pump supplies 5 L/s of syrup ($\rho = 1275$ kg/m^3) at a pump pressure difference of 600 kPa. The pump and motor efficiencies are 80% and 90% respectively. What input power is required?

4.19. A fan operating at 1750 rpm provides 5000 L/s at a total pressure difference of 0.8 kPa. What is the fan output power? What is the input power if the combined fan and motor efficiency is 70%?

4.20. The speed of the fan in the previous problem is increased to 2400 rpm. What are the flow rate, total pressure, and output power for the new operating condition?

4.21. A fan operating at 1750 rpm delivers 6000 L/s at a measured total pressure of 8 cm H_2O. The electrical input power to the motor is 6.1 kW. What is the efficiency of the fan/motor system?

4.22. The flow rate for the fan of the previous problem must be decreased to 4000 L/s. What are the fan speed, total pressure and power output for the new operating condition?

4.23. The fan of the previous two problems is too large and must be replaced with a smaller geometrically similar fan. The desired flow rate is 3000 L/s at 1750 rpm. If the impeller diameter of the previous fan was 0.8 m, what is the diameter of the replacement fan? What are the total pressure and power output for the new fan?

4.24. A calibration curve is being developed for a variable speed peristaltic pump. The pump is operated at equally spaced speed increments of 1 through 10. Collection times and amounts are given in the table below. Compute the flow rates and plot the calibration curve. Are all points reasonable? Explain.

Speed	Time (s)	Collected (kg)	Speed	Time (s)	Collected (kg)
1	40	20	6	97	360
2	80	100	7	85	360
3	58	100	8	75	360
4	120	280	9	67	360
5	60	280	10	60	360

4.25. An orifice has a constant (K) of 13.6 when units of pressure difference are mm of water and flow is in L/min. What is the flow rate for a pressure difference measuring 50 mm of water? If the flow rate is doubled, what pressure difference will be measured?

4.26. An orifice in a 50-mm diameter pipe measures a pressure difference of 16 cm of water when the flow rate is 35 L/s. What is the flow rate at a pressure difference of 8 cm of water? What is the orifice coefficient for this system? What would the orifice coefficient be for this system if the flow is to be expressed in m^3/s?

4.27. Water flows through a 90° triangular weir at a rate of 50 L/s. What is the water depth above the bottom of the weir opening (measured at a location well upstream of the weir)?

4.28. Water flows through a 90° triangular weir. Upstream of the weir, the water surface is 0.15 m above the bottom of the weir. What is the flow rate through the weir?

Heat Transfer

5

Abstract. This chapter covers the fundamentals of steady-state heat transfer. Emphasis is upon combined conduction and convection, including application to simple heat exchangers.

Keywords. Conduction, convection, energy, heat exchangers, heat transfer, radiation, thermal conductivity, thermodynamics, U-values.

5.1 Thermodynamic Concepts

Thermodynamics involves the study of thermal (heat) energy. Many basic thermodynamic concepts must be used in the analysis of heat transfer. Thus, we will first examine some key thermodynamic concepts before applying them to heat transfer.

5.1.1 Introduction to Thermodynamics

The thermodynamic concepts we will examine in this section include thermodynamic properties, thermodynamic systems, and thermodynamic laws. The explanations given here are relatively simplistic. Refer to any thermodynamics text for more rigorous explanations.

A **thermodynamic property** of a substance is a characteristic that depends only upon the state (condition) of the substance. Temperature, density, specific heat, enthalpy, and viscosity are all thermodynamic properties that we regularly use. A **thermodynamic state** is defined by values of independent thermodynamic properties. For example, we can define the state of air by specifying its temperature, relative humidity, and pressure (typically atmospheric pressure).

A **thermodynamic system** consists of a defined finite portion of matter. The system is defined in terms of its boundaries, which may be real, imaginary, or a combination of both. These systems may be either open or closed. A small balloon, filled with helium and sealed, is an example of a **closed system**. The balloon may be heated or cooled; it may change size or shape; but the same amount of helium remains inside. This is the key feature of a closed system. Energy may cross its boundaries, but matter cannot. An **open system**, however, allows both matter and energy to cross its boundaries. A typical classroom is an example of an open system. Walls, floor, ceiling, doors, and windows make up the boundaries of the room. The door opening, air supply and air return ducts, and, perhaps, open windows represent parts of the boundary that permit both matter and energy to pass.

We must define heat and work, two different forms of energy, before discussing the First and Second Laws. **Heat** is energy transferred due to a temperature difference. There can be no heat transferred unless a temperature difference exists. **Work** is defined as energy that could have the sole effect, external to the system, of raising or lowering a weight. Work done by a system (energy out) is considered positive, and work done on a system (energy in) is considered negative. On the other hand, heat transferred to a system is considered positive and heat transferred from a system is negative.

The **First Law of Thermodynamics** is simply an expression of the conservation of energy. It states that energy is conserved, and that all energy must be accounted for in any system analysis. The First Law is normally expressed in the form of an equation typically called an energy balance equation. This equation is very simple for a closed system: $\dot{Q} - W = \Delta U$. The equation for an open system is more complex, since it must account for energy in any mass crossing the system boundary. That equation is commonly written as:

$$\dot{Q} + \dot{m}_i \left(u_i + P_i v_i + \frac{u_i^2}{2g_c} + \frac{gz_i}{g_c} \right) = W + \dot{m}_e \left(u_e + p_e v_e + \frac{u_e^2}{2g_c} + \frac{gz_e}{g_c} \right) + \Delta E \qquad (5.01)$$

For these equations (see sketch at right) the variables are as follows:

$\dot{Q}$ = heat flow into the system, W

W = work done by the system, W

$\dot{m}$ = mass flow rate across boundary in or out, kg/s

u = velocity of flowing fluid, m/s

u = thermal energy of mass crossing boundary, J/kg

v = specific volume of the flowing fluid = $1/\rho$, m³/kg

z = elevation, m

ΔU = change in internal energy of the fluid, W

ΔE = change in energy (internal, kinetic, and elevation), W

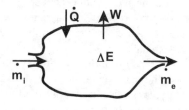

This first law equation for an open system looks very similar to the Bernoulli Equation (eq. 4.06) for fluid flow. In fact, the Bernoulli Equation is a simplified expression of the first law for an open system. The simplification results from the absence of thermal energy considerations in the Bernoulli Equation, although the friction loss term of the Bernoulli Equation represents energy dissipated as heat.

The **Second Law of Thermodynamics** is a statement that all forms of energy are *not* equal. Specifically, work can be converted completely to heat; but heat energy cannot be converted completely to work. The actual statement found in thermodynamics texts is usually more complex. One such statement is "Heat cannot, of itself, pass from a lower to a higher temperature" (Obert, 1960).

5.1.2 Energy and Power

Heat and work defined above are both forms of energy widely used in the food and processing industry. Engineers and food technologists are frequently concerned with measuring the transfer of thermal energy within a system, or between two or more systems. Energy in the form of work is also a key parameter in solid and fluids handling systems, as well as in many types of processing equipment.

Energy exists in many forms. Kinetic energy refers to energy due to motion of a substance. Potential energy is "stored" energy such as a compressed spring or water in an elevated tank. Releasing the spring, or opening the tank valve, allows the stored energy to be used. Using appropriate equipment, we can convert one form of energy to another. The energy in the elevated storage tank could be used to compress a spring, or a spring could drive a pump to move water into an elevated storage tank. Within the limits of the Second Law, we can also convert between thermal and mechanical energy. In fact, thermal energy is converted to mechanical energy in automobile engines, electric power plants, jet engines, and other similar devices. The general thermodynamic term identifying all these devices is **heat engine**. Heat engines take thermal energy from a high temperature source, convert some of it to work, and reject the remainder to a lower temperature heat sink. Heat engines are never 100% efficient. In fact, the maximum theoretical efficiency is $\eta = 1 - \dfrac{T_L}{T_H}$ where T_H is the absolute temperature of the thermal energy source and T_L is the absolute temperature of the sink to which excess heat is rejected. This efficiency applies exactly for a special theoretical engine called a Carnot (for Carnot cycle) engine. Other engines are less efficient and the maximum theoretical efficiency relationships for these engines are more complex.

Power is commonly identified as the rate of doing work. This term is used extensively in many mechanical applications. However, power is also the rate of energy transfer. The rate of electric energy use is power; and, as we will see in the next section, the rate of heat transfer also has units of power.

5.1.3 Heat Transfer— An Application of Thermodynamics

Heat transfer is the movement of energy due to a temperature difference. Thus, heat transfer can only occur in the presence of a temperature difference. The transfer of heat occurs through convection, conduction, radiation or a combination of these methods. Heat transfer is indicated as total transfer, identified by the symbol $\dot{Q}$, or heat transfer per unit area, identified by the symbol $\dot{q}$. The units of heat transfer are watts (for $\dot{Q}$) or watts/m^2 (for $\dot{q}$). Corresponding US customary units are Btu/hr and Btu/(hr ft^2).

Heat transfer may also be classified as steady state or unsteady-state (transient) heat transfer. Under steady state conditions, all parameters are stabilized with respect to time. Temperatures are constant at all locations. Many problems can be considered steady state even though there is some change with time. For example, heat flow through walls is usually considered a steady state problem even though environmental conditions may change during the day. Unsteady-state heat transfer occurs when temperature changes with time are important. Thermal processing of foods in a can is an example. The time required for the coldest spot in the can to reach a set temperature must be known. Since time is a factor, unsteady-state conditions must be considered. A similar unsteady-state condition occurs during the cooling and freezing of foods.

We will consider only steady state conditions in this chapter. Unsteady state conditions will be considered in the next chapter.

5.2 Conduction Heat Transfer

Conduction heat transfer occurs when heat moves through a material (usually a solid or a viscous liquid) due to molecular action only. Conduction heat transfer may occur simultaneously in one, two, or three directions. Many practical heat transfer problems involve heat flow in only one or two directions. Conduction along an insulated rod heated at one end is an example of conduction in one dimension. Heat flows along the length of the rod to the cooler end (one direction). If the rod is not insulated, heat is also lost to the surroundings. Thus, the rod center is warmer than the outer surface. This causes heat to flow radially outward (the second dimension). Heating and cooling of plates and fins can often be treated as two-dimensional heat transfer problems. We will emphasize one dimensional heat transfer in this analysis.

One dimensional conduction heat transfer is a function of the temperature difference, the material thickness, the area through which the heat flows, and the resistance of the material to heat flow. This relationship is expressed in equation form as:

$$\dot{Q} = -k\,A\,\frac{dt}{dx} = k\,A\,\frac{(t_1 - t_2)}{\Delta x} = \frac{A\,(t_1 - t_2)}{\left(\dfrac{1}{k}\right)\Delta x} = \frac{A\,\Delta t}{R} \tag{5.02}$$

or

$$\dot{q} = \frac{\dot{Q}}{A} = \frac{\Delta t}{R} \tag{5.03}$$

where: A = area, m^2

k = thermal conductivity, W/(m K)

$\dot{Q}$ = heat transfer, W

$\dot{q}$ = heat transfer per unit area, W/m^2

R = thermal resistance of the material $\Delta x/k$, (m^2 K)/W

t = temperature, °C (or K)

To be mathematically correct, the minus sign should be retained in Equation 5.03 and the last term of Equation 5.02 because Δt is defined as $t_2 - t_1$. However, the sign, which designates the direction of heat flow, can be ignored here. For the simple applications we will consider, we need only remember that heat flow is always from a higher temperature to a lower temperature.

The above equations serve to illustrate the factors affecting conduction. We will not be using the conduction-only equations as shown here, since most practical applications require that convection also be considered. However, you should understand the effect that each of the above factors has upon pure conduction heat transfer.

5.3 Convection Heat Transfer

Convection heat transfer is the transfer of energy due to the movement of a heated (or cooled) fluid. The movement of the fluid (liquid or gas) causes the transfer of energy from the regions of warm fluid to cooler regions in the fluid. Natural convection occurs when a heated fluid moves due to the change in fluid density. Forced convection occurs when the fluid is moved by other methods (pumps, fans, etc.). Convection effects must be considered in all analyses involving heat transfer to or from fluids (gases or liquids). Convective heat transfer between a fluid and a surface is normally written in terms of a convective heat transfer coefficient. Assuming heat transfer from the fluid to the surface, the equation is:

$$Q = hA(t_b - t_s) \text{ or } Q = \frac{A(t_b - t_s)}{R_s} \qquad (5.04)$$

where: h = convective (surface) heat transfer coefficient, $W/(m^2\ K)$
R_s = the surface resistance ($R_s = 1/h$), $(m^2\ K)/W$
t_b = bulk temperature of the fluid, °C or K
t_s = the surface temperature of the object exposed to the fluid, °C or K

5.4 Radiation Heat Transfer

Radiation heat transfer is the transfer of heat from one object directly to another without the use of an intervening medium. Thermal radiation forms a part of the electromagnetic spectrum which ranges from radio waves to gamma rays. Rules applying to other types of radiation apply also to thermal radiation. Thermal energy can be radiated through space (solar energy) and through gases (e.g., air). Thermal radiation functions much like visible light. If two objects "see" each other they can exchange radiant energy. If they cannot "see" each other, radiant energy can be transferred only if it is reflected from another surface which can "see" both surfaces.

Thermal radiation striking a surface may be reflected, absorbed, or transmitted. Polished aluminum reflects most radiant energy while flat black surfaces absorb most radiant energy. Clear glass transmits most radiation from high temperature sources, but reflects radiation from low temperature sources.

The amount of radiant energy emitted is a function of the absolute temperature of the emitter. The radiated energy is given as:

$$E = \sigma T^4 \qquad (5.05)$$

where: E = the energy radiated per unit time and per unit area, W/m^2
σ = the Stefan-Boltzmann constant ($5.669 \times 10^{-8}\ W/\ m^2\ K^4$)
T = the absolute temperature, (K), (K = 273.15 + °C)

Radiant energy exchange between two bodies is often difficult to calculate. It is a function of several factors, including (1) the temperature of each body, (2) the percentage of each body "seen" by the other body, and (3) the characteristics of each body surface (reflectivity, absorptivity, etc.).

5.5 "Practical" Heat Transfer

In the practical world, there are few heat transfer applications that can be called pure conduction, convection, or radiation. Usually, all three methods are involved to some extent. Since radiation energy increases with absolute temperature to the fourth power, it becomes very important at higher temperatures. Radiation is usually insignificant at temperatures near ambient. However, radiation from the sun (at about 5800 K) is a significant energy source. Most of the problems we shall examine will involve only conduction and convection.

These combined conduction and convection problems are common in everyday applications. Examples are heat flow through walls, heat exchangers (including heating and air conditioning systems), thermal processing, and many similar applications. All of these applications require determination of a convective heat transfer coefficient as well as thermal conductivity (or resistance) values for materials through which the heat must flow.

5.6 Heat Transfer through Walls

Heat transfer through walls is a combination of conduction, convection, and radiation, although conduction and convection are of primary importance. Radiation is likely to be a significant factor only if one surface is exposed to the sun or another very hot surface.

For heat transfer through a wall, we are normally interested in the amount of heat which will flow through a given wall with specified air temperatures on each side of the wall. The factors affecting the heat flow include (1) wall construction (thickness and material), (2) total area of heat transfer, (3) difference between air temperatures on each side of the wall, and (4) amount of air movement near the wall. A plot of temperature distribution through a wall of specified components is shown in Figure 5.01. Note the change in air temperature near each surface of the wall. This is due to a thin layer of still air near the wall. This layer serves as insulation and reduces the flow of heat. The degree of insulation varies with the amount of air movement. Outside wall surfaces are usually subject to winds which can significantly reduce the insulating value of this air layer.

The equation for heat flow through a wall can be written as:

$$q = \frac{\dot{Q}}{A} = \frac{\Delta t}{R_T} \qquad (5.06)$$

where: $R_T =$ the total resistance to heat flow, $(m^2\ K)/W$

$\Delta t =$ the difference in air temperature (K or °C)
and all other variables are as defined for Equation 5.02.

The total thermal resistance is the sum of the resistance of each wall component and the surface resistances on each side of the wall. Values of resistances for selected materials are given in Table 5.02. That table also includes values of thermal conductivity (k) and conductance (C). The thermal conductivity indicates the ease (or difficulty) with which heat is transmitted through a material. It is usually specified for a unit thickness (1 m) of a homogeneous material. Conductance is used in place of thermal conductivity for a nonhomogeneous material of specified thickness or for a homogeneous material of specified thickness other than one meter. The resistance of a material is simply the inverse of the conductivity or conductance. Note that the material thickness must be considered where thermal conductivity (k) is used.

Example 5.1

Consider the wall of Figure 5.01.
Find: (1) the overall thermal resistance of the wall, and
       (2) the heat flow through the wall.

Solution:
The overall resistance consists of the air surface resistance on each side of the wall, the resistance of the two plywood panels and the resistance of the insulation. Subscripts represent inside (i), first plywood panel ($p1$), insulation (ins), second plywood panel ($p2$), and the outside (o).

$$R_t = R_i + L_{pl}R_{pl} + L_{ins}R_{ins}\ L_{p2}R_{p2} + R_o \qquad (5.07)$$

$$= \frac{1}{h_i} + \Delta x_{pl} \times \frac{1}{k_{pl}} + \Delta x_{ins} \times \frac{1}{k_{ins}} + \Delta x_{p2} \times \frac{1}{k_{p2}} + \frac{1}{h_o}$$

$$= \frac{m^2\,K}{W} + m \times \frac{m\,K}{W} + m \times \frac{m\,K}{W} + m \times \frac{m\,K}{W} + \frac{m^2\,K}{W} \qquad \text{(units)}$$

$$R_t = 0.12 + 0.01\,(8.7) + 0.1\,(26) + 0.01\,(8.7) + 0.04 = 2.93\ \ \frac{m^2\,K}{W}$$

In this solution, the outside wall surface resistance (R_o) was taken at 12 km/h. The inside resistance (R_i) was taken at 0 km/h. (See Table 5.02.) Applying Equation 5.06:

$$\dot{q} = \frac{\Delta t}{R_T} = \frac{13 - (-18)\ K}{2.93\ \dfrac{m^2\,K}{W}} = 10.54\ \frac{W}{m^2} \qquad \textbf{ANSWER}$$

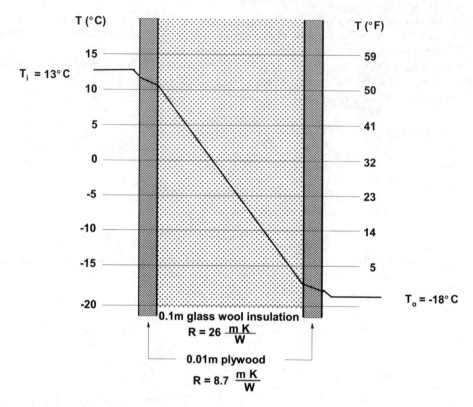

Figure 5.01. Temperature distribution through a building wall.

5.7 Heat Transfer through Pipe Walls
(Radial Heat Transfer)

Heat flow through pipe walls is a common occurrence in food processing operations. The path of energy flow may be inward (heating a fluid in the pipe) or outward (transferring energy from the fluid flowing in the pipe.) When heat flows through a pipe wall, the cross sectional area varies from the inside of the pipe to the outside. This change in the area through which the energy flows presents a complication not encountered in our study of heat flow through walls. The analysis of heat transfer through walls was relatively simple because the surface areas of all wall components remained the same. For heat transfer through walls and similar structures, the cross sectional area is constant. When the area changes, as with flow through pipe walls, it is necessary to utilize an equation which accounts for the varying cross sectional area involved in flow of the heat. For one dimensional heat flow in a circular cylinder or pipe, as shown in Figure 5.02, the heat flow becomes:

$$\dot{Q} = \frac{2\pi L k}{\ln \dfrac{r_2}{r_1}}(t_1 - t_2) \qquad \text{or} \qquad \frac{\dot{Q}}{A_1} = \frac{1}{r_1}\frac{k\,\Delta t}{\ln \dfrac{r_2}{r_1}} \qquad\qquad (5.08)$$

where: $A_1 = 2\,\pi\,r_1\,L$
L = length of the cylinder, m
k = thermal conductivity, W/(m K)

$\dot{Q}$ = heat flow, W

r_1 = cylinder inside radius, m
r_2 = cylinder outside radius, m
t_1 = temperature at the cylinder inside surface, °C or K
t_2 = temperature at the cylinder outside surface, °C or K

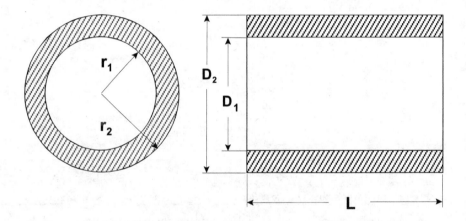

Figure 5.02. Physical dimensions for heat transfer through a pipe wall.

Example 5.2

A steel pipe is 10 m in length, with an inside radius of $r_1 = 2.50$ cm, an outside radius of $r_2 = 2.80$ cm, inside wall temperature (t_1) of 80°C, outside wall temperature (t_2) of 25°C, and $k = 45$ W/(m K). Find the heat transfer (kW) through the steel pipe due to the temperature difference between the inside and outside pipe walls. The figure below illustrates the example.

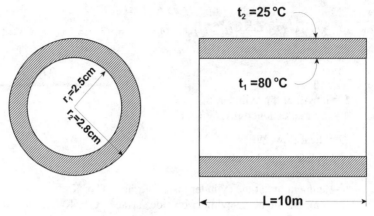

Solution:
Using Equation 5.08

$$\dot{Q} = \frac{2 \pi L k}{\ln \frac{r_2}{r_1}}(t_1 - t_2)$$

$$= \frac{2 \pi (10)(45)}{\ln \frac{2.80}{2.50}}(80 - 25)$$

$$= 1372\ 193\ W = \underline{1372\ KW} \qquad \qquad \textbf{ANSWER}$$

> Note: It is not necessary to convert the °C to K since the rate of heat transfer is due to the *difference* in temperature. Also, since we used a ratio of the inner and outer radii, it was not necessary to convert radius units to meters.

In many cases, where it is not feasible to measure the inside temperature of the pipe wall, (t_1), the temperature of the fluid (t_f) is utilized. Therefore, the estimated value of the convection heat transfer coefficient (h) or its inverse (R) must be used. Equation 5.08 can be modified to include the inside and outside convection heat transfer coefficients, h_i and h_o, respectively.

5.8 Heat Transfer through Composite Pipes and Cylinders

The previous example illustrates the problem of heat transfer through pipe walls without insulation, where a large temperature difference exists between the inside and the outside surfaces. In such cases, wrapping the pipe with appropriate insulation minimizes the heat loss. Since insulation with the highest resistance to heat flow is sometimes soft and easily damaged, an outer layer of more durable insulation is usually added.

The calculation of the heat transfer in one dimension from the inside pipe wall and through the composite insulation to the outside is illustrated below. Consider the composite section shown in Figure 5.03. In this situation, heat is transferred from a fluid at

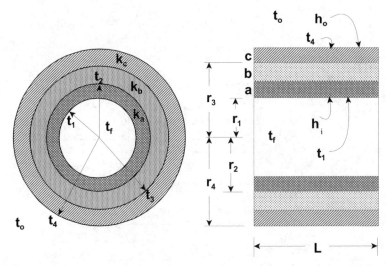

Figure 5.03. Geometry and temperature parameters for heat transfer through a composite pipe wall.

a temperature of t_f through the materials **a**, **b**, and **c** to ambient air at a temperature of t_o. Thus, we must consider surface (convective) heat transfer coefficients in addition to insulating material.

The following set of equations applies for heat flow through each element of the composite cylinder:

$$\dot{Q} = 2\,\pi\,r_1\,L\,h_i\,(t_f - t_1) \qquad \text{thus} \qquad t_f - t_1 = \frac{\dot{Q}}{2\,\pi\,r_1\,L\,h_i} \qquad \text{(Fluid to inner surface)}$$

$$\dot{Q} = \frac{2\,\pi\,L\,k_a}{\ln \dfrac{r_2}{r_1}}\,(t_1 - t_2) \qquad \text{thus} \qquad t_1 - t_2 = \frac{\dot{Q}\,\ln\,(r_2/r_1)}{2\,\pi\,k_a\,L} \qquad \text{(Through material \textbf{a})}$$

$$\dot{Q} = \frac{2\,\pi\,L\,k_b}{\ln \dfrac{r_3}{r_2}}\,(t_2 - t_3) \qquad \text{thus} \qquad t_2 - t_3 = \frac{\dot{Q}\,\ln\,(r_3/r_2)}{2\,\pi\,k_b\,L} \qquad \text{(Through material \textbf{b})}$$

$$\dot{Q} = \frac{2\,\pi\,L\,k_o}{\ln \dfrac{r_4}{r_3}}\,(t_3 - t_4) \qquad \text{thus} \qquad t_3 - t_4 = \frac{\dot{Q}\,\ln\,(r_4/r_3)}{2\,\pi\,k_o\,L} \qquad \text{(Through material \textbf{c})}$$

$$\dot{Q} = 2\pi r_4 L h_o (t_4 - t_o) \qquad \text{thus} \qquad t_4 - t_o = \frac{\dot{Q}}{2\pi r_4 L h_o} \qquad \text{(outside to surroundings)}$$

Combining to solve for $t_f - t_o$, we note that:

$$t_f - t_o = (t_f - t_1) + (t_1 - t_2) + (t_2 - t_3) + (t_3 - t_4) + (t_4 - t_o)$$

$$= \frac{\dot{Q}}{2\pi r_1 L h_i} + \frac{\dot{Q}\ln\frac{r_2}{r_1}}{2\pi L k_a} + \frac{\dot{Q}\ln\frac{r_3}{r_2}}{2\pi L k_b} + \frac{\dot{Q}\ln\frac{r_4}{r_3}}{2\pi L k_o} + \frac{\dot{Q}}{2\pi r_4 L h_o} \qquad (5.09)$$

or, after solving for $\dot{Q}$ and rearranging, the equation becomes:

$$\dot{Q} = \frac{(t_f - t_o)}{\dfrac{1}{2\pi r_1 L h_i} + \dfrac{\ln\frac{r_2}{r_1}}{2\pi L k_a} + \dfrac{\ln\frac{r_3}{r_2}}{2\pi L k_b} + \dfrac{\ln\frac{r_4}{r_3}}{2\pi L k_c} + \dfrac{1}{2\pi r_4 L h_o}}$$

$$= \frac{(t_f - t_o)}{\dfrac{1}{2\pi L}\left(\dfrac{1}{r_1 h_i} + \dfrac{\ln\frac{r_2}{r_1}}{k_a} + \dfrac{\ln\frac{r_3}{r_2}}{k_b} + \dfrac{\ln\frac{r_4}{r_3}}{k_c} + \dfrac{1}{r_4 h_o} \right)} \qquad (5.10)$$

Heat flow through composite cylinders is illustrated in the following example.

Example 5.3

The composite pipe specified below is used for pumping heated fruit puree with the following design factors:

Length of the pipe, $L = 5$ m
Inside fluid temperature, $t_f = 85°C$ (358 K)
Outside fluid (air) temperature, $t_o = 23°C$ (296 K)
Inside radius of pipe, $r_1 = 2.50$ cm (0.0250 m)
Outside radius of pipe, $r_2 = 2.70$ cm (0.0270 m)
Outside radius of first layer of insulation, $r_3 = 8$ cm (0.08 m)
Outside radius of second layer of insulation, $r_4 = 9$ cm (0.09 m)
Thermal conductivity of pipe, $k_1 = 45$ W/(m K)
Thermal conductivity of first layer of insulation, $k_2 = 0.0389$ W/(m K)
Thermal conductivity of second layer of insulation, $k_3 = 0.0228$ W/(m K)
Surface heat transfer coefficient at the pipe inside wall, $h_i = 100$ W/(m^2 K)
Surface heat transfer coefficient at the insulation outside layer, $h_o = 5$ W/(m^2 K)

Calculate the heat transfer, $\dot{Q}$ (in Watts).

Solution:

Using Equation 5.10,

$$\dot{Q} = \frac{(358 - 296)}{\frac{1}{2\pi \times 5}\left(\frac{1}{0.025 \times 100} + \frac{\ln\frac{0.027}{0.025}}{45} + \frac{\ln\frac{0.08}{0.027}}{0.0389} + \frac{\ln\frac{0.09}{0.08}}{0.0228} + \frac{1}{0.09 \times 5}\right)}$$

$$= \frac{62}{0.0318 \times (0.4 + 0.0017 + 27.9226 + 5.1659 + 2.2222)}$$

$$= \frac{62}{0.0318 \times 35.7124} = \underline{54.59 \text{ W}} \qquad\qquad \textbf{ANSWER}$$

5.9 Dimensionless Parameters

Several dimensionless ratios occur frequently in heat transfer. The use of such dimensionless numbers allows the universal application of charts, tables, and mathematical relationships. Several of the more important dimensionless numbers are presented in Table 5.01. The **Reynolds number** is a commonly occurring dimensionless parameter in fluid flow. It is, among other things, an indicator of the degree of turbulence of flow. For $Re < 2000$ (approximately), flow particles follow a very smooth path or streamline. Such flow is commonly called **laminar flow**. As Re increases above 2000, flow becomes increasingly more agitated or **turbulent**. The transition from laminar to turbulent flow can occur over a range of Reynolds numbers between 2000 and 2300 (approximately). The degree of turbulence is a significant factor in heat transfer to, or from, fluids. Higher velocity, resulting in more turbulent flow, tends to increase convective (surface) heat transfer coefficients and, thus, the overall heat transfer.

The **Prandtl number** is another dimensionless parameter that affects the surface heat transfer coefficient. It is a dimensionless parameter relating the relative thickness of hydrodynamic and thermal boundary layers. It is a fluid property that varies with temperature. The Prandtl number is defined as:

$$Pr = \frac{v}{\alpha} = \frac{\frac{\mu}{\rho}}{\frac{k}{\rho c_p}} = \frac{\mu c_p}{k}$$

Reynolds number and Prandtl number are two of the dimensionless parameters commonly used in convection heat transfer calculations. Other parameters in the table will be introduced in later sections of this text.

Example 5.4

Find the Prandtl number for water at 100°C.

Solution:

The properties of water at 100°C are (from Table 9.05):

$$k = 0.682 \frac{W}{m\,K} = 0.682 \frac{J}{s\,m\,K} = 0.682 \times 10^{-3} \frac{kJ}{s\,m\,K}$$

Note: For ease of canceling units, convert the thermal conductivity to $\dfrac{kJ}{s\,m\,K}$.

$$c_p = 4.211 \frac{kJ}{kg\,K}$$

$$\mu = 2.775 \times 10^{-4} \frac{N\,s}{m^2}$$

$$Pr = \frac{\mu\,c_p}{k} = \frac{2.775 \times 10^{-4} \dfrac{N\,s}{m^2} \times 4.211 \dfrac{kJ}{kg\,K}}{0.682 \times 10^{-3} \dfrac{kJ}{s\,m\,K}} = 1.72 \frac{N\,s^2}{m\,kg} = \underline{1.72}$$

ANSWER

Note that in SI units $g_c = 1 \dfrac{kg\,m}{N\,s^2}$ or $1\,kg = 1 \dfrac{N\,s^2}{m}$ Thus, the units cancel and *Pr* is dimensionless.

Table 5.01. Dimensionless[a] ratios commonly used in heat transfer.[b]

Name	Formula	Used In	Physical Meaning
Biot[c]	$Bi = \dfrac{h\delta}{k_s}$	Transient heat transfer	$\left[\dfrac{\text{HT body} - \text{to} - \text{fluid}}{\text{HT within body}}\right]$
Fourier	$Fo = \dfrac{\alpha\theta}{\delta^2}$	Transient heat transfer	
Graetz	$Graetz = \dfrac{Q_m c_p}{kL}$	Fluid Flow	$\left[\dfrac{\text{fluid thermal capacity}}{\text{conductive HT}}\right]$
Grashof	$Gr = \dfrac{\rho^2 gL^3 \beta \Delta t}{\mu^2}$	Free convection	$\left[\dfrac{\text{inertia} \times \text{buoyant forces}}{(\text{viscous force})^2}\right]$
Nusselt[c]	$Nu = \dfrac{hD}{k_f}$	Convection heat transfer	$\left[\dfrac{\text{total HT}}{\text{conductive HT}}\right]$
Peclet	$Pe = Re_d\, Pr$	Heat transfer	$\left[\dfrac{\text{convection HT}}{\text{conduction HT}}\right]$
Prandtl	$Pr = \dfrac{\nu}{\alpha} = \dfrac{\mu\, c_p}{k}$	A material property	$\left[\dfrac{\text{momentum diffusivity}}{\text{thermal diffusivity}}\right]$
Reynolds	$Re = \dfrac{uD}{\nu}$	With flowing fluids	$\left[\dfrac{\text{inertia force}}{\text{viscous force}}\right]$
Thermal diffusivity[a]	$\alpha = \dfrac{k}{\rho\, c_p}$	Transient heat transfer	$\left[\dfrac{\text{heat conduction}}{\text{heat storage}}\right]$

[a] Thermal diffusivity is *not dimensionless*. It has units of m^2/h or m^2/s.

[b] A more detailed discussion of dimensionless parameters relevant to food and biological materials is given by Dekas (1992)

[c] Thermal conductivity (k) used in the Nusselt number is that of a flowing fluid. In the Biot number it is that of the object being heated.

5.10 Heat Transfer to Flowing Fluids

Many heating and cooling systems use a flowing fluid as a heating or cooling medium. Refrigeration systems, steam jacketed kettles, and plate heat exchangers are examples of this application. It is usually important to know how much heat can be transferred to (or from) a fluid flowing in such a system. Under these conditions other factors, in addition to those already discussed, may affect the heat flow. These include: fluid flow rate, fluid properties, thickness of fluid layer, and pipe diameter or other characteristic length.

For heat transfer to a flowing fluid, the heat transfer is usually given by the expression:

$$\dot{q} = h(t_w - t_b) \tag{5.11}$$

where: t_w = temperature of the pipe wall
t_b = bulk (average) temperature of the fluid

This equation is written for heat flow from the wall to the fluid. If heat is flowing from the fluid to the pipe wall, the temperature difference for Equation 5.11 is $(t_b - t_w)$. The temperatures are usually easily determined; however, estimating the convective (surface) heat transfer coefficient (h) is more difficult. Theory and experimental verification have shown that equations grouping the relevant parameters into dimensionless numbers usually give a good approximation to the surface heat transfer coefficient. Either of two similar equations involving dimensionless parameters is widely used to estimate h for turbulent flow in tubes:

$$Nu_D = 0.023 \, Re_D^{\,0.8} \, Pr^n \tag{5.12}$$

where: $n = 0.4$ for fluid heating
$n = 0.3$ for fluid cooling

or
$$Nu_D = 0.027 \, Re_D^{\,0.8} \, Pr^{\frac{1}{3}} \left[\frac{\mu}{\mu_w} \right]^{0.14} \tag{5.13}$$

Except for μ_w, all fluid properties in the above equations are evaluated at the bulk temperature of the fluid. Note that these two equations give estimates of h, not exact values. Results from the equations may differ by as much as 20%, with Equation 5.13 typically giving higher values.

The convective (surface) heat transfer coefficient is slightly affected by the direction of heat flow. This effect is obvious in Equation 5.12 since an exponent must be determined based upon the direction of heat flow. Equation 5.13 accounts for the direction of heat flow with the different absolute viscosity values. The ratio of these values is greater than one for heating and less than one for cooling.

A similar equation is used for forced convection in laminar flow; however, the length of the pipe is also a factor in laminar flow calculations:

$$Nu_D = 1.86 \, (Pe)^{\frac{1}{3}} \left[\frac{D}{L} \right]^{\frac{1}{3}} \left[\frac{\mu}{\mu_w} \right]^{0.14} \qquad \text{for} \qquad Pe\left(\frac{D}{L} \right) \rangle 10 \tag{5.14}$$

Once the Nusselt number (Nu) is determined for the flow condition of interest, we can then calculate the surface heat transfer coefficient (h). The above equations are valid only for certain ranges of Re, Pr, d/L, and Δt. Limits for these equations and alternate equations for other conditions are given by Holman (1986) and Heldman and Lund (1992). For simplicity, we will assume the equations are valid for all conditions we encounter.

Example 5.5

Water (at 100°C) flows with a velocity of 1 m/s in a 0.02-m diameter pipe (see sketch). The pipe wall temperature is 70°C. What is the heat transfer from the fluid to the pipe wall?

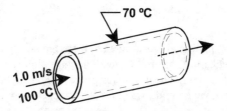

Solution:
If flow is turbulent, either Equation 5.12 or 5.13 can be used to solve for the Nusselt number (and h) once the Reynolds number and Prandtl number are known. From Table 9.05, at 100°C, $Pr = 1.75$, $k = 0.682$ W/m K, and $\nu = 0.294 \times 10^{-6}$ m^2/s.

Thus, $Re_D = \dfrac{u\,D}{\nu} = \dfrac{1\,\dfrac{m}{s} \times 0.02\ m}{0.294 \times 10^{-6}\ \dfrac{m^2}{s}} = 68030$ \qquad (Flow is clearly turbulent.)

$$Nu_D = 0.023\,(68030)^{0.8}\,(1.75)^{0.3} \qquad \text{(Using Equation 5.12)}$$

$$Nu_D = 0.023\,(7348)\,(1.18) = 200$$

But: $Nu_D = \dfrac{h\,D}{K}$

Thus: $h = \dfrac{k\,Nu_D}{D} = \dfrac{0.682\,\dfrac{W}{m\,K} \times 200}{0.02\ m} = 6800\,\dfrac{W}{m^2\,K}$

Returning to Equation 5.11, written for heat flow from the fluid:

$$\dot{q} = h(t_b - t_w) = 6800\,(100 - 70) = 204\,\frac{kW}{m^2} \qquad \textbf{ANSWER}$$

We can follow a similar process using Equation 5.13. We also need values for μ (at 100°C) and μ_w (at 70°C). The values are found from Table 9.05. Using these, and previously determined values, Equation 5.13 becomes:

$$Nu_D = (0.027)(68030)^{0.8} (1.75)^{\frac{1}{3}} \left[\frac{277.52 \times 10^{-6}}{404.03 \times 10^{-6}} \right]^{0.14}$$

$$Nu_D = (0.017)(7348)(1.205)(0.9488) = 227$$

Then: $h = \dfrac{0.682(227)}{0.02} = 7740 \, \dfrac{W}{m^2 \, K}$

and: $\dot{q} = h\,(t_b - t_w) = 7740 \,(100 - 70) = \underline{232 \, \dfrac{kW}{m^2}}$ **ANSWER**

Note that the two equations give somewhat different solutions. This is not unexpected since the equations are not exact. They are simply two relationships approximating a very complex heat transfer process. Thus, while the results should be reasonably close, we should expect differences.

5.11 Heat Exchangers

Heat exchangers are used extensively in many industrial applications. They are especially important in processing applications where many heating and cooling operations are involved. The basic function of a heat exchanger is to transfer heat from one fluid to another. In some applications, the fluids may be mixed, as when steam is added to water. In most cases, the fluids must be physically separated by a plate, pipe wall, or other good heat conductor.

A simple heat exchanger can be constructed by mounting one pipe inside another as shown in Figure 5.04. Heat would be transferred to the cooler of the two fluids as they flow through the exchanger. This double-pipe heat exchanger is excellent for analyzing heat exchanger characteristics. However, other heat exchanger types are much more efficient in most applications.

One widely used type of heat exchanger is the shell-and-tube exchanger. This exchanger has tubes mounted inside an outer shell (Figure 5.05). One fluid flows through

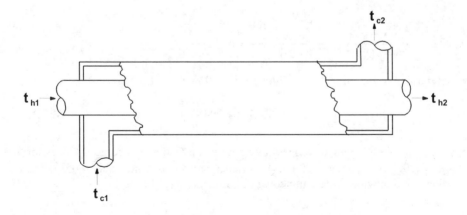

Figure 5.04. Double-pipe heat exchanger with parallel flow.

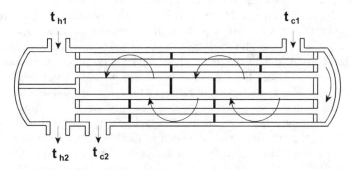

Figure 5.05. Shell-and-tube heat exchanger with baffles.
This unit has one shell pass and two tube passes.

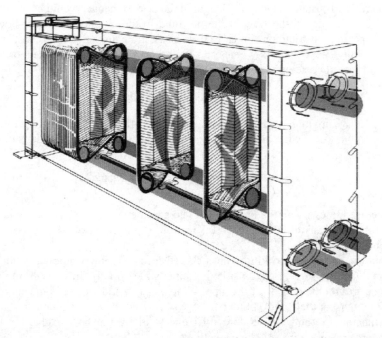

Figure 5.06. Plate-type heat exchanger. Hot fluid enters the upper left pipe, flows
downward between plates and exits through the lower left pipe. The cold fluid
enters the pipe at lower right and exits through the pipe at upper right.
(Used by permission; Paul Mueller Company Bull. TP-108-9 © 1994.)

the tube while the other fluid is in the shell surrounding the tubes. Several tube-and-shell flow patterns are possible with different baffle and tube arrangements. Plate heat exchangers (Figure 5.06) are used extensively in the dairy industry. These units are made with multiple plates shaped to provide flow channels between adjacent plates. Heat is then transferred through the plates from one fluid to another. Note that hot and cold fluids must alternate between plates along the length of the heat exchanger. Different flow patterns between the individual plates are possible depending upon plate design. Typically, plates can be added or removed to adjust the total heat transfer area.

Heat exchangers are also identified by the flow pattern of the fluids in the exchanger. The double-pipe heat exchanger of Figure 5.04 is a parallel-flow unit since both fluids flow in the same direction. Reversing either fluid would produce a counter-flow system with fluids flowing in opposite directions. In some heat exchangers, the fluids flow perpendicular to each other, producing a cross-flow system. Units may be further complicated by using combinations of the flow systems noted.

5.12 Analysis of a Simple Heat Exchanger

In this section, we will study the simple double-pipe heat exchanger shown in Figure 5.07a. We will assume the hot fluid is flowing in the inner pipe, while the cooler fluid flows in the outer pipe. As shown in the sketch, the flow is parallel. Under this condition, the temperature distribution along the length of the heat exchanger would be as shown in Figure 5.07b. Reversing the flow of the hot fluid would produce a counter-flow unit, with a temperature distribution similar to that shown in Figure 5.07c. The exact shape of the curves will depend upon flow rates and fluid properties. The heat gained, or lost, by either fluid is easily determined by a simple energy balance:

$$\dot{Q} = \dot{m}_h \, c_{ph} \Delta t_h = \dot{m}_c \, c_{pc} \Delta t_c \qquad (5.15)$$

However, we are more concerned with the factors affecting the rate of heat transfer. Based upon our knowledge of heat transfer we could assume that a relationship of the form:

$$\dot{Q} = \frac{A \, \Delta t}{R_T} = U A \, \Delta t \qquad \text{where} \qquad U = \frac{1}{R_T} \qquad (5.16)$$

might be used to evaluate the heat flow. (The parameter U in this equation is called the overall heat transfer coefficient.) Inspection of this equation reveals two potential problems:

1. We are no longer working with a flat surface. The inner pipe has a thickness such that the surface area inside that pipe is measurably different from the surface area on the outside of the pipe. Which area should we use in the equation?
2. For both parallel- and counter-flow systems, we have continuously changing temperatures (and temperature differences) along the heat exchanger length. What Δt should we use in the equation?

We resolve the first problem by stating that either the inside or outside surface area may be used provided the overall thermal resistance (R_T) is evaluated based upon that area. It can be further shown that Equation 5.16 applies as written provided the log-mean temperature difference is used. The log-mean temperature difference is defined as:

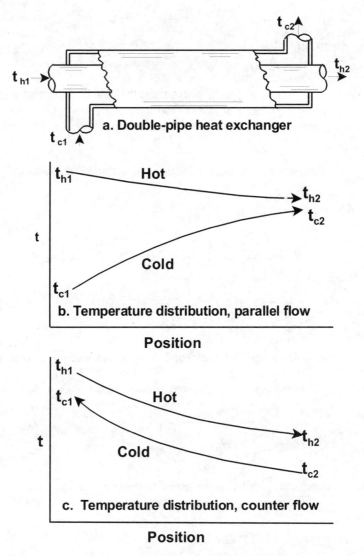

a. Double-pipe heat exchanger

b. Temperature distribution, parallel flow

Position

c. Temperature distribution, counter flow

Position

Figure 5.07. Temperature distribution in a double-pipe heat exchanger.

$$\Delta t_{1m} = \frac{\left(t_{h1} - t_{c1}\right) - \left(t_{h2} - t_{c2}\right)}{\ln\left[\dfrac{t_{h1} - t_{c1}}{t_{h2} - t_{c2}}\right]} = \frac{\Delta t_1 - \Delta t_2}{\ln\left[\dfrac{\Delta t_1}{\Delta t_2}\right]} \tag{5.17}$$

where Δt_1 and Δt_2 are temperature differences at each end of the heat exchanger.

Example 5.6

Water at 20°C is heated to 80°C by condensing steam in a heat exchanger. Saturated steam is supplied at a rate of 100 kg/h and a temperature of 200°C. It leaves the exchanger at a quality of 0.05. How much water can be heated?

Solution:

This solution is a simple energy balance: heat lost by the steam $\left(\dot{Q}_s \right)$ must

equal heat gained by the water $\left(\dot{Q}_w \right)$:

$$\dot{Q}_s = \dot{m}_s \, \Delta h_s = \dot{m}_s \, [h_g - (h_f + x h_{fg})] = \dot{Q}_w = \dot{m}_w \, c_{pw} \Delta t_w$$

or

$$\dot{m}_w = \frac{\dot{m}_s [h_g - (h_f + x h_{fg})]}{c_{pw} \Delta t_w} = \frac{100 \times (2791 - 949)}{4.178 \times 60} = \frac{100 \times 1842}{251} = 735 \frac{kg}{hr}$$

ANSWER

Note: The steam properties are found from Table 9.02 at a temperature of 200°C.

Example 5.7

For the heat exchanger of Example 5.6, find the log mean temperature difference and compute the value for U if the heat exchanger surface area is 0.35 m².

Solution:

Solving Equation 5.17 for Δt_{lm}:

$$\Delta t_{lm} = \frac{\Delta t_1 - \Delta t_2}{\ln \left[\dfrac{\Delta t_1}{\Delta t_2} \right]} = \frac{(200 - 20) - (200 - 80)}{\ln \left[\dfrac{200 - 20}{200 - 80} \right]} = \frac{180 - 120}{\ln \left[\dfrac{180}{120} \right]}$$

$$= \frac{60}{\ln (1.5)} = \frac{60}{0.41} = \underline{148°C}$$

ANSWER

The problem statement did not indicate if flow was parallel or counter. This solution is based upon an assumption of parallel flow. A solution assuming counter flow will produce the same numerical answer since the steam temperature does not change.

Solving Equation 5.16 for U:

$$U = \frac{\dot{Q}}{A\,\Delta t_{1m}} = \frac{\dot{m}_w c_p \Delta t_w}{A\,\Delta t_{1m}} = \frac{735\left[\dfrac{\text{kg}}{\text{hr}}\right] \times 4.178\left[\dfrac{\text{kJ}}{\text{kgK}}\right] \times (80-20)\,\text{K}}{0.35\,\text{m}^2 \times 148\,\text{K}}$$

$$= \frac{184250}{51.8} = 3557\,\frac{\text{kJ}}{\text{hr m}^2\text{K}}$$

Converting units:

$$U = 3557\,\frac{\text{kJ}}{\text{hr m}^2\text{K}} \times 1000\,\frac{\text{J}}{\text{kJ}} \times \frac{1\,\text{hr}}{3600\,\text{s}}$$

$$= 988\,\frac{\text{J}}{\text{s m}^2\,\text{K}} = 988\,\frac{\text{W}}{\text{m}^2\,\text{K}} \qquad \textbf{ANSWER}$$

5.13 Thermal Resistance in a Heat Exchanger

The effectiveness of a heat exchanger is substantially affected by the overall thermal resistance, R_T (or $1/U$). For the double-pipe heat exchanger discussed earlier, this resistance includes the inside surface resistance, the resistance of the pipe wall, and the surface resistance on the outside of the smaller pipe.

The surface resistances may be estimated using Equation 5.12 or a similar relationship. The resistance of the pipe wall can be determined from tables of metal properties. With this information, we can calculate the heat transfer under ideal conditions. However, another factor compounds the problem. Scale deposits often build up on the heat exchanger surfaces. These deposits may cause a substantial increase in thermal resistance. Typical values of overall thermal resistances for selected "heat exchangers" are shown in Table 5.04. Table 5.05 lists values of scale resistance for selected conditions.

Table 5.02. Conductivity/Resistance values of selected materials.[a]

Material	Conductivity		Resistance	
	k	C	$1/k$	$1/C$
Masonry				
Brick, common	0.7	--	1.4	--
Concrete, stone aggregate	2.2	--	0.45	--
Stone, typical	2.0	--	0.50	--
Concrete blocks, 3-oval core				
Stone aggregate, 200 mm (8 in.)	--	5.4	--	0.19
300 mm (12 in.)	--	4.6	--	0.22
Cinder aggregate, 200 mm (8 in.)	--	2.8	--	0.36
300 mm (12 in.)	--	2.4	--	0.42
Metals				
Aluminum	221	--	0.0045	--
Cast iron	47.7	--	0.021	--
Copper	393	--	0.00254	--
Steel	45	--	0.022	--
Steel, 316 stainless	15	--	0.067	--
Wood and panels				
Hardwood	0.17	--	5.9	--
Softwood	0.13	--	7.7	--
Plywood	0.12	--	8.7	--
Plywood, 13 mm (1/2")	--	9.1	--	0.11
Gypsum board, 9.5 mm (3/8")	--	17.6	--	0.057
13 mm (1/2")	--	12.6	--	0.079
Particle board, medium density	0.135	--	7.41	--
high density	0.170	--	5.88	--
Insulation				
Glass wool	0.038	--	26	--
Expanded polystyrene, extruded	0.029	--	35	--
Expanded polyurethane	0.024	--	42	--
Blanket or bat type	0.040	--	25	--
Other materials				
Bakelite	17	--	0.059	--
Cardboard	0.07	--	14	--
Cotton (fiber)	0.042	--	24	--
Glass, heat resistant	1.0	--	1.0	--
Ice, at 0°C	2.24	--	0.446	--
Paper	0.13	--	7.7	--
Paraffin	0.24	--	4.2	--
Plastic film	4	--	0	--
Acrylic glass (Plexiglas)	0.184	--	5.43	--

Polyvinyl chloride (PVC)	0.15	--	6.7	--
Pyrex	1.06	--	0.94	--
Floor				
Carpet and fibrous pad	--	2.73	--	0.37
Carpet and rubber pad	--	4.60	--	0.22
Tile, asphalt, etc.	--	113.6	--	0.009
Wood subfloor, 19 mm	--	6.0	--	0.17
Glass				
Single	--	56.7	--	0.02
Double	--	3.97	--	0.25
Other				
Air space, 2 cm to 4 cm	--	6.2 [b]	--	0.16 [b]
Surface, vertical, still air	--	8.29 [c]	--	0.12 [c]
horizontal, still air, HT up	--	9.26 [c]	--	0.11 [c]
horizontal, still air, HT down	--	6.13 [c]	--	0.16 [c]
Wall surface, 3.33 m/s air velocity	--	22.7 [c]	--	0.04 [c]
Wall surface, 6.67 m/s air velocity	--	34.0 [c]	--	0.03 [c]

[a]Values shown here are based upon information from several sources. These values should be used as approximations only. Thermal conductivity can vary significantly with temperature. Other factors also affect thermal conductivity. Material density is important in determining thermal conductivity of insulating materials. Direction of heat flow (e.g., along or across wood grain) is also a factor. Thus, values shown here should be considered as good approximations, but not exact values. Consult ASHRAE (1997) for extensive information regarding thermal properties.

[b]Can be used as approximate value for vertical, horizontal, or sloped air space.

[c] These are convective (surface) heat transfer coefficient (h) values.

Notes:

k is in units of W/m K.

C is in units of W/m^2 K for the thickness, or conditions, given.

R, the resistance to heat flow, is simply the inverse of C (m^2 K/W) or k (m K/W). Note, however, that k is based upon a unit thickness. To find R for a specified thickness, R (or $1/k$) must be multiplied by the thickness.

Table 5.03. Approximate[a] range of convective (surface) heat transfer coefficient (h).

Condition	h (W/m^2 K)	$R_s = 1/h$ (m^2 K/W)	h (Btu/hr ft^2 °F)
Gases (natural convection)	5 - 28	0.04 - 0.2	0.9 - 5
Gases (forced convection)	11 - 280	0.004 - 0.09	2 - 50
Viscous liquids (forced convection)	57 - 570	0.02 - 0.002	10 - 100
Water (forced convection)	570 - 5700	0.002 - 0.002	100 - 1000
Liquid metals (forced convection)	5700 - 28,000	0.00004 - 0.002	1000 - 50,000
Boiling water	1700 - 57,000	0.00002 - 0.0006	300 - 10,000
Condensing steam	2800 - 28,000	0.004 - 0.00004	500 - 5000

[a] These numbers give approximate ranges only. Numbers have been rounded to avoid implying excess accuracy. Thus conversions between units may not be exact for the numbers shown.

Table 5.04. Approximate values of thermal resistance for selected heat transfer conditions.[a]

Condition	$U = \dfrac{W}{m^2\,K}$	$R_T = \dfrac{m^2\,K}{W}$
Plate glass window	6.2	0.16
Frame wall, insulated	0.40	2.5
Steam condenser	1100 - 5600	0.00018 - 0.00091
Freon 12 condenser with water coolant	280 - 850	0.0012 - 0.0036
Water-to-water heat exchanger	850 - 1700	0.00059 - 0.0012
Finned tube (water in tubes to air across tubes)	25 - 55	0.018 - 0.040
Gas-to-gas heat exchanger	10 - 40	0.025 - 0.10

[a] Based on data from Holman (1986).

Table 5.05. Thermal resistance (R_s)[a] of scale deposits from water at water temperatures and velocities shown.

	$t < 52°C$		$t > 52°C$	
Water Type	$u < 0.9$ m/s	$u > 0.9$ m/s	$u < 0.9$ m/s	$u > 0.9$ m/s
Distilled	8.8×10^{-5}	8.8×10^{-5}	8.8×10^{-5}	8.8×10^{-5}
Sea water	8.8×10^{-5}	8.8×10^{-5}	1.8×10^{-4}	1.8×10^{-4}
Treated boiler feed water	1.8×10^{-4}	8.8×10^{-4}	3.5×10^{-4}	1.8×10^{-4}
City well, Great Lakes	1.8×10^{-4}	1.8×10^{-4}	3.5×10^{-4}	3.5×10^{-4}
Brackish, clean river water	3.5×10^{-4}	1.8×10^{-4}	5.3×10^{-4}	3.5×10^{-4}
Muddy river water	5.3×10^{-4}	3.5×10^{-4}	7.0×10^{-4}	5.3×10^{-4}
Hard water	5.3×10^{-4}	5.3×10^{-4}	8.8×10^{-4}	8.8×10^{-4}

Based upon data from Avallone and Baumeister (1986).
[a] Units of R_s are (m^2 K)/W.

List of Symbols

A area, m^2
Bi Biot number, dimensionless
c_p specific heat capacity at constant pressure, J/(kg K) or kJ/(kg K)
C thermal conductance, W/(m^2 K)
D diameter, m
E energy radiated, W/m^2
Fo Fourier number, dimensionless
Gr Grashof number, dimensionless
h convective (surface) heat transfer coefficient, W/(m^2 K)
h enthalpy, kJ/kg
k thermal conductivity, W/(m K)
L a characteristic length, m
$\dot{m}$ mass flow rate, kg/s
Nu Nusselt number, dimensionless
Pe Peclet number, dimensionless
Pr Prandtl number, dimensionless
$\dot{q}$ heat transfer rate per unit area, W/m^2
$\dot{Q}$ heat transfer rate, W
r radius, m
R thermal resistance, (m^2 K)/W

R_T total resistance to heat flow, $(m^2\ K)/W$
Re Reynolds number, dimensionless
t temperature, °C
Δt temperature difference, °C
T absolute temperature, K
u velocity, m/s
$\dot{u}$ thermal energy of mass crossing a boundary
U overall heat transfer coefficient, $W/(m^2\ K)$
α thermal diffusivity, m^2/s
δ characteristic length, m
θ time, s
μ dynamic (or absolute) viscosity, Pa s or $(N\ s)/m^2$
ρ density, kg/m^3
σ Stefan-Boltzmann Constant $(5.669 \times 10^{-8}\ W/m^2\ K^4)$
v kinematic viscosity (μ/ρ), m^2/s

Subscripts
1,2,3   position identification
b bulk (average)
c cold fluid
D diameter
f fluid state
h hot fluid
i inside
lm logarithmic mean
o outside
s steam
s solid
s surface
T total
w wall

References

1. ASHRAE. 1997. *Handbook of Fundamentals*. Chapter 24: Thermal and Water Vapor Transmission Data; Chapter 36: Physical Properties of Materials. ASHRAE, Inc., Atlanta, GA.
2. Avallone, Eugene A., and Theodore Baumeister III. 1986. *Marks' Standard Handbook for Mechanical Engineers*, 9th ed., McGraw Hill, New York, NY.
3. Dakas, Vassilis. 1992. *Transport Phenomena of Food and Biological Materials*. CRC Press, Boca Raton, FL.
4. Heldman, Dennis R., and Daryl B. Lund. 1992. *Handbook of Food Engineering*. Marcel Dekker, Inc., New York, NY.
5. Holman, Jack P. 1986. *Heat Transfer*. McGraw-Hill, New York, NY.
6. Obert, Edward F. 1960. *Concepts of Thermodynamics*. McGraw Hill, New York, NY.

Problems

5.1. Compute the heat flow per unit area through the materials listed in the following table. All temperatures are surface temperatures.

Material	Thickness	t_1 (°C)	t_2 (°C)	Comments
Brick, common	8 cm	23	7	Compare to plywood
Concrete block, cinder	200 mm	20	–4	
Steel plate	100 mm	23	7	
Plywood	13 mm	23	–5	
Expanded polyurethane	10 mm	25	–10	Compare to plywood
Plexiglas	7 mm	25	–10	Compare to Pyrex
Pyrex glass	7 mm	55	20	
Cardboard	7 mm	25	–10	Compare to Plexiglas

5.2. Repeat Problem 5.1 using the temperatures given as *air temperatures*, rather than *surface temperatures*. For each material, assume still air along one surface and a velocity of approximately 6.7 m/s over the other surface.

5.3. Using the results of the previous problem, estimate the surface temperature on the still air side of each material.

5.4. An uninsulated retort is made of 1 cm steel. The steam temperature inside the retort is 125°C and the outside air temperature is 35°C. Compute the heat flow per unit area through the retort wall. For simplicity, treat the wall as a flat surface for this analysis.

5.5. Estimate the outside surface temperature for the retort of Problem 5.4.

5.6. A 5-cm layer of glass wool insulation is added to the outer surface of the retort of Problem 5.4. Compute the percent reduction in heat loss from the retort.

5.7. A glass window separates rooms at temperatures of 25°C and –15°C, respectively. What is the heat flow through the window? A second pane of glass is added to the window with a 0.02 m air space between panes. What is the heat flow now?

5.8. How will the result of the previous problem be changed (give revised heat flow calculations) if the second "pane" is simply a plastic sheet instead of glass?

5.9. What is the "R value" for a wall made up of 0.1 m common brick, 1.5 cm sheathing, 2 cm air space, and 8 cm bat-type insulation? What is the "U value"? Ignore surface resistance.

5.10. Repeat the previous problem replacing the air space and bat-type insulation with 10 cm of blanket insulation.

5.11. What is the "R value" for a wall made up of 200 mm concrete blocks (stone aggregate), 25 mm expanded polystyrene, plastic film, and 13 mm plywood. What is the "U value"?

5.12. Compute the heat flow through the wall for inside and outside air temperatures of 23°C and –7°C, respectively. For these temperatures, what is the temperature at the interface between the plywood and the plastic film?

5.13. A wall is made up of 0.15 cm steel sheet, 10 cm of blanket insulation, and 1.3 cm plywood. Compute the heat flow through the wall for an inside air temperature of 25°C and an outside air temperature of –5°C.

5.14. A metal pipe has an inside diameter of 2.50 cm and an outside diameter of 2.70 cm. The thermal conductivity of the pipe material is 50 W/(m K). The inside and outside surface heat transfer coefficients are 100 and 5 W/(m² K) respectively. Compute the heat transfer per square meter of inside surface if the inside liquid temperature is 80°C and the outside air temperature is 30°C.

5.15. The pipe of the previous problem is insulated with a 2-cm layer of polyurethane. If all other parameters remain the same (including the outside air temperature and outside surface heat transfer coefficient), compute the heat transfer per square meter of inside surface.

5.16. Repeat the previous problem for a pipe with inside and outside diameters of 7.50 and 7.70 cm respectively. All other parameters, including the insulation thickness, remain the same.

5.17. For turbulent flow inside tubes, the following equation is often used to calculate the film coefficient:

$$Nu = 0.027 \, R_e^{\,0.8} \, Pr^{\frac{1}{3}} \left(\frac{\mu_b}{\mu_w} \right)^{0.14}$$

Find the film coefficient (h) for water at 85°C (bulk temperature) flowing at 1.5 m/s through a 0.03-m pipe if the wall temperature of the pipe is 65°C.

5.18. Repeat the previous problem for a bulk temperature of 65°C and a wall temperature of 85°C (fluid heating).

5.19. You are asked to estimate the heat flow through the wall of a refrigeration unit. The inside and outside temperatures are 1°C and 26°C, respectively. The wall is made up of 0.1 m of urethane sealed between 0.0025 m sheets of aluminum. You know that this urethane has an average thermal conductivity of $0.0173 \dfrac{\text{Watts}}{\text{m K}}$. What would you estimate the heat loss to be if the refrigerator has 25 m² of surface area?

5.20. Explain the significance of:

a. Reynolds number	e. Prandtl number
b. Nusselt number	f. thermal diffusivity
c. absorptivity	g. reflectivity
d. black body	h. surface heat transfer coefficient.

5.21. 30 kg/h of saturated steam at 500 kPa are used in a counter-flow heat exchanger. The steam leaves with a quality of 5% (5% vapor and 95% liquid). How many kilograms per hour of milk can be heated from 20°C to 120° in this unit?

5.22. A single pass heat exchanger is used to cool milk from 65°C to 20°C using water initially at 10°C. The exit water is at 24°C.

a. Is this a parallel- or counter-flow unit?

b. If $U = 2500 \dfrac{W}{m^2K}$, what is the heat transferred per square meter of heat exchanger area?

5.23. A single pass counter-flow heat exchanger is used to cool water used in a processing plant. The water enters at 50°C and exits at 25°C. The cooling brine enters at 0°C and exits at 15°C.

a. If the water flow rate is 500 kg/h, what is the rate of heat transfer from the water to the cooling brine?

b. What is the required flow rate for the cooling brine if it has a specific heat of 3.3 kJ/kg K?

c. If the incoming water temperature remains at 50°C while the flow rate is increased by 50%, what is likely to happen regarding other temperatures, and the overall heat transfer?

Transient Heat Transfer

6

Abstract. *This unit introduces the concept of transient, or unsteady-state, heat transfer. The special case of uniform internal temperature (Newtonian heating) is considered. The more general case of high thermal resistance materials is discussed and the graphical solution approach is discussed for one-dimensional and multi-dimensional applications.*

Keywords. *Biot number, Fourier number, Heisler charts, Newtonian heating, Schneider charts, transient heat transfer, unsteady-state heat transfer.*

6.1 Factors Affecting Transient Heat Transfer

As noted in the previous heat transfer chapter, transient (or unsteady-state) heat transfer involves changes in conditions with time. Where changes are slight, we can often ignore them. However, in many applications, these changes are important. This is typically the situation when we wish to raise or lower the temperature of an object. The heating and cooling of foods during thermal processing are applications where change in temperature with time is a factor of primary interest. Thus an unsteady-state heat transfer analysis must be performed for such applications.

We must look at additional parameters, beyond those affecting steady-state heat transfer, when considering unsteady state conditions. Time and the thermal storage capacity of the material are two important new parameters. The ratio of surface resistance to internal resistance is also important. If the internal resistance of an object is very low compared to its surface resistance, the inside temperature will be nearly uniform throughout. A can of water heated in a retort would exhibit this characteristic. The water would circulate by natural convection as it is heated, producing a nearly uniform temperature throughout. (This is effectively a low internal resistance even though convection rather that conduction is the cause of the near uniform temperature.) Cream style corn and mashed potatoes would exhibit very high internal resistances compared to the surface resistance at the can. Thus, there would be a large temperature gradient in cans of these products. The analyses in this unit assume convection heat transfer to the outside surface, but conduction heating only inside the container.

The governing equation for unsteady-state heat transfer may be written as:

$$\frac{k}{\rho\,c_p}\left(\frac{\partial^2 t}{\partial x^2} + \frac{\partial^2 t}{\partial y^2} + \frac{\partial^2 t}{\partial z^2}\right) = \frac{\partial t}{\partial \theta} \tag{6.01}$$

where: θ = time, s

$\rho\, c_p$ = thermal storage capacity, kJ/m^3 K

$$\frac{k}{\rho\, c_p} = \alpha = \text{thermal diffusivity} = \frac{\text{conducting ability}}{\text{storage capacity}}\,,\ \frac{m^2}{s}$$

In solving problems of this type, dimensionless numbers and ratios are widely used to produce "universal" solutions. For unsteady-state heat transfer, a dimensionless temperature ratio in the following form is commonly used:

$$T = \frac{t_o - t}{t_o - t_i} \tag{6.02}$$

where: t = the temperature of the object at any time θ
         t_i = the initial temperature of the object under consideration
         t_o = the temperature of the surrounding medium

6.2 Transient Heat Transfer with Uniform Internal Temperature (Newtonian Heating)

For the can of water noted above, and for many metal products (high thermal conductivity), we can assume a uniform internal temperature. This type of heating is called **lumped capacity** or **Newtonian heating**. This constant internal temperature assumption is valid because the internal thermal resistance is very low compared to the surface resistance. Since t does not change with position (only with time) and the thermal conductivity (k) is very large, the left side of Equation 6.01 becomes ambiguous (it approaches $\infty \times 0$). A new equation is, thus, written for this special case. It states, simply, that heat flow through the surface of the object must equal the heat gained by the object. Thus:

$$h\, A(t_o - t) = \rho\, V\, c_p\, \frac{dt}{d\theta} \tag{6.03}$$

Rewriting the equation, we get:

$$\frac{dt}{d\theta} = \frac{h\,A}{\rho\,V\,c_p}\,(t_o - t) = \frac{h\,A}{m\,c_p}(t_o - t) \tag{6.04}$$

Since the temperature is uniform throughout the object, an exact solution to Equation 6.04 can be obtained. That solution, written in the form of the dimensionless temperature ratio, is:

$$T = \frac{t_o - t}{t_o - t_i} = \exp\left(\frac{-h\,A\,\theta}{\rho\,V\,c_p}\right) = \exp\left(\frac{-h\,A\,\theta}{m\,c_p}\right) = \exp\left(\frac{-A\,\theta}{m\,c_p R_T}\right) \tag{6.05}$$

where: A = the surface area through which heat is transferred, m^2
         c_p = the thermal capacity, or specific heat, of the object, kJ/(kg K)

h = the surface heat transfer coefficient, W/(m² K)
m = the total mass of the object ($m = \rho V$), kg
R_T = the overall surface resistance to heat flow (1/h).
V = the object volume, m³
ρ = the density of the object, kg/m³
θ = time, s

Note that Equation 6.05 is truly applicable only to bodies that are homogeneous throughout, e.g., a block of copper. In applying it to the can of water, we either consider only the water (ignoring the can) or use weighted averages for the can and water to compute m and c_p. For Newtonian heating described here, the surface heat transfer coefficient, h, controls the heat flow into a can. For normal heating, on the other hand, the limiting factor is the thermal conductivity, k. When thermal conductivity is limiting, heat can be transferred to the surface much more rapidly than it can be transferred within the object.

With Newtonian heating, the shape of bodies being analyzed is important only as it affects surface area. Since the internal temperature is uniform throughout, only surface area, surface resistance, thermal capacity, and time are significant.

Example 6.1

A 5.0-cm diameter copper sphere (ρ = 8954 kg/m³, c_p = 0.3831 kJ/kg K) is initially at a uniform temperature of 10°C. The sphere is placed inside an environment having a temperature of 200°C. The surface heat transfer coefficient is h = 10 W/(m² K). Under these conditions, we can assume uniform internal temperature for the sphere.

What is the temperature inside the sphere after 10 minutes in this environment?

Solution:
We will solve Equation 6.05 using the first form of the exponential expression:

$$T = \exp\left(\frac{-10\dfrac{W}{m^2\ K} \times \pi(0.05)^2\ m^2 \times (10 \times 60)\ s}{8954\dfrac{kg}{m^3} \times \dfrac{\pi(0.05)^3}{6}\ m^3 \times 383.1\dfrac{J}{kg\ K}}\right) =$$

$$= \exp\left(\frac{-10 \times 0.007854 \times 600}{8954 \times 0.00006545 \times 383.1}\right) = \exp\left(\frac{47.12}{224.5}\right) = \exp(0.2099) = 0.8107$$

Thus, $t = t_o - (t_o - t_i) \times T = 200 - (200 - 10) \times 0.8107 = 200 - 154 = \underline{46°C}$

ANSWER

Example 6.2

The 5.0 cm copper sphere of Example 6.1 is reshaped into a rectangular plate 5.0 cm × 13.09 cm × 1.0 cm. The total volume, mass, and thermal properties remain the same. Determine the internal temperature under the same exposure conditions as for Example 6.1.

Solution:

The solution procedure is exactly the same as for the previous example, but the surface area of the object is much larger:

$$T = \exp\left(\frac{-10\,\frac{W}{m^2\,K}\,\left[2(.05\times.1309) + 2\,(.01\times.05) + 2\,(.01\times.1309)\right]m^2\times(10\times60)\,s}{8954\,\frac{kg}{m^3}\times(0.05\times0.1309\times0.01)m^3\times383.1\,\frac{J}{kg\,K}}\right)$$

$$= \exp\left(\frac{-10\times0.01671\times600}{8954\times0.00006545\times383.1}\right) = \exp\left(\frac{-100.3}{224.5}\right) = \exp(-0.4466) = 0.6398$$

Thus, $t = t_o - (t_o - t_i)\times T = 200 - (200-10)\times0.6398 = 200 - 121.6 = \underline{78.4°C}$

ANSWER

The increased surface area results in a much more rapid heating of the plate.

6.3 Materials Having High Thermal Resistances

Most food materials have high thermal resistance such that the surface thermal resistance (R_s) of a food container is low compared to the thermal resistance (R_p) of the food product inside. Analytical solutions of the governing equation are complex under these conditions, and graphical solutions are often used. These graphical solutions make use of dimensionless parameters to permit universal application. These dimensionless parameters are the Biot number (Bi), the Fourier number (Fo), position ratio (δ/δ_o), and the dimensionless temperature ratio (T). They are frequently presented in a form known as the Heisler chart published in many heat transfer texts. As noted later, we will use a modified, and more easily read, form of these charts. This modified form of the charts was originally published by Schneider (1963).

6.4 Use of the Solution Charts

6.4.1 Parameters Used in the Solution

For heat transfer in one direction only, the solution of Equation 6.01 can be shown to be of the form:

$$T = f\left[\left(\frac{h\delta_o}{k}\right),\left(\frac{\delta}{\delta_o}\right),\left(\frac{\alpha\theta}{\delta_o^2}\right)\right] = f\left[(Bi),\left(\frac{\delta}{\delta_o}\right),(Fo)\right] \qquad (6.06)$$

where: $T = \dfrac{t_o - t}{t_o - t_i}$

Bi = Biot number = $\dfrac{h\delta_o}{k}$

δ_o = characteristic length [radius (r_o) or half thickness (L_o)] depending upon the object's shape

δ = length measurement showing position within an object. (For a cylinder, $\delta = r$ and is zero at the center. For a plate, δ is measured from the center and $\delta = L_o$ at the surface.)

Fo = Fourier number = $\dfrac{\alpha\theta}{\delta_o^2}$

Heat flow to (or from) a sphere, an infinite cylinder, or an infinite plate is described by the functional relationship of Equation 6.06. However, actual numeric solutions are much more difficult than simply showing this general form of the solution. Thus, either computer programs or graphical solutions are typically used. We will use the dimensionless parameters shown in Equation 6.06, presented in graphical form, to obtain solutions. Each graph represents conditions at a specific position (δ/δ_o) in a given geometry, e.g., the center of an infinite cylinder ($\delta/\delta_o = 0$), or midway between the center and the surface of a sphere ($\delta/\delta_o = 0.5$). For the specified position, the graph shows T as a function of Fo using a family of curves, each representing a different Bi value. Figures 6.03 through 6.08 represent such graphs.

Many conditions in which we are interested, including many food-processing applications, involve low values of the Fourier number. Thus, using a logarithmic scale for the Fourier number is desirable since it is easier to read the chart at low Fo values. Figures 6.03 through 6.08 represent such logarithmic plots. The graphs are based upon mathematical solutions of Equation 6.01, simplified for one-directional heat flow in a plate, cylinder, or sphere. These graphs may be used to solve for transient heat transfer to or from the geometry indicated. Since many food-processing applications involve low values of the Fourier number, Figures 6.03 through 6.08 will be more useful to us than the Heisler charts. Other than the scale for the Fourier number, these "Schneider" charts differ from the non-logarithmic (Heisler) charts, presented in many heat transfer texts, in that the Heisler charts plot a family of curves for the inverse of the Biot number while the Schneider graphs show curves for the Biot number.

The temperatures of interest to us are usually the center temperatures. The shapes of primary interest are an infinite plate, an infinite cylinder, and a sphere. Temperatures at location other than the center may be found using other Schneider charts (Schneider, 1963).

Consider the plate section shown in Figure 6.01a. The plate has a thickness of $2 L_o$ and is infinite in length and width. Thus heat flows toward the center from the top and bottom (or away from the center toward the top and bottom). Knowing the plate thickness $(2L_o)$, plate thermal properties (k, ρ, c_p), the surrounding temperature (t_o), the plate initial temperature (t_i), and the surface heat transfer coefficient (h), the center temperature can be found for any time (θ). Similarly, for the infinite cylinder shown in Figure 6.01b and for a sphere, heat flows radially toward (or from) the center. Using the previously identified parameters, a center temperature can be determined for each.

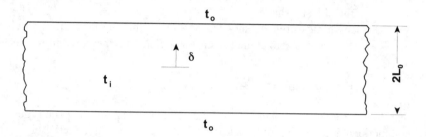

Figure 6.01a. Infinite plate of thickness 2 L_o and initial temperature t_i subjected to ambient temperature t_o.

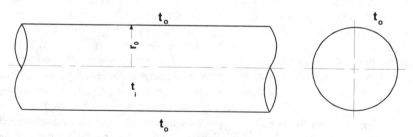

Figure 6.01b. Infinite cylinder of radius r_o and initial temperature t_i subjected to ambient temperature t_o.

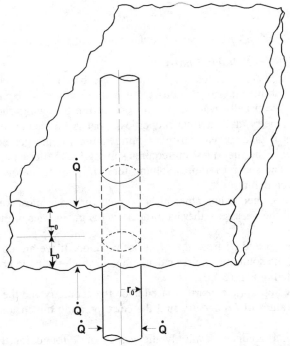

Figure 6.02. Representation of heat flow into a finite cylinder of radius r_o and height $2L_o$ by superimposing an infinite cylinder onto an infinite plate.

A short cylinder (e.g., a can) can be represented by a cylinder cutting through a plate (Figure 6.02). The temperature within such a finite cylinder is given by:

$$T = T_p \times T_c \qquad (6.07)$$

where:
$$T = \frac{t_o - t}{t_o - t_i} \qquad (6.08)$$

The subscript p represents the infinite plate and the subscript c represents an infinite cylinder. The temperatures t_o and t_i have been previously defined and t represents the center temperature. Note that we must solve for the plate and cylinder temperature ratios and multiply the two to obtain the dimensionless "can" temperature ratio.

The procedure outlined for analyzing a short cylinder can also be used for analyzing temperatures at the center of a rectangular parallelepiped (a box shape). In this case, we must have three mutually perpendicular infinite plates intersecting to produce the desired shape. The thickness of each plate must correspond to the one of the dimensions of the "box." Heat flow into or out of the object can be along three axis. Thus, the equation comparable to that for a cylinder (Equation 6.07) is:

$$T = T_{p1} \times T_{p2} \times T_{p3} \qquad (6.09)$$

where the subscripts $p1$, $p2$, $p3$ represent the three mutually perpendicular plates.

6.4.2 Steps in Use of Solution Charts

The solution charts (Figures 6.03 to 6.08) are based upon relationships among dimensionless parameters (Fo, Bi, and T). If we know two of these parameters, we can find the third. We usually want to answer one of the following questions: (1) for a given time, geometry, and thermal properties, what is the center temperature or (2) how long does it take to reach a given temperature for the geometry and thermal properties given? The first question requires solving for T after calculating the values of Fo and Bi. The second requires solving for Fo. Steps to follow in each solution process are given below.

To solve for center temperature at any given time, we must know the physical dimensions and the necessary thermal properties (as given later in the examples). We then:

1. Calculate Fo and Bi from the given information. If we are considering a short cylinder, the solution requires calculations for both the plate and the cylinder as represented in Figure 6.02.
2. Select the appropriate chart(s) based upon the geometry and the value of Bi.
3. For the values of Fo and Bi, find the corresponding dimensionless temperature ratio, T.
4. (For a short cylinder, multiply the values of T found for the plate and the cylinder to obtain a value of T for the short cylinder. See Equation 6.07.)
5. Solve for the temperature using Equation 6.08.

To solve for the time required to reach a specified center temperature:

1. Calculate T and Bi from the given information.
2. Select the appropriate chart.
3. For the values of T and Bi, find the corresponding Fo.
4. Compute the time ($\theta = Fo\ \delta^2/\alpha$).

This procedure for determining the time is suitable for a sphere, long cylinder, or large flat plate. For a short cylinder, we must use an iterative solution. From the specified temperature, we can determine T for the short cylinder, but we do not know the values for the plate (T_p) and the cylinder (T_c). The most straightforward approach in this case (or for a box shape) is as follows:

1. Assume a time (θ) and determine the corresponding temperature using steps 1 to 5 in the temperature solution above.
2. Based upon the temperature determined in step 1, assume a longer or shorter time and repeat the calculations.
3. Continue the iterations until your solution is sufficiently close to the center temperature originally specified.

Example 6.3

A "can" 0.2 m high and 0.2 m in diameter has thermal properties as follows:

$$\rho = 980 \text{ kg/m}^3 \qquad c_p = 3.77 \text{ kJ/(kg K)} \qquad k = 0.64 \text{ W/(m K)}$$

The initial temperature of the can is 70°C. What is the can center temperature after exposure to an ambient temperature of 120°C for one hour? Assume a surface heat transfer coefficient of 500 W/(m² K).

Solution:

The solution is straightforward; but, to find α, we must convert from Watts to Joules per second and from Joules to kiloJoules. The thermal diffusivity is:

$$\alpha = \frac{k}{\rho c_p} = \frac{0.64 \dfrac{W}{m\ K} \times \dfrac{1 \text{ J/s}}{1\ W} \times \dfrac{1 \text{ kJ}}{1000 \text{ J}} \times \dfrac{3600 \text{ s}}{1\ h}}{980 \dfrac{kg}{m^3} \times 3.77 \dfrac{kJ}{kg\ K}} = 6.236 \times 10^{-4} \ \frac{m^2}{h}$$

We must now calculate Fo and Bi for both the plate ($L_o = 0.1$ m) and the cylinder ($r_o = 0.1$ m):

$$Fo_p = \frac{\alpha \theta}{L_o^2} = 6.236 \times 10^{-4} \ \frac{m^2}{h} \times \frac{1 \text{ hr}}{(0.1)^2 \text{ m}^2} = 0.06236$$

$$Fo_c = \frac{\alpha \theta}{r_o^2} = 6.236 \times 10^{-4} \ \frac{m^2}{h} \times \frac{1 \text{ hr}}{(0.1)^2 \text{ m}^2} = 0.06236$$

Since $L_o = r_o = 0.1$, Fo_p and Fo_c are equal.

Similarly, $Bi_p = Bi_c$. Thus:

$$Bi_p = Bi_c = \frac{h\ r_o}{k} = \frac{500 \text{ W/(m}^2 \text{ K)} \times (0.1 \text{ m})}{0.64 \text{ W/(m K)}} = \frac{50}{0.64} = 78$$

Using Figure 6.05 (at $Fo_p = 0.06236$ and $Bi_p = 78$), we find $T_p = 0.99$.

Similarly, from Figure 6.03 (at $Fo_c = 0.06236$ and $Bi_c = 78$), $T_c = 0.97$.

Solving for T: $\qquad T = T_p \times T_c = 0.99 \times 0.97 = 0.960$.

Since $T = \dfrac{t_o - t_c}{t_o - t_i}$ we can solve for t_c.

$t_c = 120 - 0.960\ (120 - 70) = 120 - 0.960(50) = 120 - 48.0 = \underline{72.0°C}$

ANSWER

Example 6.4

Repeat Example 6.3 using a can that is 0.111 m high and 0.081 m in diameter. (This is a typical can size. The "can" of Example 6.1 is much larger than a typical food container.)

Solution:

All thermal properties, including thermal diffusivity, are unchanged. Thus, we can solve directly for Fo and Bi, noting that $L_o = 0.0556$ m and $r_o = 0.0405$.

$$Fo_p = \frac{\alpha\,\theta}{L_o^2} = 6.236\times10^{-4}\ \frac{m^2}{h}\times\frac{1\ hr}{(0.0506)^2\ m^2} = 0.2436$$

$$Fo_c = \frac{\alpha\,\theta}{r_o^2} = 6.236\times10^{-4}\ \frac{m^2}{h}\times\frac{1\ hr}{(0.0405)^2\ m^2} = 0.3802$$

$$Bi_p = \frac{h\,L_o}{k} = \frac{500\ W/(m^2\ K)\times(0.0556\ m)}{0.64\ W/(m\ K)} = \frac{27.8}{0.64} = 43.44$$

$$Bi_c = \frac{h\,r_o}{k} = \frac{500\ W/(m^2\ K)\times(0.0405\ m)}{0.64\ W/(m\ K)} = \frac{20.25}{0.64} = 31.64$$

Using Figure 6.05 (at $Fo_p = 0.2436$ and $Bi_p = 43.44$), we find $T_p = 0.695$.

Similarly, from Figure 6.03, (at $Fo_c = 0.3802$ and $Bi_c = 31.64$), $T_c = 0.2$.

Solving for T: $T = T_p \times T_c = 0.695 \times 0.2 = 0.139$

Since $T = \dfrac{t_o - t_c}{t_o - t_i}$, we can solve for t_c:

$t_c = 120 - 0.139(120 - 70) = 120 - 0.139(50) = 120 - 7 = \underline{113.0^\circ C}$

ANSWER

Note that the center temperature (72°C) of the large container in Example 6.1 had changed very little in one hour, while the center temperature (113°C) of this smaller container was approaching the temperature of the surroundings (120°C).

Example 6.5

A spherical food product, initially at 30°C, is suddenly exposed to an environment of 5°C. The surface heat transfer coefficient is 15 W/(m² K). The food product properties are: $\rho = 990$ kg/m³, $c_p = 3.77$ kJ/(kg K), and $k = 0.64$ W/(m K). How long will it take for the center temperature of the product to reach 10°C if the diameter of the product is 100 mm?

Solution:
To find the required cooling time, we must follow the reverse of previous steps. We must determine the dimensionless temperature ratio (T); calculate the Biot number; use the appropriate chart to find Fo; and determine the time corresponding to this value of Fo.

$$T = \frac{t_o - t}{t_o - t_i} = \frac{5 - 10}{5 - 30} = 0.20$$

The Biot number is: $Bi = \dfrac{h\, r_o}{k} = \dfrac{15\dfrac{W}{m^2\,K} \times 10\ m}{0.64\dfrac{W}{m\,K}} = 234$

Using Figure 6.07 at $T = 0.2$ and $Bi = 234$, we find $Fo = 0.24$. Note: the Biot number of 234 falls within the narrow band between the 100 and 1 000 000 curves on the chart.

We must now calculate the thermal diffusivity before solving for the time:

$$\alpha = \frac{k}{\rho\, c_p} = \frac{0.64\dfrac{W}{m\,K} \times \dfrac{1\ J/s}{1\ W} \times \dfrac{1\ kJ}{1000\ J}}{990\dfrac{kg}{m^3} \times 3.77\dfrac{kJ}{kg\,K}} = 1.715 \times 10^{-7}\ \frac{m^2}{s}$$

Solving for the time:

$$F_o = \frac{\alpha\,\theta}{r_o^2} \quad \text{or} \quad \theta = \frac{F_o \times r_o^2}{\alpha} = \frac{0.24 \times (0.10)^2\ m^2}{1.715 \times 10^{-7}\dfrac{m^2}{s}} = 13996\ s$$

Thus, $\theta = 13\ 996$ s $= 233.3$ min $= \underline{3.888\ hours}$ **ANSWER**

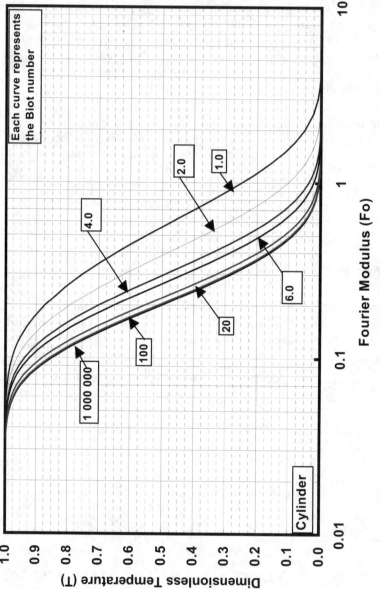

Figure 6.03. Dimensionless center temperature for an infinite cylinder (high Biot number).

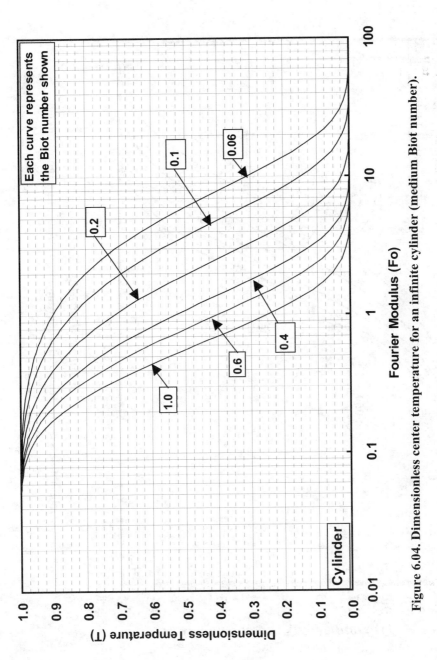

Figure 6.04. Dimensionless center temperature for an infinite cylinder (medium Biot number).

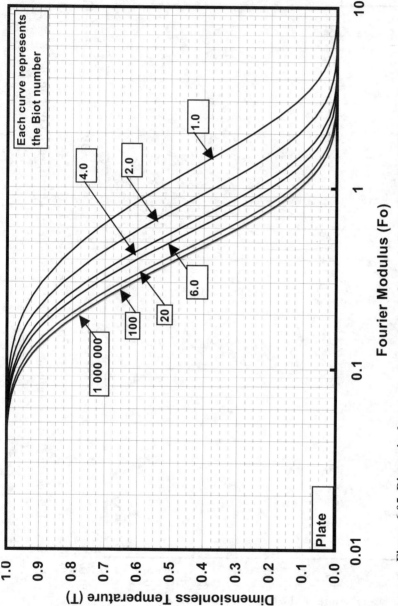

Figure 6.05. Dimensionless center temperature for an infinite plate (high Biot number).

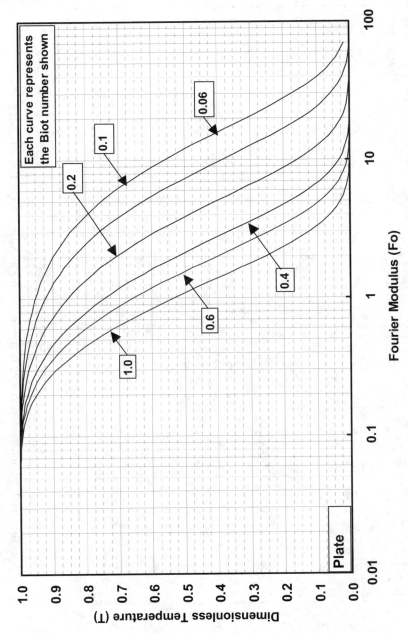

Figure 6.06. Dimensionless center temperature for an infinite plate (medium Biot number).

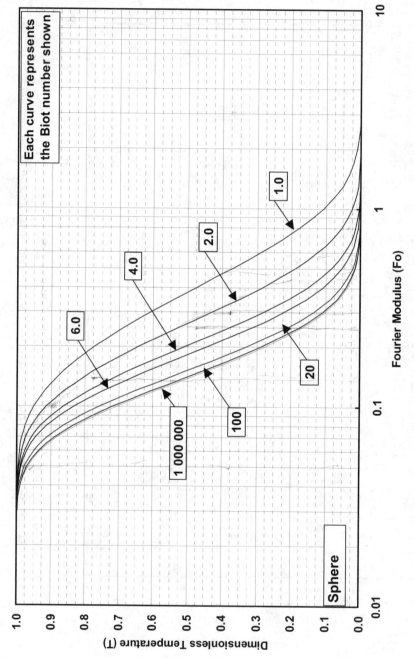

Figure 6.07. Dimensionless center temperature for a sphere (high Biot number).

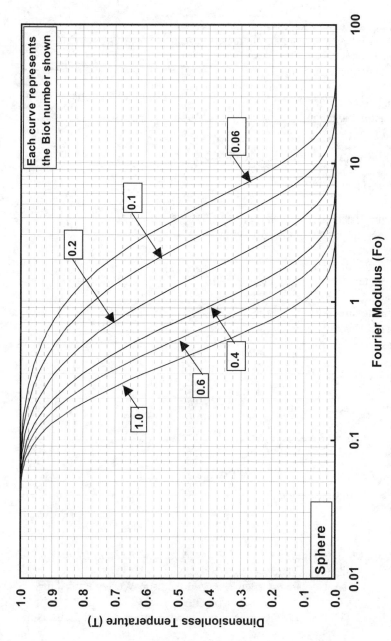

Figure 6.08. Dimensionless center temperature for a sphere (medium Biot number).

List of Symbols

A area, m^2

Bi Biot number, dimensionless

c_p specific heat capacity at constant pressure, J/(kg K) or kJ/(kg K)

C Thermal conductance, W/(m^2 K)

Fo Fourier number, dimensionless

h surface heat transfer coefficient, W/(m^2 K)

k thermal conductivity, W/(m K)

L a characteristic length, m

m mass, kg

$\dot{q}$ heat transfer rate per unit area, W/m^2

$\dot{Q}$ heat transfer rate, W

r radius, m

R thermal resistance, (m^2 K)/W

R_T total resistance to heat flow, (m^2 K)/W

t temperature, °C

Δt temperature difference, °C

T temperature ratio, dimensionless, $(t_o - t)/(t_o - t_i)$

V volume, m^3

x,y,z coordinate directions

α thermal diffusivity, m^2/s

δ characteristic length, m

θ time, s

ρ density, kg/m^3

Subscripts

c infinite cylinder

i initial

o surrounding or reference condition

p plate

References

1. Arpaci, V. S. 1966. *Conduction Heat Transfer*. Addison-Wesley Publishing Co., Reading, MA.
2. Holman, J. P. 1986. *Heat Transfer*. 6th ed. McGraw-Hill Book Company, New York, NY.
3. Rohsenow, W. M., J. P. Harnett, and Y. I. Cho. 1988. *Handbook of Heat Transfer*, 3rd ed. McGraw Hill Book Company, New York, NY.
4. Schneider, P. J. 1955. *Conduction Heat Transfer*. Addison-Wesley Publishing Co., Reading, MA.
5. Schneider, P. J. 1963. *Temperature Response Charts*. John Wiley and Sons, New York, NY.
6. Wong, H. Y. 1977. *Handbook of Essential Formulae and Data on Heat Transfer for Engineers*. Longman Inc., New York, NY.

Problems

6.1. Calculate the thermal diffusivity of the following materials:

Material	k (W/m k)	ρ (kg/m^3)	c_p (kJ/kg K)
Meat	0.61	1200	3.35
Pea puree	0.83	1090	3.81
Ice	2.21	910	1.93
Water	0.568	1000	4.21

6.2. Consider the following object shapes, having the properties noted in the table. Thermal conductivity (k) is very high for each object.

a. For each, plot the object temperature as a function of time based upon an initial object temperature of 50°C and a surrounding temperature of 120°C.

b. As a separate exercise, verify that the areas shown in the table are correct.

Object Description (all have the same volume, 0.000125 m^3)	Area (m^2)	ρ (kg/m^3)	c_p (kJ/kg K)	h (W/m^2 K)
Cube: 5 cm × 5 cm × 5cm	0.0150	8954	0.3831	10
Sphere: 6.205 cm diameter	0.01210	8954	0.3831	10
Cylinder: 5 cm long by 5.642 cm dia	0.01386	8954	0.3831	10
Cube: 5 cm × 5 cm × 5cm	0.0150	1000	4.18	30
Sphere: 6.205 cm diameter	0.01210	1000	4.18	30
Cylinder: 5 cm long by 5.642 cm dia	0.01386	1000	4.18	30

6.3. Consider an orange as a sphere with uniform thermal properties as follows: c_p = 3.70 kJ/(kg K), k = 0.52 W/(m K), and a density of 966 kg/m^3. Calculate the center temperature of the orange for the following conditions. (Note: for the diameter given the surface area of a sphere is 2.011×10^{-2} m^2 and the volume is 2.681×10^{-4} m^3.)

Item	Dia. (mm)	Time (s)	h (W/m^2 K)	t_i (°C)	t_o (°C)
A	80	15	10	30	0
B	80	30	10	30	0
C	80	60	10	30	0
D	80	120	10	30	0
E	80	15	100	30	0
F	80	30	100	30	5
G	80	60	100	25	0
H	80	120	100	25	5

6.4. Numbers such as 202 × 204 and 301 × 411 designate Can sizes. These numbers represent diameters and heights respectively of the cans. The first of the three digits in a number represents inches. The next two represent sixteenths. Thus, a 211 × 414 can is 2 11/16" in diameter and 4 14/16" (or 4 7/8") high. Plot the can center temperature as a function of time for the following conditions:

Item	Retort Temp. (°C)	Initial can Temp. (°C)	Can Size (in. × in.)	k (W/m K)	ρ (kg/m^3)	c_p (kJ/kg K)	h (W/m^2 K)
A	116	66	211 × 400	0.52	960	3.98	60
B	116	66	211 × 200	0.52	960	3.98	60
C	121	66	300 × 400	0.83	1090	3.81	100
D	93	38	303 × 406	0.61	1200	3.35	30
E	116	66	211 × 400	0.52	960	3.98	500
F	116	66	211 × 200	0.52	960	3.98	500
G	121	66	300 × 400	0.83	1090	3.81	500
H	125	21	300 × 400	0.83	1090	3.81	500

Thermal Processing

7

Abstract. This unit introduces the concepts relative to thermal processing. The concept of thermal death of microorganisms is presented. Procedures for determining adequacy of thermal death at constant temperature and for changing temperatures are discussed. Additional topics include heat penetration analyses for retort processing and the relationship between experimental and theoretical heat penetration data.

Keywords. Aseptic processing, heat penetration curves, microorganisms, retorts, sterilization, thermal death.

7.1 Introduction

Food spoilage has been a serious problem since food was first collected for preservation. The lack of a good quality food supply contributed significantly to human diseases, many of them nutritional in origin. Eventually, primitive societies learned a form of preservation—drying and salting of fish, meat, and other products. Other preservation methods including cooking and fermentation also developed over time. The modern era of food preservation began in 1810 when Nicholas Appert, of France, invented the art of canning. He heat-treated perishable food in glass jars and bottles, thus making one of the most important advances in the history of food processing. Shortly thereafter, two Englishmen, Donkin and Hall, began to can food using tin plate instead of glass. By 1839, American canneries had adopted this English practice.

We now know that food products contain many microorganisms that can cause spoilage of food, and illness and death. For our health, and to store food for extended periods, some type of food preservation is necessary. The most practical method of preservation for many foods is the thermal processing (sterilization) technique developed by Appert. This processing typically involves sealing the food inside a container and placing that container into a retort for a specified time period. **Retorts** are containers that can be sealed and filled with steam under pressure. (For some special applications, water, or a mixture of steam and air, may be used.) The high temperature condensing steam provides the heat energy needed for sterilization. The canner traditionally used for canning foods in the home is a small-scale retort. Aseptic processing, a different sterilization method, is discussed later in this chapter. For additional thermal processing information, consult Stumbo (1965), Larousse and Brown (1997), and similar publications.

Modern food processing utilizes knowledge about microorganisms and biochemical reactions to enhance food products. The use of heat allows the food industry to create safe, lasting, and enjoyable foodstuffs. This unit emphasizes the heat transfer aspects of thermal processing; however, a brief coverage of microbiology is needed to understand the sterilization process.

7.2 Microorganisms

The food industry is quite familiar with microorganisms, for they play a large role in the production of food products such as cheese, alcoholic beverages, and yogurt. However helpful a few of these organisms may be, others are troublesome because their metabolic activities result in the spoilage of foodstuffs.

Microorganisms are subdivided into many classes. **Yeasts** and **molds,** which are types of **fungi,** and **bacteria** pose the greatest spoilage threats to food. The category of bacteria is further broken down into three types based upon the oxygen requirements of the organisms:

1. **Obligate aerobes**. Obligate aerobes are those that require the presence of molecular oxygen to grow and to survive.
2. **Facultative anaerobes**. Facultative anaerobes are the group of bacteria that normally grow best in the presence of oxygen but can also survive in its absence.
3. **Obligate anaerobes**. Obligate anaerobes are the group of bacteria that live in the absence of oxygen.

The capability of bacteria to survive without oxygen is a key factor in food spoilage, especially of canned foods. Canned foods have very low levels of molecular oxygen, thus making facultative and obligate anaerobes the likely culprits of food spoilage. Bacteria pose another dilemma to the food processing industry in that some of these organisms produce spores that are resistant to heat treatment. Spores are the result of reproduction and remain dormant until favorable conditions arise for growth.

Fungi also produce spores. Both yeasts (which are unicellular fungi) and molds are important spoilage agents in foods with a high acidity level and low water activity. However, the survival of bacteria, especially in low acid foods, is usually the greatest concern in food processing.

Microorganisms are also classified according to the temperature ranges in which they optimally grow (Figure 7.01). Bacteria possess an amazing ability for adaptation as demonstrated by their ability to thrive in hostile environments from the arctic tundra to the great depths of the oceans. The three main temperature categories of microorganisms are psychrophilic, mesophilic, and thermophilic. **Psychrophilic microorganisms** grow in temperature ranges of −10° to 10°C (14° to 50°F). These organisms are responsible for spoilage of food in refrigerators. **Mesophilic microorganisms** optimally grow within the temperature range of 10° to 40°C (50° to 104°F). The majority of microorganisms fall into this category. The final category of temperature classifications is the thermophilic microorganisms. **Thermophilic microorganisms** survive and often thrive at high temperatures ranging from 40° to 80°C (104° to 176°F). The food industry is quite concerned with these microorganisms because of their ability to survive at high temperatures. Proper thermal processing is necessary to ensure the destruction of thermophilic microorganisms and spores.

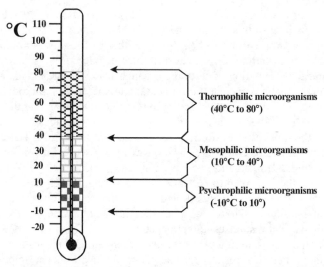

Figure 7.01. Optimum temperature range for microorganisms.

Many different spoilage organisms exist in our environment. A few of the major spoilage organisms are:

- *Clostridium botulinum*: *C. botulinum*, a food spoilage organism whose toxin is labeled the deadliest in the world, is responsible for botulism food poisoning. This organism normally exists in soil and water as non-harmful vegetative cells; however, in the absence of air, it becomes deadly. In only a few days, with suitable conditions, *C. botulinum* can produce the toxin. It is found mainly in canned and bottled products that have received an inadequate heat process.

- *Salmonella* spp.: *Salmonella* is an organism that is commonly associated with seafood, poultry, and uncooked eggs. Great care is taken in the food industry to place strict standards on the testing of foods for this organism.

- *Shigella* spp.: *Shigella* is often found with water and fresh fruit and vegetables that have been exposed to fecal contamination.

- Enteropathogenic *Escherichia coli*: *E. coli* is one of the most widely known bacterial species. Many strains of *E. coli* exist. The species resides in the intestines of animals. The food industry is primarily concerned with the contamination of ground beef and other undercooked or raw foods (FAO, 1976). Such contamination has received considerable media attention in recent years, with the evolution of strains that can cause serious illness and death.

7.3 Thermal Processing

Thermal processing uses heat to produce desired changes in food. These changes may include improved food quality and additional ease in further processing; however, the primary desired result is food preservation. Microorganisms pose the greatest threat in the spoilage of food products. To ensure safe food, we must know the appropriate temperature and duration of heating to achieve sterilization. For simplicity, the word organism (or microorganism) will be used to represent both vegetative cells and spores in the remainder of this discussion.

Microorganisms are resistant to heat for a number of reasons. The three most important variables contributing to the heat resistance of microorganisms are the type of microorganism, the incubation conditions in which the microorganisms are growing, and the conditions that are present during heat treatment. Just as microorganisms vary in size and shape, they differ in their ability to resist heat, even among different strains of the same species. Spores have a greater level of resistance than their parents, making spores the most difficult form of microorganism to destroy. The conditions in which the microorganisms and spores have grown are a second determining factor in thermal processing. An incubation condition in which spores are formed at high temperatures enables the organism to better resist processing at high temperatures. Additionally, the age of the microorganisms and the medium in which they are present affect their heat resistance. These characteristics are not unique to microorganisms. Animals exhibit similar responses to thermal stress.

The condition of the food in which the microorganisms and spores are present has a major effect upon their heat resistance. The pH of the medium is an important indicator of the resistance of spoilage bacteria, yeasts, and fungi. Bacteria prefer an acidity level near neutral while yeasts and fungi are more resistant to heat at mildly acidic conditions. Spores are more resistant to moist heat than to dry heat while bacteria prefer the opposite. Also, microorganisms have a greater heat resistance in foods high in fats, proteins, and sucrose.

7.3.1 Sterilization

The purpose of sterilization is to insure that spoilage organisms are inactivated and that pathogenic microorganisms and spores are destroyed. The spores of *C. botulinum* are quite resistant to heat processing and, therefore, are a common target of the sterilization process. Some nonpathogenic spoilage microorganisms have a heat resistance higher than *C. botulinum*, thus preventing a food product from achieving complete sterility. A completely sterile food item would have no surviving microorganisms or spores remaining after thermal processing. Complete sterilization is not practical, however, because sterilization time increases greatly as the number of organisms approaches zero. Thus, sterilization, as used here, is actually commercial sterilization—a degree of sterilization that is sufficient to achieve an acceptable reduction in microorganisms.

The degree of sterilization is measured by the **sterilization value** (*SV*). A sterilization value of 12*D* means a 12 decimal reduction in the number of spores of a specific strain of microorganism present. For example, assume a process designed to reduce the number of spores of a specific microorganism by 6 decimal reductions (6*D*) is applied to pears containing 10^2 of these spores per container. Thermal processing would reduce the number of spores of this microorganism in the pears to 10^{-4} spores per container, which is the equivalent of one spore per 10,000 containers. A sterilization value of 12*D* reduces the number of the specified microorganism to 10^{-10} organisms per container with the likelihood of a surviving microorganism reduced to one in 10^{10} containers. The value of 12*D*, based on the destruction of *Clostridium botulinum*, has been a long-time industry standard.

Example 7.1

A food process engineer is using thermal processing to sterilize a can of green beans. The engineer feels that sterilization will be achieved once 99.9999% of the *C. Botulinum* organisms are inactivated. What is the sterilization value of this process?

Solution:

The percentage of organisms remaining after processing is:

$$100\% - 99.9999\% = 0.0001\%$$

The ratio of initial organisms to final organisms is:

$$100\% / 0.0001\% = 1,000,000$$

The number of decimal reductions is then:

$$\log 1,000,000 = 6$$

The sterilization value of the process is $\underline{6D}$. **ANSWER**

7.3.2 Thermal Death Calculations

Knowledge about microorganisms and their relationship with various foodstuffs gives us the ability to calculate the processing times required to achieve a commercially sterile product. To examine this concept, we will first look at an idealized constant-temperature sterilization process. At constant temperature, the death rate of spores for a specific organism is a function of heating time. Figure 7.02 is a typical graph of such a death rate. This graph shows the typical logarithmic death curve—a straight line on a semi-logarithmic plot. This straight line relationship results from the fact that the rate of decrease in viable organisms is proportional to the number of organisms present. This can be represented as shown in Equation 7.01 where k is simply a constant for a particular organism, and N is the number of organisms at any time θ.

$$\frac{dN}{d\theta} = -kN \tag{7.01}$$

We can find the total change in N over any time period, θ, by rearranging (separating the variables) and integrating (note that at $\theta = 0$, $N = N_0$ and at any other time, θ, $N = N$):

$$\int_{N_0}^{N} \frac{dN}{N} = -k \int_{0}^{\theta} d\theta$$

The result of this integration is:

$$\ln \frac{N}{N_0} = -k_1 \theta \tag{7.02}$$

To express the relationship of Equation 7.02 on a semi logarithmic chart such as Figure 7.02, we must first convert from natural logarithms to common (base 10) logarithms. This is easily done by noting that:

$$\ln x = 2.3026 \log x$$

Thus:

$$\ln \frac{N}{N_0} = 2.3026 \log \frac{N}{N_0} - k_1 \theta \quad \text{or} \quad \log \frac{N}{N_0} = -\frac{k_1}{2.3026} \theta = k_2 \theta$$

where $k_2 = k_1/2.3026$.

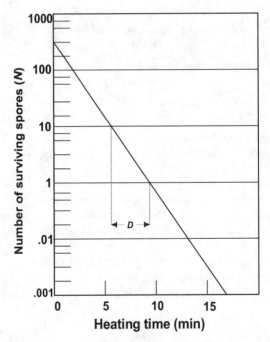

7.02. Death rate curve at constant temperature.

Thus, we see that Equation 7.02 represents the straight line of Figure 7.02. Remember that D represents the heating time required for one log reduction in the number of microorganisms. Note also that one log cycle reduction represents a 90% decrease (100 to 10, 10 to 1, 1 to 0.1, etc.). Thus, a $2D$ reduction is a 99% reduction; a $3D$ reduction is a 99.9% reduction, etc.

We now look at the effect of both time and temperature upon sterilization. To do this, we will define a relationship between the time and the temperature required to achieve sterilization. We first define F_0 as the time required at a reference temperature of 121.1°C (250°F) to achieve a desired sterilization value. However, we also need a method to calculate the time required for the desired sterilization at other temperatures. If we select a specific sterilization value (e.g., 12*D*) as that needed for thermal death of a particular organism, we can then graph the time required for thermal death as a function of temperature. Figure 7.03 shows such a graph for a hypothetical organism. We will develop the equation for this straight line in the following paragraphs. This development helps provide a review of algebra, and the use of logarithms in equations.

We begin with the general equation for a straight line: $y = mx + b$. The Y axis is logarithmic, thus $Y = \log \theta$. The slope m is $\Delta y/\Delta x$, and, for any full cycle, $\Delta y = -\log 10 = -1$. The corresponding value of Δx is the change in temperature corresponding to one full log cycle. We will define this value as z. Substituting into the straight line equation, we have:

$$\log\theta = -\frac{\log 10}{z} \times t + b = -\frac{1}{z} \times t + b = -\frac{t}{z} + b \tag{7.03}$$

We now know that the slope of this line is $-1/z$. This slope and an intercept (coordinates of any point on the line) fully define the straight line. The point selected is the location where the line crosses the 121.1°C (250°F) temperature line. The value of time (θ) at this temperature of 121.1°C is defined as F_0. Substituting into Equation 7.03 and solving for b:

$$\log F_0 = -\frac{121.1}{z} + b$$

$$b = \log F_0 + \frac{121.1}{z} \tag{7.04}$$

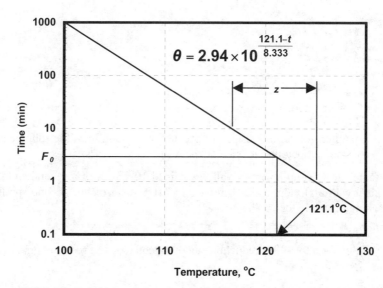

Figure 7.03. Plot of thermal death time for hypothetical organism XZYZX.

Substituting for b in Equation 7.03, we obtain:

$$\log\theta = -\frac{t}{z} + \log F_0 + \frac{121.1}{z}$$

Combining terms, we obtain the common form of the equation relating θ and F_0:

$$\log\frac{\theta}{F_0} = \frac{121.1 - t}{z} \qquad (t \text{ in } °\text{C}) \tag{7.05}$$

or, converting to exponential form:

$$\frac{\theta}{F_0} = 10^{\frac{121.1-t}{z}} \qquad (t \text{ in } °\text{C}) \tag{7.06}$$

For Figure 7.03, F_0 is 2.94 minutes, corresponding to the thermal death time at 121.1°C. The thermal death line traverses one full log cycle in a temperature increment of 8.333°. Thus, $z = 8.333°$.

If we know F_0 and z for any microorganism in a food product (see Table 7.01 for typical examples), we can compute the thermal death time, for that organism and food product, at any temperature. Recall that the sterilization value (SV) of a process (i.e., $12D$ or $18D$) is defined as the number of decimal reductions in the spores. Using this information, and noting that D represents one decimal reduction, we can relate F_0 and D, for any given temperature by:

$$F_0 (\text{min}) = D\left(\frac{\text{min}}{\text{cycle}}\right) \times SV (\text{cycles}) \quad \text{or} \quad SV = \frac{F_0}{D} \tag{7.07}$$

Example 7.2

A can of chicken noodle soup was processed at a constant soup temperature until a 99.999% reduction in *C. botulinum* was obtained. *C. botulinum* has a D value of 0.6 min for conditions of this process. How long must the soup be held at this constant temperature to achieve the result?

The same can of soup also originally contained 10 spores of a second spoilage organism with a D value of 2.1 minutes. What percent of this second spoilage organism remains in the can?

Solution:

The D value for a 99.999% reduction can be calculated. The reduction ratio is:

$$\frac{100\%}{(100-99.999)} = \frac{100}{0.001} = 10^5$$

Thus, the sterilization value of the process is 5D. The time required to destroy 99.999% of *C. botulinum* can now be calculated. This is the total time of the process.

$$SV_{C.bot.} = \frac{F}{D_{C.bot.}} = 5 \quad \text{or} \quad \frac{F}{0.6} = 5 \quad \text{and} \quad F = 3 \text{ minutes} \quad \textbf{ANSWER}$$

This time is then used to determine the sterilization value of the second spoilage organism.

$$SV_{new} = \frac{3\min}{D_{new}} = \frac{3\min}{2.1\min} = 1.429$$

Thus, we only have a 1.429 reduction in the second spoilage organism, and the percent remaining is:

$$\text{Percent remaining} = \frac{1}{10^{1.429}} = 0.037 \times 100\% = \underline{3.7\%} \qquad \textbf{ANSWER}$$

Example 7.3

A manufacturer of canned corn desires to reduce the sterilization time by raising the corn temperature to 135°C. Previously, the cans of corn had been processed at a corn temperature of 121°C. Assume $F_0 = 2.5$ minutes and $z = 10°C$. Determine F_{135}.

Solution:
Use Equation 7.05:

$$\log\left(\frac{\theta_{135}}{F_0}\right) = \log\theta_{135} - \log F_0 = \frac{121.1-135}{10} = -1.4$$

$$\log\theta_{135} = \log 2.5 - 1.4 = 0.3979 - 1.4 = 1.0021$$

$$\theta_{135} = \frac{1}{10^{1.0021}} = 0.09953 = \underline{0.10 \text{ minutes}} \qquad \textbf{ANSWER}$$

The constant temperature exposure time required for equivalent thermal death is substantially reduced (from 2.5 minutes at 121°C. to 0.1 minutes at 135°C). Note that both Example 7.2 and 7.3 assume a constant temperature of the processed material. Actual product temperatures vary with time, and this must be taken into account.

Table 7.01. Thermal processing data for selected microorganisms.

Microorganism	Z value(°C)	D_{121} value (min)	Typical foods
Thermophilic (35° to 55°C)			
Bacillus stearothermophilus	10	4.0	Vegetables, milk
Clostridium thermosaccharolyticum	7.2-10	3.0-4.0	Vegetables
Mesophilic (10° to 40°C)			
Clostridium sporogenes	8.88-11.1	0.8-1.5	Meats
Bacillus subtilis	4.1-7.2	0.5-0.76	Milk products
C. botulinum toxins A and B	5.5	0.1-1.3	Low-acid foods
Psychrophilic (–5° to 1.5°C)			
C. botulinum toxin E	10	3.0 (60°C)	Low-acid foods

From Fellows (1988).

7.3.3 Sterilization Equipment (Retorts)

The information presented in the previous section is based upon constant temperature sterilization. In actual processing operations, temperatures change with time. It is not possible, for example, to immediately change the temperature of an entire can of corn from 30°C to 70°C. Instead, the can must be heated from the outside, with the contents near the center being the last to reach the desired temperature. Since bacteria live longest at the lowest temperature in a container, we will always be interested in the "cold spot" during thermal processing. In the absence of convective circulation of liquids, the cold spot is the geometric center of the can. If circulation is present, the cold spot will be a function of can orientation. For vertical cans, it should be along the center axis of the can, but below the geometric center.

The physical device used to achieve this sterilization process is commonly called a **retort**. Since retorts play such an important role in the processing of foods, we will examine some commonly used types of retorts.

7.3.3.1 Still Vertical and Horizontal Steam Retorts

These retorts are cylindrical vessels positioned in either a vertical or horizontal orientation. They operate in a batch mode. While retort designs differ, the common feature is a chamber that can be filled, sealed, pressurized with steam for the desired time, depressurized, and emptied. These batch systems can be adapted for different products and container sizes by adjusting the steam pressure and/or holding time.

With older (and still widely used) retort models, prefilled cans are placed into crates or baskets that are then placed into the retort. In **vertical retorts** (Figure 7.04), the crates are raised and lowered by a hoist. In **horizontal retorts** (Figure 7.05) the crates are placed on a wheeled carrier that rolls on metal tracks into the retort. These systems are very labor intensive since the crates are filled, placed into the retort, removed from the retort, and emptied—all operations requiring human labor.

Vertical crateless retorts eliminate much of the labor involved in processing. These retorts can be filled and emptied automatically. The typical process is as follows: the retort is filled with water to cushion the fall of cans into it; a conveyor then dumps cans through an opening in the top, allowing the cans to displace the water; when filled the water is drained and the retort is sealed; steam is supplied and the processing is completed; the retort may then be filled with water for pressure cooling or it may then be depressurized; and cans are dumped from the bottom of the retort into water for cooling (Figure 7.06).

The operating method for all these retorts is simple. The retorts are filled and sealed. Steam is then injected into the retort and the retort is vented to remove all air. The presence of air inside the retort can affect heat transfer characteristics and temperature uniformity within the retort. In addition, it can result in a lower processing temperature if pressure is used to regulate temperature. (See the Steam-Air Mixtures section of the psychrometrics chapter.) Once the air is removed, the vent is closed. Pressure then increases until the desired operating temperature is reached. Since wet steam is used, maintaining a fixed pressure insures that a constant, and known, temperature is also maintained. However, most controls now use temperature sensors to determine if pressure changes are needed to adjust temperature. The retort is held at the operating conditions for the required amount of time based upon the container size and the product being processed. Pressure cooling may then be required to protect the containers. The retort is then depressurized and the containers are removed.

The above description applies for both glass and metal cans. In actual practice, glass is much more sensitive to thermal gradients; thus, special care must be taken when heating and cooling glass containers. The heating and cooling must be more gradual, and additional care must be taken in handling the glass containers. Precautions must also be taken to insure that internal can pressures are not high enough to cause failure of the can.

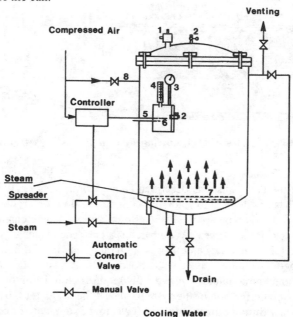

Figure 7.04. Vertical crate type retort. Numbered components are:
(1) safety valve; (2) steam bleed; (3) pressure gage; (4) thermometer;
(5) sensing element for controller; (6) thermo-box; (7) steam distribution section;
(8) air inlet for pressure cooling (from Rees and Bettison, 1991).

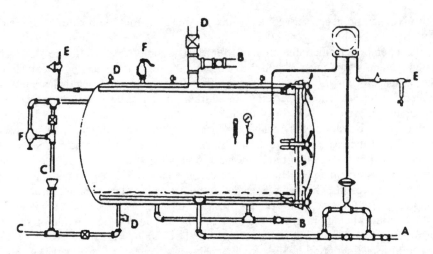

Figure 7.05. Horizontal retort. Letters represent (A) steam supply; (B) water source; (C) drain and/or overflow; (D) vents and bleeder valve; (E) air supply; and (F) safety, pressure relief, and manual control valves (from Rees and Bettison, 1991).

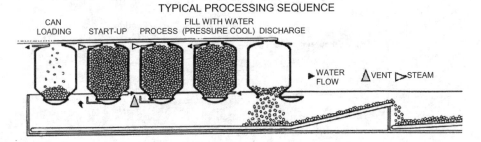

Figure 7.06. Vertical crateless retort showing steps in processing (www.maloinc.com).

7.3.3.2 Continuous Systems

In addition to the batch systems described above, continuous sterilization systems are also used. These systems allow for the continuous flow of product through the sterilizer. Systems of this type are well suited to operations where changes in product and/or container size are infrequent. With batch systems, each batch can be a different product or a different container; and processing conditions for the new batch can be modified as needed. Continuous systems do not allow this easy modification. Conversion to a new product or container size typically requires completion of processing for the current run and modification of the system to meet the needs for the new product.

A **multi-shell continuous horizontal rotary retort** is one type of continuous system. Most systems have three or more shells. These systems use a special continuous rotary feed valve to bring food containers into the shell. The cans then travel along the shell wall in a spiral motion between a wheel and the shell wall. Upon reaching the end of the shell, another rotary valve transfers the cans to the next shell. Subsequent shells can be used for additional heating or cooling as needed for the product being processed.

As the cans move along the wall of the shell, they rotate about their axes. This rotation encourages movement of the head space in the can and, thus, agitation of the can contents. For liquid contents, rotation and the resulting agitation speeds heating of the product. The rotation has little effect upon the heating of cans containing solids or highly viscous products.

Another example of a continuous system is the **hydrostatic retort**. This system uses hydrostatic pressure to maintain the desired steam pressure in a continuous flow process. This operating concept is shown in Figure 7.07. Cans enter the system from a conveyor belt and travel to the top of the structure where the cans enter the water-filled bring-up leg. As the cans travel down this leg, the water temperature continuously increases. Cans then enter the steam dome where they are exposed to the required retort temperatures. Holding time in the steam is controlled by the conveyor speed. Cans exit the retort through the bring-down leg and are discharged. Steam pressure inside a hydrostatic retort is maintained by the height of water in the entrance and exit legs of the unit. Hydrostatic retorts are distinguished by the tall enclosures required to house them, since a substantial depth of water is necessary to produce the desired retort pressure.

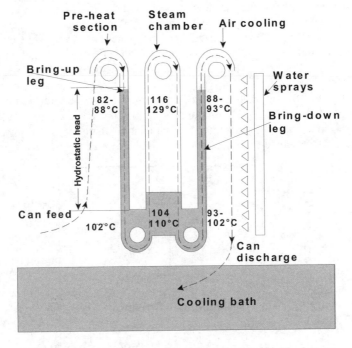

Figure 7.07. Continuous hydrostatic retort showing typical temperatures.

The systems described here may be used to process different products and/or different container sizes. They can be adapted for these changes by adjusting the steam pressure and/or holding time.

Aseptic processing is a third example of a continuous flow system. This process involves sterilizing a product and then placing it into presterilized containers in a sterile environment. Aseptic processing will be discussed later in this unit.

7.4 Heat Penetration During Processing

The sterilization analyses discussed earlier assume constant temperature throughout the process. However, we have already noted that no real processing operation can instantaneously raise the temperature of a product to a desired value and then hold that temperature for the desired time. Thus, none of the retort operations discussed in the previous section are constant temperature processes. Containers must be heated from the outside, and temperatures throughout the container are continuously changing during the heating and the cooling processes. These changes in temperature with time (including both the heating and cooling stages) must be considered in any analysis of thermal processing.

The transient heat transfer analysis techniques discussed in the transient heat transfer chapter can be used to estimate thermal processing temperatures. These techniques require knowledge of material properties (ρ, c_p, k) and the heat transfer coefficient (h), in addition to container geometry. Often, a more suitable method is to use experimental heating and cooling data to analyze the heat penetration process. Consider the processing of a single can of food inside a retort. The can at some initial temperature (t_i) is placed inside the retort. The retort is filled with steam, and after some time has elapsed, the temperature inside the retort stabilizes at t_r. The magnitude of t_r is controlled by the retort pressure since wet steam is used. Since the retort temperature is greater than the temperature of the product inside the can ($t_r > t_i$), the product will be heated. An ordinary plot of temperature as a function of time produces a nonlinear graph (Figure 7.08). However, we can normally obtain a straight-line relationship if

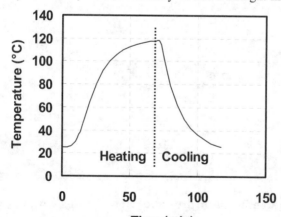

Figure 7.08. Can center temperature as a function of time during thermal processing.

we plot the *temperature difference* as a function of time using a semi-logarithmic graph. For heating, this difference would be the retort temperature minus the can temperature $(t_r - t)$. This approach applies for the temperature at any location in the can; however, we are normally interested only in the cold spot at the center of the can.

Figure 7.09 is an example heat penetration plot for the heating portion of Figure 7.08. Remember, we are plotting the temperature difference $(t_r - t)$ on the logarithmic scale. However, we are interested in the temperature inside the can, not the temperature difference. We resolve this problem by plotting the temperature difference on the right side of the graph and the corresponding actual temperature on the left. (Note that the graph paper is inverted for this plot.) Remember, temperatures on the left side are simply the difference on the right side subtracted from the retort temperature [$t = t_r - (t_r - t)$]. We normally begin the first cycle at the top of the chart at one degree below the retort temperature; however, we could begin at 0.1 or 0.01 degrees below the retort temperature.

After an initial transition period, the typical plot is a straight line as shown in Figure 7.09. Sometimes food properties change during heating and the curve may contain a break that can be best represented by two straight lines covering different periods of the heating process (Heid and Joslyn, 1963-1964). In our review, we will only consider the single straight line heating. To make the information from this graph more usable, we need to determine the equation representing this straight line. This is commonly done by writing the equation as follows:

$$\theta = f_h \log\left(j \frac{t_r - t_i}{t_r - t} \right) \qquad (7.08)$$

where: f_h = the time required for the temperature plot (straight line) to cross one full log cycle, min

t = the temperature at any time θ, °C

t_r = the retort temperature, °C

t_i = the initial temperature inside the container, °C

θ = elapsed time from a corrected zero, min

θ_o = corrected zero for the process (58% of the come up time), min

j = an offset parameter defined as

$$j = \frac{t_r - t_i'}{t_r - t_i} \qquad (7.09)$$

Note that $j\left(\dfrac{t_r - t_i}{t_r - t} \right) = \left(\dfrac{t_r - t_i'}{t_r - t_i} \right)\left(\dfrac{t_r - t_i}{t_r - t} \right) = \left(\dfrac{t_r - t_i'}{t_r - t} \right)$.

Thus, we can also write Equation 7.08 as $\theta = f_h \log\left(\dfrac{t_r - t_i'}{t_r - t} \right)$. The pseudo-initial temperature (t_i') is found graphically. This pseudo-initial temperature and a related parameter, the corrected zero (θ_o) for the process, are discussed in the following paragraphs.

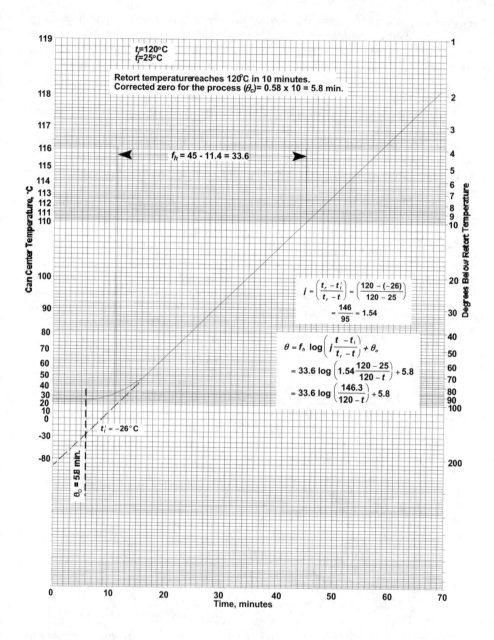

Figure 7.09. Product temperature record during thermal processing.

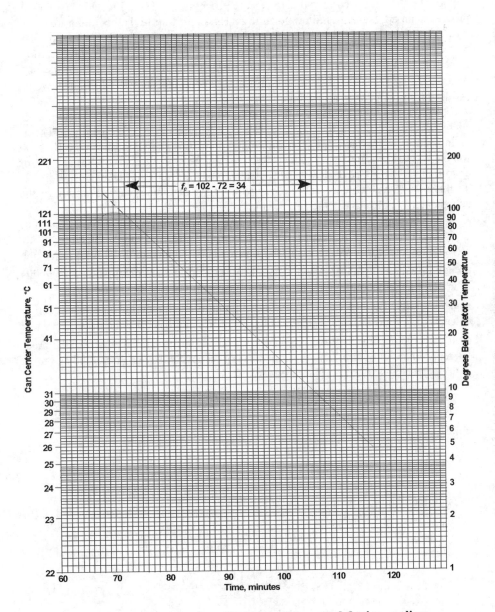

Figure 7.10. Continuation of temperature record during cooling with water at 21°C.

Examining the data of Figure 7.09, we see that the retort temperature is 120°C and the initial temperature of the product is 25°C. To obtain parameters for the equation, the straight line portion of the actual temperature data is extended downward until it crosses the time for a corrected zero for the process (θ_o). The corrected zero for the process is an adjustment to allow for bringing the retort up to the operating temperature. This time required to reach operating temperature is called the come-up time. Studies have shown that only about 42% of the come-up time can be considered as effective processing time. Thus, the remaining 58% is removed by setting the corrected zero (θ_o) at 58% of the come-up time. A come-up time of 12 minutes would result in a corrected zero at 7 minutes ($\theta_o = 0.58 \times 12$).

Using Figure 7.09, we can see how the equation for the straight line is determined. As previously noted, f_h is the time required for the line to cross a full log cycle. This is an indication of the line slope. The determination of f_h is shown for the cycle 10 - 100 (on the right-side scale). It could just as easily have been cycle 2 - 20, 3 - 30, 5 - 50, or any other full cycle. Note that it is necessary to use the straight line extension in this example. Note also that we never measure from the beginning curved portion of the actual data. We always use the straight line to find f_h.

With the slope determined, we now need an intercept to complete the definition of the straight line. This intercept is the temperature corresponding to the straight line crossing of the corrected zero for the process. This temperature (t_i') is called the pseudo initial temperature since it is not measured during the process. In fact, as in this example, this temperature may be negative. Care must be used in determination of t_i' from the graph. Often a small error in positioning the value on the chart can result in an error of several degrees. With t_i' determined, we can calculate the parameter j and write the equation for the time required to reach any given temperature. For the process represented in Figure 7.09, the equation can be developed and simplified as shown in the steps below. The governing equation is:

$$\theta_f = f_h \log\left(j \frac{t_r - t_i}{t_r - t} \right) + \theta_o$$

Solving for j:

$$j = \left(\frac{t_r - t_i'}{t_r - t_i} \right) = \left(\frac{120 - (-26)}{120 - 25} \right) = 1.54$$

Substituting into the governing equation,

$$\theta_t = 33.6 \log\left(1.54 \frac{120 - 25}{120 - t} \right) + 5.8$$

$$\theta_t = 33.6 \log\left(\frac{146.3}{120 - t} \right) + 5.8 \tag{7.10}$$

where θ_t is the time measured from the actual time zero, not from the corrected zero (θ_o).

The parameters j and f_h of Equation 7.08 can be related to the thermal properties used in the theoretical calculations of the transient heat transfer chapter. That relationship is exact for Newtonian heating (Equation 6.05).

For Newtonian heating, Equation 6.05 can be written as $\ln\left(\dfrac{t_o - t_i}{t_o - t}\right) = \dfrac{A\theta}{mc_p R_T}$.

Thus, $\theta = \dfrac{mc_p R_T}{A} \times \ln\left(\dfrac{t_o - t_i}{t_o - t}\right)$.

But $\ln X = 2.3026\log_{10} X$. Thus, $\theta = \dfrac{2.3026 mc_p R_T}{A} \times \log_{10}\left(\dfrac{t_o - t_i}{t_0 - t}\right)$.

Comparing this equation to Equation 7.08 we see that, for Newtonian heating, j and f_h are defined as follows:

$$j = 1 \qquad \text{and} \qquad f_h = \frac{2.3026\, m\, c_p\, R_t}{A}$$

These relationships are for uniform internal temperature. Note that the number 2.3026 in the relationship for f_h is due to the conversion from natural logarithms to common (base 10) logarithms. The remaining parameters are simply coefficients of θ in the exponential term of Equation 6.05.

For the general case (Equation 6.06), only an approximate relationship can be obtained because of the infinite series solutions to that equation. Using only the first term of the two infinite series (one for the plate shape and one for the cylinder) to represent the solution shown in Equation 6.07, the solution is approximately:

$$T = \frac{t_0 - t}{t_0 - t_i} \approx 2.0396 \exp\left[-\left(\frac{(2.4048)^2}{r_0^2} + \frac{\pi^2}{L_0^2}\right)\alpha\,\theta\right]$$

This equation can be written as:

$$\theta \approx \frac{1}{\left[\left(\dfrac{2.4048}{r_o}\right)^2 + \left(\dfrac{\pi}{L_o}\right)^2\right]\alpha} \times \ln\left(2.0396\,\frac{t_o - t_i}{t_o - t}\right)$$

Converting the expression to common logarithms gives:

$$\theta \approx \frac{2.3026}{\left[\left(\dfrac{2.4048}{r_o}\right)^2 + \left(\dfrac{\pi}{L_o}\right)^2\right]\alpha} \times \log\left(2.0396\,\frac{t_o - t_i}{t_o - t}\right)$$

Comparing this equation to Equation 7.08, we find that j and f_h are approximated as follows:

$j \approx 2.0396$ or 2.04

$$f_h \approx \frac{2.3026}{\left[\left(\dfrac{2.4048}{r_0}\right)^2 + \left(\dfrac{\pi}{L_o}\right)^2\right]\alpha} \quad \text{or} \quad f_h \approx \frac{2.3026\,\rho c_p}{\left[\left(\dfrac{2.4048}{r_0}\right)^2 + \left(\dfrac{\pi}{L_o}\right)^2\right]k} \quad \text{since} \quad \alpha = \frac{k}{\rho c_p}$$

Example 7.4

For the process identified by Figure 7.09, find the time required for the can center temperature to reach 119.1°C if the heating process is continued. The time should be measured from the actual beginning of the process.

Solution:

θ_t for this process has already been expressed in equation form (Equation 7.10). Substituting the desired final temperature in this equation:

$$\theta_t = 33.6\log\left(\frac{146.3}{120-119.1}\right)+5.8$$

$$= 33.6 \log (162.56) + 5.8 = 74.29 + 5.8$$

$$= \underline{80.1 \text{ min}}$$ **ANSWER**

The act of thermal processing continues as the can is removed from the retort and cooled. The center temperature will continue to increase for a short while, then the cooling process will produce a straight-line plot as shown in Figure 7.10. Note that this plot is very similar to that for the heating curve. However, the graph paper is not inverted, and the right-hand scale is a plot of degrees *above* the cooling water temperature. Figures 7.09 and 7.10 could be connected to produce a continuous plot by connecting them at the common point (68 minutes and 117.8°C). This entire heating-cooling process comprises the thermal processing operation.

> Note:To achieve the straight line heating and cooling graphs, the retort and cooling water temperatures must be constant. Changes in these temperatures affect the Y-axis scale, making a normal plot impossible.

7.5 Adequacy of Sterilization

With thermal death data and a record of thermal processing temperatures we can determine the adequacy of a sterilization process. We begin with the equation for thermal death of a given organism (Equation 7.06), which can be rewritten as:

$$\frac{F_0}{\theta} = 10^{\frac{t-121.1}{z}}$$ (7.11)

Equation 7.11 can then be expressed as:

$$F_0 = \theta \times 10^{\frac{t-121.1}{z}} \qquad (t \text{ and } z \text{ for } °C)$$ (7.12)

or, for degrees Fahrenheit:

$$F_0 = \theta \times 10^{\frac{t-250}{z}} \qquad (t \text{ and } z \text{ for } °F)$$ (7.13)

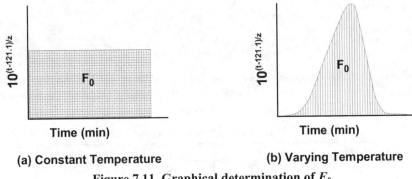

(a) Constant Temperature   (b) Varying Temperature

Figure 7.11. Graphical determination of F_0.

Equation 7.12 (or 7.13) represents the condition when sterilization is achieved. If the time of processing is extended beyond that required by these equations we have exceeded the minimum time required for sterilization. The same holds true if the temperature is exceeded. In other words, sterilization is accomplished if the right-hand side of the equation exceeds F_0. Thus the time-temperature combinations for processing must be such that F_0, as given by Equation 7.12 or 7.13 is equaled or exceeded. For a constant temperature process this is simply the rectangular area shown in Figure 7.11a. That area must exceed F_0 to insure sterilization. Since actual sterilization processes involve changing temperatures, Figure 7.11b is more representative of the actual area to be measured. The area determination here is more complex and is usually done by looking at small time steps of the process. The contribution of each step is then added. Thus:

$$F_0 = \Delta\theta_1 \times 10^{\frac{t_1 - 121.1}{z}} + \Delta\theta_2 \times 10^{\frac{t_2 - 121.1}{z}} + \ldots + \Delta\theta_n \times 10^{\frac{t_n - 121.1}{z}} \qquad (7.14)$$

where $\Delta\theta_1$, $\Delta\theta_2$,... $\Delta\theta_n$ represent time intervals over which the corresponding values of t_i are evaluated. This is shown in integral form as:

$$F_0 = \int_{\theta=0}^{\theta=0} 10^{\frac{t-121.1}{z}} \, d\theta \qquad (7.15)$$

Mathematical evaluation of Equation 7.15 is normally very difficult. Thus, we will use the graphical summation process of Equation 7.14. Note that we can use either °F or °C simply by changing units in the exponent (see Equations 7.12 and 7.13). For both Equation 7.14 and 7.15, F_0 is given by the area under the curve obtained by plotting $10^{\frac{t-121.1}{z}}$ as a function of time θ. Thus, our problem is to find the area under the plotted curve. If that value exceeds the required value of F_0, then sterilization is accomplished.

Example 7.5

A product has a F_0 value of 10.3 minutes and a z value of 23. The thermal processing temperature record is shown in the table below. (This is the process shown in Figure 7.08.) Was the sterilization adequate?

Table 7.02. Thermal processing example data.

θ (min)	t (°C)	θ (min)	t (°C)
0	25.0	60	116.4
10	30.0	70	118.15
20	64.7	80	78.5
30	92.1	90	49.5
40	106.0	100	36.0
50	112.9	110	28.7
55	115.0	117	25.8

Solutions:

Two solution methods will be demonstrated. The first is a simple graphical approach. We simply calculate $10^{\frac{t-121.1}{z}}$ for each of the temperatures in the above table and plot those values as shown in Figure 7.12. We can then use graphical averaging to estimate the area under the curve. This averaging procedure involves drawing a series of rectangles to represent the area under segments of the curve. The top of each rectangle should be located such that the area which is within the rectangle but above the curve is equal to the area under the curve but outside the rectangle. Rectangle widths (time intervals) may vary. However, where equal widths are possible, the calculation is simplified. For this example, we have used increments of ten minutes and drawn the rectangles as shown in Figure 7.12. This approach still includes the data at 55 minutes since the "inside = outside" requirement must hold for the interval between 50 and 60 minutes. In this plot, that requirement is easy to meet since all lines except between 50 and 60 minutes are straight lines. Thus, the "y" value for each rectangle is simply the average of the beginning and ending values for that time interval. The value of F_0 (area under the curve) is then estimated as:

$$F_0 = 10\ (0.029 + 0.137 + 0.330 + 0.534 + 0.686 + 0.379 + 0.007) = 10\ (2.102)$$

$$= 21.02 \text{ minutes}$$

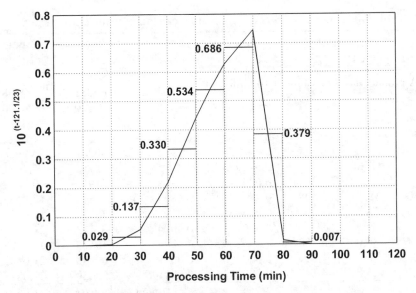

Figure 7.12. Data from graphical solution to determine F_0.

The second solution method shows how a spreadsheet can be used to solve the problem. We would certainly want to use a spreadsheet if the above data had been recorded at one minute intervals for the entire period. Spreadsheets allow us to create a set of equations that can be copied for as many observations as desired. With a spreadsheet, we can process 2000 points almost as easily as we can process 10 points. See section 11 of the introductory chapter for more information regarding spreadsheet use.

The numerical data in Table 7.03 represents the results that would be obtained using a spreadsheet. Column headings show the calculations performed for each column in the spreadsheet. The first two columns contain the original data. The remaining columns are step-by-step calculations to allow calculation of the data points that could be used for plotting the graph, and additional calculations to determine the area under the curve using Equation 7.14. Note that values in the Average column, excluding the value at 55 minutes, are essentially the same as the "y" values used in the previous graphical solution. The result (21.08) is essentially the same as the 21.02 value found in the graphical solution.

ANSWER: With these results, we can now decide if the sterilization was adequate. Since both values are well above the 10.3 minutes specified for F_0, sterilization was adequate. In fact, sterilization was achieved after 60 minutes, when the cumulative summation reaches 10.37. Note that the continued high temperature after the can is removed from the retort (at 68 minutes) contributes significantly to the lethality of the process.

Table 7.03. Thermal processing example calculations for Example 7.5.

θ (min)	t (°C)	$\dfrac{t-121.1}{23}$	$10^{\frac{t-121.1}{z}}$	Average[a]	Time interval × Average[b]	Summation[c]
0	25.0	-4.178	0.000066			
10	30.0	-3.961	0.000109	0.0001	0.00088	0.00088
20	64.7	-2.452	0.003530	0.0018	0.01820	0.01908
30	92.1	-1.261	0.054844	0.0292	0.29187	0.31095
40	106.0	-0.657	0.220535	0.1377	1.37690	1.68785
50	112.9	-0.357	0.440026	0.3303	3.30281	4.99066
55	115.0	-0.265	0.542978	0.4915	2.45751	7.44817
60	116.4	-0.204	0.624672	0.5838	2.91913	10.36729
70	118.15	-0.128	0.744285	0.6845	6.84478	17.21208
80	78.5	-1.852	0.014055	0.3792	3.79170	21.00378
90	49.5	-3.113	0.000771	0.0074	0.07413	21.07790
100	36.0	-3.700	0.000200	0.0005	0.00485	21.08276
110	28.7	-4.017	0.000096	0.0001	0.00148	21.08423
117	25.8	-4.143	0.000072	0.0001	0.00059	21.08482
					Computed area (F_0) =	21.08

[a] This is the average of $10^{\frac{t-121.1}{z}}$ between the current and the previous measurement.

[b] This product of the average and the time interval is the area of a rectangle for that specific time interval. For 10-minute intervals, this is equivalent to the rectangles drawn in Figure 7.12.

[c] This is simply a cumulative summation of the areas.

7.6 UHT—Ultrahigh Temperature (Aseptic) Processing

The concept of aseptic or ultrahigh temperature (UHT) processing is simple. Instead of packaging the food and then sterilizing it, the food is first sterilized and then packaged into sterile containers. The entire process must take place in a sterile environment to avoid recontamination of the product or the presterilized containers. The process typically occurs at a much higher temperature than normal retort processing. In addition, the product being processed flows through small tubes (Figure 7.13), or in thin layers, (tube or plate heat exchangers) such that all the product can be quickly heated. Thus, actual processing times are greatly reduced (Figures 7.14 and 7.15). Additional details regarding the history and application of UHT processing can be found in Reuter (1989) and Catsberg and Kemplen-Van Dommelen (1990).

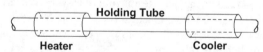

Figure 7.13. Schematic diagram of an aseptic processing system for product sterilization.

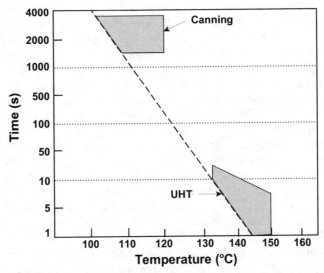

Figure 7.14. Comparison of microbial destruction rates in
UHT processing and conventional canning. The UHT and canning ranges
shown are approximate ranges only.

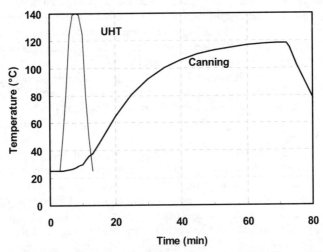

Figure 7.15. Comparison of time-temperature profiles for canning and
UHT processing. The two treatments have equal sterilization effect.

The concept of aseptic processing appeared in the early part of the 20th century
when a man from Denmark patented the first process in which milk was sterilized by
ultra-heat and aseptically packaged. The introduction of steam to sterilize cans and lids
so that they could then be filled with a sterilized product was introduced in the United
States in 1917. After decades of work, the first commercial aseptic filling plant was

built. Typical foods processed by UHT include milk, fruit juices, wine, ice cream, puddings, baby foods, and tomato products. The process works best with homogeneous liquid products. Solid particulates tend to heat at different rates from the liquid, creating non-uniform sterilization rates. Thus, analysis of aseptic processing of non-homogeneous foods is more complex.

The goal of UHT processing is the same as any other heat processing technique in that it attempts to achieve commercial sterilization. The practice of UHT is based upon the principle that, for a defined temperature increase, the rate of microbial destruction occurs at a faster rate than the rate of destruction of the food's nutrients and sensory elements. Canning applies the same principles of microbial death rate under heat processing as does UHT. However, in the canning process, the majority of the destruction of microorganisms occurs at the end of the heating stage and the beginnings of the cooling stage. This period is when temperatures are at their highest. In UHT, the food is rapidly heated to the desired temperature and held there for a short period of time. The majority of microbial destruction in UHT occurs at the near constant holding temperature. UHT processing is able to do this because the food is heated outside the storage/shipping container. A significant lag time does not exist in UHT processing as in canning, and concern about the time required to reach the desired can center temperature is no longer a factor.

UHT processing offers significant advantages over traditional canning. Damage to foods by destruction of nutrients and sensory components is kept to a minimum because under UHT processing, the food is heated for only a short amount of time. With canning, however, the heat is gradually added to the food until the desired temperature is met. The outer portion of the can is heated for a longer period of time than the center of the can (since the center of the can must reach the required processing temperature). Processing times are much lower for UHT due to the short amount of time that it takes to achieve the desired temperature. Additionally, since UHT processing heats the food outside of the container, the size of the container is not a restriction as in canning. Table 7.04 summarizes comparison data provided by Fellows (1988). The reduction in processing time is dramatic. UHT processing requires only 0.07% of the time required for processing in an A2 can.

An important aspect of UHT is that sterilization occurs before packaging, and containers do not have to withstand a heated sterilization process. Consequently, the containers are often selected for economical reasons, and cartons are widely used. Limitations to UHT mainly concern cost. The plant and equipment needed to conduct UHT processing requires a sizeable initial capital investment. Additional expenses include maintaining a sterile environment to package the product into the containers. Additional expenses also are incurred due to the higher skill levels required of workers.

Table 7.04. Comparison of conventional retort and UHT processing of vegetable soup.

	Conventional retorting		UHT
	A2 cans	A10 cans	
Temperature	121°C	121°C	140°C
Time required	120 minutes	218 minutes	5 seconds

As noted, the general procedure for UHT processing is to quickly heat the food in a continuous heat exchanger. This step allows operators to maintain close control over the sterilization temperatures and holding times. A second heat exchanger works to cool the newly sterile product. The product is cooled to a suitable temperature for packaging the foodstuff safely into the pre-sterilized containers. UHT processing equipment should have the following engineering related characteristics:

- ability to operate at higher temperatures;
- exposure of a small volume of product to a large surface area to produce maximum heat transfer;
- provisions to establish and maintain turbulence (where possible) in the product, resulting in higher heat transfer rates;
- use of pumps that provide consistent flow rates; and
- continuous cleaning of the system to maximize heat transfer rates at heating surfaces and reduce burning of product.

Note that control and effectiveness are the two features emphasized in these characteristics. For a given system, flow of the product can be increased as the heat transfer increases. The increased flow rate results in a higher production rate. Control is also an important feature of UHT systems. Sterilization is affected by both temperature and time of exposure to that temperature. Thus, close control of both temperature and flow rate is required to insure a consistent product. Since time of exposure is a function of heat exchanger length and product flow rate, both must be taken into account in analyzing the process.

List of Symbols

D time required a given temperature required to destroy 90% of the spores of an organism

f_c cooling curve slope parameter, the time required for the temperature plot (straight line) to cross one full log cycle

f_h heat penetration curve slope parameter, the time required for the temperature plot (straight line) to cross one full log cycle

F_0 time required at 121.1°C (250 °F) to obtain a desired sterilization value

j an offset parameter or lag factor used in developing equation for heat penetration

N number of organisms at any time θ

N_o initial number of organisms (at $\theta = 0$)

SV sterilization value, decimal reduction, or log cycles

t temperature at any time θ, °C

t_i initial temperature inside the container, °C

t_i' a pseudo-initial temperature used in heat penetration analysis, °C

t_r retort temperature, °C

z temperature difference required for thermal destruction to result in a change of one log cycle (or a 90% reduction in spores of the organism), °C

θ time, s

θ_o corrected zero for a process (58% of the come-up time), s or min

Subscript

o property evaluated at $\theta = 0$

References

1. Catsburg, C. M. E., and G. J. M. Kemplen-Van Dommelen. 1990. *Food Handbook.* Ellis Horwood, Ltd., Chichester, England.
2. FAO, 1976. *Guidelines for Developing an Effective National Food Control System.* FAO, Rome.
3. Fellows, P. 1988. *Food Processing Technology: Principles and Practice.* Ellis Horwood, Ltd., Chichester, England.
4. Heid, J. L., and M. A. Joslyn. 1963-64. *Fundamentals of Food Processing Operations.* Volume 2 (of three volumes). AVI. Westport, CT.
5. Larousse, J., and B. E. Brown. 1997. *Food Canning Technology.* Wiley-VCH. New York, NY.
6 . Rees, J. A. G., and J. Bettison, eds. 1991. *Processing and Packaging of Heat Preserved Foods.* AVI, New York, NY.
7. Reuter, H. 1989. *Aseptic Packaging of Food.* Technomic Publishing Co. Inc., Lanacaster, PA.
8. Stumbo, C. R. 1965. *Thermobacteriology in Food Processing.* Academic Press, New York, NY.

Problems

7.1. Complete the following table relating F_0, D, and sterilization value (SV).

F_0 (min.)	D (min./cycle)	SV (cycles)
	2.1	6
20		6
	2.1	12
20		12
	2.1	18
20		18
	4.2	18

7.2. What percentage of microorganisms are inactivated for a sterilization value of 6? For $SV = 8$? For $SV = 12$?

7.3. Thermal Death Time curves for products with a specific organism are defined as:

Product	F	z (for °F)	z (for °C)
Green beans	19.8	17.8	9.89
Peas, fresh	20.2	16.9	9.39
Pumpkin puree	17.5	23.2	12.9
Spinach	24.7	20.8	11.6

a. What is the processing time in minutes for each of the above products to achieve thermal death if the temperature is 250°F (121.1°C)?

b. If the processing temperature is increased to 280°F (137.8°C), how much time would be required for each product?

c. Repeat part b for T = 212°F (100°C).

7.4. The table below shows limited time-temperature data for plots similar to Figures 7.09 and 7.11. Plot heat penetration curves similar to those figures. Determine the slope of each curve and write the equation for the straight-line heat penetration curve.

t_r (°C)	117	119	121	123
t_i (°C)	17	54	57	33
θ (min.)	t (°C) Process 1	t (°C) Process 2	t (°C) Process 3	t (°C) Process 4
0	17	54	57	33
10	23	65	69.8	44.5
20	61	82.3	87.3	78.3
30	87	94	98.8	99.5
40	101.3	101.9	106.4	110.5
50	108.6	107.3	111.4	116.4
60	112.6	111.1	114.7	119.5
70	114.7	113.6	116.8	121.2

7.5. Consider the thermal processes outlined in the table below. Temperatures were measured only at the times shown. Assume a straight-line relationship between points. For each process, $z = 12$ and F_0 is 3.0. Determine if sterilization was achieved in each process.

Time (min.)	Temperatures (°C)				
	Process 1	Process 2	Process 3	Process 4	Process 5
0	23	23	27	23	23
0.1	100		28		25
10			42	70	250
20			66	135	23
30		110	83	70	
40			95	23	
50			102		
59.9	100				
60	30	23	108		

Refrigeration Systems

8

Abstract. *This chapter provides a brief coverage of refrigerants and vapor compression refrigeration systems. Refrigeration loads and freezing/thawing times are also reviewed.*

Keywords. *Coefficient of performance, cooling, freezing, refrigerants, refrigeration cycles, refrigeration systems.*

8.1 Introduction

The Romans used ice for cooling over 2000 years ago. Collecting ice and storing it in insulated buildings for later use was a common method of cooling for centuries. Commercial ice production became widespread in the United States in the late 1800's. By 1900 commercial production and sale of ice for use in home iceboxes was common. In some households, "kerosene refrigerators" soon replaced the iceboxes. The availability of electricity and "electric refrigerators" made home refrigeration available to almost everyone in the United States by the mid-1900's.

The cooling methods noted above make use of latent heat to accomplish the cooling. The latent heat of fusion for ice (heat required to melt it) provided the cooling effect for the icebox. For every kilogram of ice melted, approximately 335 kJ of heat is removed. (Actually somewhat more cooling is obtained because the actual initial ice temperature is almost certainly below 0°C.) Now, imagine that the ice is replaced by a container of liquid Refrigerant 134a (R-134a). At atmospheric pressure, R-134a boils at −26.1°C (Table 8.01). Thus it will immediately begin to boil, removing 216.8 kJ of energy for each kilogram of refrigerant evaporated. This is an effective cooling method, but the loss of evaporating refrigerant is a potential pollution problem. In addition, the cost of refrigerant for this process would be quite high. These problems are removed by keeping the refrigerant inside a closed system and taking advantage of the fact that the boiling temperatures of refrigerants vary with pressure. This pressure effect is clearly shown in Table 8.01. We know that, at atmospheric pressure, water boils at 100°C. For those conditions, 2257 kJ of energy is needed to evaporate one kilogram of water. If we increase the pressure to 1.0 MPa, the boiling point increases to 179.9°C and the latent heat of vaporization decreases to 2013.6 kJ/kg. Further increase in pressure to the critical point produces a condition where the latent heat of vaporization is zero. This occurs at the top of the vapor dome (refer to pages 234 to 237 of Chapter 9 for additional details).

Table 8.01. Boiling point and latent heat of vaporization as a function of pressure for selected materials.[a]

Material	Absolute Pressure		Boiling Point		Latent Heat of Vaporization	
	MPa	psi	°C	°F	kJ/kg	Btu/lb
Water	0.10132	14.7	100.0	212.0	2256.6	970.2
Water	1.0	145.0	179.9	355.8	2013.6	865.7
Water	22.064	3200	374.0	7505.2	0	0
Ammonia	0.10132	14.7	−33.3	−28.0	1369.6	588.8
Ammonia	1.0	145.0	24.9	76.8	1165.7	501.1
Ammonia	2.0	290.1	50.7	123.2	1053.2	452.8
Refrigerant 12	0.10132	14.7	−29.8	−21.6	165.9	71.3
Refrigerant 12	1.0	145.0	41.7	107.1	128.6	55.3
Refrigerant 22	0.10132	14.7	−40.8	−41.4	233.8	100.5
Refrigerant 22	1.0	145.0	23.4	74.1	184.0	79.1
Refrigerant 23	0.10132	14.7	−82.0	−115.7	238.8	102.7
Refrigerant 23	1.0	145.0	−30.4	−22.7	186.6	80.2
Refrigerant 134a	0.10132	14.7	−26.1	−14.9	216.8	93.2
Refrigerant 134a	1.0	145.0	39.4	102.9	163.9	70.5
Nitrous Oxide	0.10132	14.7	−88.3	−127.0	377.5	162.3
Nitrous Oxide	1.0	145.0	−37.6	−35.7	321.1	138.1

[a] Computed from data in ASHRAE (1997) and (for Nitrous Oxide) ASHRAE (1959).

Most refrigerants have temperature enthalpy charts similar in form to that for water. Two such charts are shown at the end of this chapter. Temperatures, pressures, and latent heats of vaporization differ, but the form of response does not. Pressure-enthalpy and temperature-enthalpy charts have a liquid area, a superheated vapor area, and a transition area beneath a vapor dome that consists of a combination of liquid and vapor. This region beneath the vapor dome is very important for analysis of the widely used vapor compression refrigeration cycle.

8.2 Refrigeration Cycles

The food industry makes use of two types of refrigeration cycles. Both cycles use the pressure-temperature effect noted in Table 8.01. Many large systems use an absorption cycle while other systems (including home refrigeration appliances) use a vapor compression cycle.

A vapor-compression refrigeration cycle is shown in Figure 8.01. A refrigerant with a low boiling point (e.g., Refrigerant 134a) is compressed. The compressed gas, now with a much higher boiling point, moves to the condenser. The boiling point of the refrigerant is now higher than the temperature of the surrounding air. Therefore, the gas will give up heat and condense (the latent heat of vaporization is given up to the surroundings). The high-pressure liquid refrigerant then flows to the evaporator. As it enters the evaporator, it flows through a restriction (expansion valve or capillary tube), which produces a substantial pressure drop. This lowers the boiling point of the

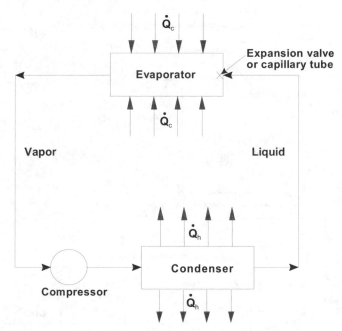

Figure 8.01. Vapor compression refrigeration cycle.

liquid to a very low value—well below the temperature around the evaporator coils. Heat gained by the evaporator coils causes the liquid to boil. The low pressure vapor then flows to the compressor where it is compressed to continue the cycle.

This vapor compression refrigeration cycle is commonly used in the refrigerators, freezers, and air conditioners used in the home and in many commercial applications. The "standard" for refrigerants used in the compression refrigeration cycle was Refrigerant 12 (commonly called Freon 12) until the early 1990's. Refrigerant 12 possesses the desirable properties for a refrigerant: low boiling point, non-poisonous, non-explosive, non-corrosive, and it mixes with oil. The last property is needed to permit internal lubrication of the compressor during operation. Refrigerant 12, however, possesses one very undesirable property. It is a chlorofluorocarbon (CFC) that, when released to the upper atmosphere, degrades to produce chlorine (Rowland, 1997). This chlorine has a powerful ability to destroy ozone in the upper atmosphere. New refrigeration systems no longer use Refrigerant 12 and other CFC's that are major chlorine producers. One of the replacement refrigerants is Refrigerant 134a.

The other cycle commonly used in refrigeration employs heat to produce cold! It is commonly called the ammonia absorption cycle. This cycle makes use of the ability of water to absorb ammonia. Heat is then used to "drive" the ammonia from the water. An ammonia absorption cycle is shown in Figure 8.02. The cycle uses a pump to produce the high pressure in the generator and condenser. Note that, even with the absorption cycle, a pressure difference must be present between the condenser and the evaporator.

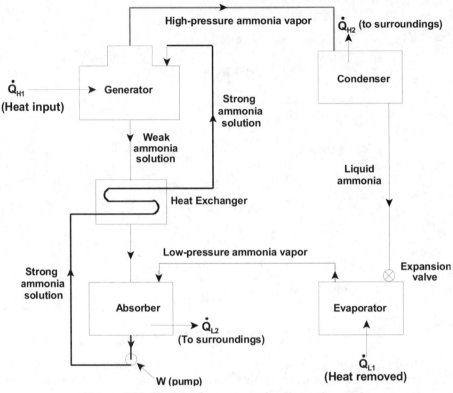

Figure 8.02. Sketch of an ammonia absorption cycle.

8.3 Analysis of the
Vapor-Compression Refrigeration Cycle

To analyze refrigeration cycles, we must use charts (Figures 8.04 and 8.05, pages 209 and 211) or thermodynamic tables of properties (Tables 8.02 and 8.03, pages 210 and 212). The full refrigeration cycle is best represented on a pressure-enthalpy diagram for the refrigerant used. Figure 8.03 represents such an ideal cycle for a typical refrigerant. The high-pressure vapor (at point D) is usually cooled at the specified pressure until it becomes a saturated liquid. That defines state point A on the curve. The refrigerant flows through the expansion valve with no change in energy content (constant enthalpy) and begins to evaporate at the lower pressure. The process B–C represents constant pressure evaporation (boiling at a very low temperature). At point C, the refrigerant is 100% vapor. It is then compressed reversibly (constant entropy) to the high-pressure value (point D). Our analysis will consider only this **ideal** cycle. However, you should be aware that real cycles deviate from the cycle shown. In real cycles, pressure drops in the system plumbing prevent constant pressure operations for processes B–C and D–A. In addition, there are no abrupt changes in processes at points A, B, C, and D. Real processes do not permit the sharp changes in direction shown on the chart. Each change is gradual, producing rounded corners rather than the sharp changes noted.

As we analyze the ideal vapor compression refrigeration cycle we must note the following energy changes:

1. The amount of cooling provided by process B–C is the energy required for evaporation $(h_g - h_L)$.
2. The work of compression, process C–D, is given by $(h_H - h_g)$.
3. The heat rejected by the system (condenser heat transfer, process D–A) is $(h_H - h_L)$.

The efficiency of this cycle is the ratio of output to input. It is called coefficient of performance (COP):

$$COP = \frac{\text{Cooling Produced}}{\text{Work Input}} = \frac{h_g - h_L}{h_H - h_g} \qquad (8.01)$$

The coefficient of performance is usually greater than one.

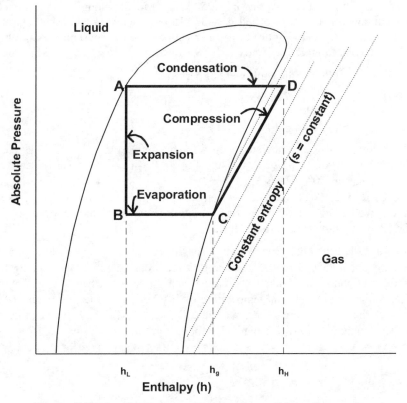

Figure 8.03. An ideal vapor-compression refrigeration cycle.

Example 8.1

An ideal refrigerant cycle using Refrigerant 12 operates between refrigerant temperatures of –30°C and 50°C. Find the operating pressures and the coefficient of performance.

Solution:
Use Figure 8.04 to locate the state points A, B, C and D as identified in Figure 8.03. The input parameters are: $t_H = 50°C$, $t_L = -30°C$. Temperatures are shown as small tic marks on the saturated liquid curve. Since 50°C and –30°C are not shown, we must interpolate along the curve. Doing so, we find the corresponding pressures to be: $P_h = 1.2$ MPa and $P_L = 0.10$ MPa. Following the cycle as sketched in Figure 8.03, we find $h_L = 250$ kJ/kg. Moving along $P = 0.10$ MPa to the saturated vapor line, we find $h_g = 339$ kJ/kg. Following a constant entropy line of 1.58 (by interpolation) to its intersection with the constant pressure line ($P = 1.2$ MPa, Point D), we find $h_H = 388$.

We can now solve for the coefficient of performance:

$$COP = \frac{h_g - h_L}{h_H - h_g} = \frac{339 - 250}{388 - 339} = \frac{89}{49} = \underline{1.82} \qquad \textbf{ANSWER}$$

Note: We can also use tabulated values for the refrigerants to more accurately determine most of the properties. Using Table 8.02 (the data for Refrigerant 12), we find that at 50°C, $P_h = 1.2171$ kPa and $h_L = 249.51$ kJ/kg. Similarly, for –30°C, $P_L = 0.10044$ kPa and the enthalpy of saturated vapor is $h_g = 338.81$ kJ/kg. We cannot determine h_H since it is in the superheated vapor region and the table only covers saturation values.

Note also that the highest temperature for the cycle, in the superheat region, is actually about 75°C. However that temperature drops quickly as the superheated refrigerant condenses. Once the saturated vapor line is reached, the heat rejection continues at a constant temperature of 50°C. Most of the heat removal occurs at this temperature. Thus, we typically identify the high temperature as 50°C even though it exceeds that value for a short time.

Example 8.2

Repeat Example 8.1 using Refrigerant 134a.

Solution:
Figure 8.05, for Refrigerant 134a, is read in the same manner as Figure 8.04, used for the previous example. We find the following results:

$P_L = 0.084$ MPa $P_H = 1.3$ MPa
$h_L = 272$ kJ/kg $h_g = 380$ kJ/kg $h_H = 440$ kJ/kg

$$COP = \frac{h_g - h_L}{h_H - h_g} = \frac{380 - 272}{440 - 380} = \frac{108}{60} = 1.80 \quad \textbf{ANSWER}$$

The coefficient of performance for Refrigerant 134a is quite close to that for Refrigerant 12 operating under the same conditions. In general, the coefficients of performance will be different for systems using different refrigerants but operating at the same pressures.

8.3.1 Heat Pumps

The refrigeration cycle is actually a cycle that "pumps" thermal energy from a region of lower temperature to a region of higher temperature. The examples we have looked at involve using this pumping cycle to cool. Refrigeration systems are also used to provide heat. When used for this purpose they are called heat pumps. This is most easily visualized by imagining a window air conditioner installed in reverse, such that the condenser coils (hot air) are inside the room and the evaporator coils (cold air) are outside the room. The exact mechanism used for an actual air conditioner/heat pump is more complicated since changes from heating to cooling are implemented by changing the direction of refrigerant flow.

If a system is being used as a heat pump, then the useful output is heat rejected at the condenser—not heat absorbed in the evaporator. Thus, the coefficient of performance for a heat pump is higher than for a cooling system operating between the same pressures. The equation for COP is then:

$$COP_{HP} = \frac{\text{Heat rejected}}{\text{Work input}} = \frac{h_H - h_L}{h_H - h_g}$$

For Example 8.2, using R-134a, the heat pump coefficient of performance is:

$$COP_{HP} = \frac{440 - 272}{440 - 380} = \frac{168}{60} = 2.80$$

Example 8.3

An ideal refrigerant cycle using Refrigerant 134a operates between pressures of 0.3 and 1.5 MPa. Determine the evaporator and condenser temperatures and calculate the coefficient of performance.

Solution:

We will use Figure 8.05 to obtain the required information. However, most points can also be found using Table 8.03. Where available, interpolated values from this table are also shown (in parenthesis) as a check of the chart results.

The temperatures corresponding to the specified pressures are:

condenser temperature: $t_H = 55°C$ (55.23°C)

evaporator temperature: $t_L = 1\ °C$ (0.6°C)

The enthalpy and entropy values corresponding to the saturated liquid (L) and saturated vapor (g) points on the cycle are:

$h_L = 280$ kJ/kg (279.8 kJ/kg)

$h_g = 400$ kJ/kg (399.0 kJ/kg)

$s = 1.74$ kJ/kg K (1.73 kJ/kg K)

Following the constant entropy line (s = 1.74) to the high pressure of 1.5 MPa, we find:

$h_H = 435$ kJ/kg

$t \approx 63°C$ (this temperature quickly drops to 55°C as condensation begins)

Knowing the enthalpy values, we can now calculate the coefficient of performance:

$$COP = \frac{400 - 280}{435 - 400} = \frac{120}{35} = \underline{3.43} \qquad \textbf{ANSWER}$$

8.4 Refrigeration Capacity

The capacity of a refrigeration system is a function of the refrigerant, the operating pressures, and the mass of refrigerant circulated $\left[\dot{Q} = \dot{m}(h_g - h_L) \right]$. In Example 8.1, we calculated a heat removal of 89 kJ for one kg of refrigerant ($h_g - h_L$). The cooling capacity will depend upon both this heat removal and the circulation (evaporation) rate of the refrigerant. If the circulation rate is 2 kg/min, then the cooling capacity for the system is:

$$\dot{Q} = 2\ \frac{kg}{min} \times \frac{1\ min}{60\ s} \times 89\ \frac{kJ}{kg} = 2.97\ kW$$

> Refrigeration capacity of cooling systems is sometimes given in "tons." This rating is based upon the cooling capacity of one ton of ice melted over a 24-hour period [(2000 lb × 144 BTU/lb)/24 hr = 12,000 BTU/hr = 3.5 kW]. While the use of "ton" to indicate cooling capacity does have a logical basis this is another example of using one unit (mass) to represent something completely different (rate of energy transfer, or power).

8.5 Refrigeration Loads

Refrigeration systems are widely used for cooling, freezing, and refrigerated storage of food and other products. Refrigeration units used for these applications must be sized to overcome heat gain through the walls of the system and also perform the desired functional operation. For example, freezing a food product may be considered as a three-step operation: (1) the product is cooled to its freezing point, (2) it is frozen at constant temperature, and (3) the frozen product is further cooled to the desired final temperature. The energy required to do this can be computed as:

$$\dot{Q} = \dot{m}c_P(t_1 - t_f) + \dot{m}h_{sf} + \dot{m}c'_P(t_f - t_2) \tag{8.02}$$

where: c_p, c'_p = specific heat values above and below freezing, respectively, kJ/(kg K)

h_{sf} = the latent heat of fusion, kJ/kg

$\dot{m}$ = the mass of product being frozen, kg

$\dot{Q}$ = the total energy removed in the cooling operation, (kJ) and

t_1, t_2, t_f = the initial, final and freezing point temperatures, respectively, °C or K.

Appendix Table A.5 lists the necessary thermal properties to make the above calculation for selected food products.

Example 8.4

Twenty kilograms of strawberries at 22°C are to be frozen to –24°C. What amount of energy must be removed from the strawberries?

Solution:

We can use Equation 8.02 to solve for Q.

From Table A.5, c_p = 3.89, c'_p = 1.94, and h_{sf} = 307. Thus:

Q = 20 kg [3.89 kJ/kg K(22– –0.8)K + 307 kJ/kg + 1.94.kJ/kg K(–0.8– –24)K]

= 20 [3.89 (22.8) + 307 + 1.94 (23.2)] kJ

= 20 [88.69 + 307 + 45.01] = 20 (440.7) kJ

= 8814 kJ   **ANSWER**

Considerable refrigeration may also be required for refrigerated storage. Fresh products must be cooled to the desired storage temperature and held at that temperature. These products are living organisms and produce heat as a part of their life processes. This heat of respiration, while small on a unit mass basis, is a major source of heat where large masses of products are handled (e.g., apple storage warehouses). Heat of respiration varies with products and increases with temperature for all products (Appendix, Table A.8).

8.6 Food Freezing

Consumption of frozen foods has increased because of demand for high quality products and increased use of home microwave ovens for rapid meal preparation. Proper freezing retains food color, texture, and nutrient quality for long time periods provided storage temperatures are maintained sufficiently low. The storage life of foods is extended by lowering temperature and greatly extended by freezing the product. Lowering temperature reduces the microbial growth rate which is temperature dependent. Freezing foods reduces the amount of water in liquid form that is available for microbial activity. Production volume freezing is done quickly but requires significant energy. The amount of energy to freeze food materials has been determined and is fairly predictable in most cases. The time required to accomplish freezing is less predictable, depending on properties of the food, physical characteristics of the particular equipment, and operation of the system.

Removing sufficient energy from a food product to change its state from "liquid-like" to "solid-like" is a process known as freezing. The temperature at which a food freezes depends on its constituents. Although foods contain a substantial amount of water, they behave differently from pure water. The freezing point of foods is lowered below that of water by an amount known as the freezing point depression. The presence of a solute in water lowers its freezing point. Depressions are typically 1° to 5°C for many foods, i.e., they freeze at −1°C and lower (Appendix, Table A.5). Also, the freezing process for a food material occurs over a range in temperatures rather than at a single temperature like pure water. For example, ice cream products begin to freeze at −2°C and 50% of the water is frozen at −5°C. When 80% of the water is frozen, the remaining unfrozen portion has a freezing point of −15°C. The last 5% to 15% of the water in foods may never be frozen. (data from ASHRAE [1998] *Handbook of Refrigeration*, Table 9, Chapter 19).

Freezing foods involves the removal of energy from the food. The energy removed to freeze foods is partially the sensible cooling required to lower the temperature to the freezing point, but the primary energy removed is the latent energy for phase change. The latent heat of freezing for water, 335 kJ/kg, is many times larger than the sensible energy removed to lower the temperature by one degree. Latent heat values are used to compute the amount of energy removed for freezing. The thermal conductivity of water and food materials increases greatly at below freezing temperatures; the increase is fourfold for water (Figure 2.08). Other thermal properties change, but to a lesser degree, during freezing.

Freezing time, *FT*, for foods and other products can be computed by an equation known as Plank's formula:

$$FT = \rho \, h_{sf} \frac{\left(\dfrac{Pd}{h} + \dfrac{Rd^2}{k} \right)}{t_f - t_a} \tag{8.03}$$

where: d = product thickness (smallest dimension), m
FT = freezing time, s
h = convective heat transfer coefficient, W/(m^2 K)
h_{sf} = latent heat of fusion, kJ/kg
k = thermal conductivity of frozen product, W/(m K)
t_f = initial freezing temperature of product, from Table A.5, °C or K
t_a = temperature of refrigerated air, °C or K
ρ = density of frozen product, kg/m^3
P and R are constants depending on product shape

The constants for "standard" shapes are $P = 1/2$ and $R = 1/8$ for an infinite plate (slab); $P = 1/4$ and $R = 1/16$ for a long cylinder; and $P = 1/6$ and $R = 1/24$ for a sphere. The equation includes a term, $\Delta h_{sf} R d^2/k$, for heat flow from the inside to the surface, i.e., heat transfer controlled by food properties, and a term $\Delta h_{sf} Pd/h$ for heat flow from the food's surface, i.e., heat transfer controlled by the equipment and its operation. The temperature difference, $t_f - t_a$, is the usual temperature difference term found in heat transfer equations. This equation estimates the time only for phase change, excluding time to lower temperature either above or below the freezing point. Plank's equation can be used to estimate freezing time, or graphs are available based on the equation. ASHRAE's *Handbook of Refrigeration* (1998) has freezing time graphs for meat (Chapter 16), poultry (Chapter 17), and fishery products (Chapter 18). Plank's equation has numerous assumptions and limitations; but it is simple, includes the pertinent factors, and is sufficiently accurate for most applications. The equation tends to under-estimate freezing times of food products of non-ideal, irregular shape. There are other, more complicated, equations to predict freezing time for specific products and for particular situations. However, it is more common to use Plank's simpler equation recognizing that it predicts times 10% to 30% less than actual freezing times.

Example 8.5

Beef patties for hamburgers are being frozen in an air-blast freezer having air at –22°C and a convective heat transfer coefficient of 50 W/(m^2 K). A patty averages 1 cm thick and is circular with a diameter of 8 cm. Frozen ground beef has a density of 1050 kg/m^3, a thermal conductivity of 1.4 W/(m K), a latent heat of fusion of 250 kJ/kg, and begins to freeze at –2°C. Compute the time to freeze the product using Plank's equation.

Solution:
Assume the shape of the patty is a slab (thickness is small compared to other dimensions). Thus, P and R are 1/2 and 1/8, respectively.

Using Plank's equation:

$$FT = \rho \, h_{sf} \frac{\left(\dfrac{Pd}{h} + \dfrac{Rd^2}{k}\right)}{t_f - t_a}$$

$$FT = 1050 \frac{kg}{m^3} \times 250 \frac{kJ}{kg} \frac{\left[\dfrac{0.01\,m}{2 \times 50 \dfrac{W}{m^2\,K}} + \dfrac{(0.01\,m)^2}{8 \times 1.4 \dfrac{W}{m\,K}}\right]}{(-2)-(-22)\,K}$$

$FT = 262\ 500$ kJ/m3 [0.000 100 m3 K/W + 0.000 008 9 m3 K/W] / 20 K

$FT = 1\ 429$ J/W $= 1\ 429$ J/ (J/s) $= 1\ 429$ s $= \underline{23.8\ min}$ **ANSWER**

Notice that no consideration was given to the initial temperature of the product in the above example. The computed time starts with the unfrozen product, at a temperature of –2°C. Starting at higher temperatures will require allowance for time to lower the product temperature to –2°C.

How do product dimensions affect freezing time? For example, how long will it take to freeze a patty of twice the thickness? Consider the previous problem with all the parameters the same except that d is changed from 0.01 m to 0.02 m. Plank's equation now becomes:

$FT = 262,500$ kJ/ m³ K ([0.000 200 m³ K/W + 0.000 035 7 m³ K/W) / 20 K

$FT = 3.094$ kJ/W $= 3094$ sec $= 51.6$ min.

We see that doubling the product's thickness will require slightly more than doubling of the freezing time, i.e., 2.17 times longer to freeze. The assumed value of h (50 W/m² K) for the equipment was for high velocity air blast freezing. With less efficient cooling (values of h are 5 to 10 for still-air freezing systems, 100 for plate freezing, and 600 W/(m² K) for liquid-immersion systems), freezing time (FT) would increase. With thin products like the patty of this example, h is the controlling factor. With thicker products like a side of beef carcass, d is larger and the second term in the parenthesis in Plank's equation contributes more to the total freezing time. Also, increases in thickness in this situation will have a non-linear (d^2) effect on freezing time. Thus, a small reduction in d of a thick product will cause a relatively large reduction in freezing time for low efficiency equipment systems.

Freezing time is important in determining the capacity of equipment and quality of product. The freezing rate establishes the type of ice crystal formation. Slow heat removal from a food causes a few large crystals to form while rapid heat removal causes formation of many small crystals. The smaller the size of the ice crystals in the frozen product, the better the texture of the subsequent food product.

Analogous to the often-used freezing time computation is the occasional need to predict the thawing time. Plank's formula can be used for computing the thawing time by substituting the food property values for density and conductivity of the unfrozen material. Since the thermal conductivity of unfrozen material is less than for frozen material, thawing time is longer than freezing time for the same food material and same operating conditions, i.e., temperature difference and convective heat transfer coefficient.

Example 8.6

The frozen beef patties of Example 8.4 are being thawed in open air with the same convective heat transfer coefficient and temperature difference. Compute the time to thaw the product and compare with the freezing time.

Solution:
The numbers to be used in Plank's equation are the same as for freezing except that the thermal conductivity now is 0.4 W/m K (unfrozen meat). The resulting equation then becomes:

$$TT = 1050 \frac{kg}{m^3} \times 250 \frac{kJ}{kg} \left[\frac{\dfrac{0.01\ m}{2 \times 50\ \dfrac{W}{m^2 K}} + \dfrac{(0.01\ m)^2}{8 \times 0.4 \dfrac{W}{m\ K}}}{20\ K} \right]$$

$$TT = 1.723\ kJ/W = 1723\ s = \underline{28.7\ min} \qquad \textbf{ANSWER}$$

Note that, assuming all factors are the same, thawing of these relatively thin patties takes 20% longer than freezing. This is due to the difference in thermal conductivity of frozen and unfrozen material.

List of Symbols

c_p	specific heat capacity at constant pressure, J/(kg K) or kJ/(kg K)
c_p'	specific heat capacity below freezing at constant pressure, J/(kg K) or kJ/(kg K)
COP	coefficient of performance, dimensionless
d	product thickness, m
FT	freezing time, s
h	enthalpy, kJ/kg
h	surface heat transfer coefficient, W/(m² K)
h_{sf}	$(h_f - h_s)$ latent heat of fusion, kJ/kg
k	thermal conductivity, W/(m K)
m	mass, kg
$\dot{m}$	mass flow rate, kg/s
P	pressure, Pa
P	Plank Equation constant, a function of product shape
Q	energy, J
$\dot{Q}$	heat transfer rate, W
R	Plank Equation constant, a function of product shape
s	entropy, kJ/(kg K)
t	temperature, °C
TT	thawing time, s
ρ	density, kg/m³

Subscripts

1,2	initial and final temperatures
a	air (or dry air)
f	frozen product
f	freezing point
g	gaseous state
H	highest enthalpy value of refrigeration cycle
HP	heat pump operation
L	liquid

References

1. ASHRAE. 1959. *Refrigerant Tables, Charts, and Characteristics*. ASHRAE, Inc., Atlanta, GA.
2. ASHRAE. 1997. *Handbook of Fundamentals*, Chapter 18: Refrigerants; Chapter 19: Thermophysical Properties of Refrigerants. ASHRAE, Inc., Atlanta, GA.
3. ASHRAE. 1998. *Handbook of Refrigeration*. ASHRAE, Inc., Atlanta, GA.
4. ASHRAE. 1999. *Handbook of HVAC Applications*. ASHRAE, Inc., Atlanta, GA.
5. Rowland, F. S. 1997. Stratospheric ozone depletion: Identifying the problem and the solution. *ASHRAE Journal* 39(9): 29-31.
6. Van Wylen, Gordon J., and Richard E. Sonntag. 1986. *Fundamentals of Classical Thermodynamics*. 3rd ed. John Wiley & Sons, New York, NY.

Problems

8.1. Complete the following table of refrigerant properties. Abbreviate state codes as SL = saturated liquid, SV = saturated vapor, and SH = superheated vapor.

Item	Refrigerant	t (°C)	P (MPa)	h (kJ/kg)	s (kJ/kg K)	x	State
A	R-12		1.0		--	0	
B	R-12		0.1			1	
C	R-12	80	1.5			--	
D	R-134a		1.0		--	0	
E	R-134a		0.1			1	SV
F	R-134a	-30				1	
G	R-134a	50			--	0	
H	R-134a		0.1		--	0.5	--

8.2. A cooler uses Refrigerant 134a and operates between 2.0 MPa and 0.15 Mpa. Refrigerant flow is 0.1 kg/s. Find:
   a. operating temperatures
   b. cooling per kilogram of refrigerant
   c. *COP*
   d. cooling capacity in Watts and tons

8.3. Repeat Problem 8.2 using Refrigerant R-12.

8.4. A refrigeration system is to be installed which will produce a temperature of −30°C at the evaporator and 45°C at the condenser. What pressures (MPa) would be required to produce those temperatures for: (a) Refrigerant 12; (b) Refrigerant 134a? Compute the coefficient of performance for each refrigerant operating at these conditions.

8.5. Assume the system of problem 8.2 is to be operated as a heat pump. Find the:
   a. operating temperatures
   b. heat output per kilogram of refrigerant
   c. *COP*
   d. heating capacity in watts

8.6. Repeat Problem 8.5 using Refrigerant R-12.

8.7. How much energy (kJ) is required to freeze one ton of water at 0°C to ice at 0°C?

8.8. How much energy (kJ) is required to produce one ton of −15°C ice from water at 10°C?

8.9. How many kg of ice are needed to cool 1000 kg of apples from 20°C to 0°C if only the latent heat of fusion is available for cooling?

8.10. A processor plans to freeze 1000 kg of strawberries from 20°C to −18°C in 24 hours in a perfectly insulated freezer. Calculate for this processor the:
   a. cooling needed to bring the temperature of the berries to the freezing point (kJ)
   b. heat (latent) that must be removed to freeze them (kJ)
   c. cooling needed to further lower the temperature of the berries to −18C (kJ)
   d. average cooling rate for the 24 hours (watts)
   e. power for the refrigeration unit if the input power must be 50% of the cooling rate

8.11. Repeat Problem 8.10 for 1000 kg of blueberries.

8.12. If the freezer of problem 10 is 3 m × 5 m × 3 m, has a "U" factor of 1.2 W/(m² K), and is in a location where the outside temperature is 26°C, what is the total heat loss (watts) from the freezer if the inside temperature is –18°C? How much would this increase the power requirement for the refrigeration unit?

8.13. A food freezer has dimensions (average of inside and outside) of 0.6 m × 0.8 m × 1.8 m. Its walls are made up of inner and outer stainless steel sheets (1.6 mm) with 50 mm of polyurethane insulation between them. The freezer is loaded with 160 kg of beef (at 20°C) which is to be frozen to –18°C in 24 hours. The freezer is inside a room at 20°C temperature.

a. Calculate the heat gain through the freezer walls in watts (assume an average freezer inside temperature of –20°C and no air movement in the room or in the freezer).

b. Calculate the heat that must be removed from the meat to lower temperature to the freezing point.

c. Calculate the heat that must be removed to freeze the meat.

d. Calculate the heat that must be removed from the frozen meat to lower its temperature to –18°C.

e. Calculate the the average cooling load (J/s) of the beef for a 24-hour period (use the total of b, c, and d).

f. Calculate the total cooling load on the freezer (beef plus heat gain).

g. Calculate the power required if the refrigeration system requires a power source equal to 30% of the total removal rate.

8.14. Consider a hamburger patty identical to that of Example 8.5 except that the diameter is 10 cm. Compute the time to freeze and compare to the time for the 8-cm patty of the example.

8.15. The beef patties of Example 8.5 are placed in a freezer now set to –27°C. Assuming all other parameters remain the same, compute the time to freeze with this colder freezer temperature.

8.16. The beef patties of Example 8.5 are placed in a different freezer having less air movement (the convective heat transfer coefficient is 10 W/m² K).

a. Compute the time to freeze assuming all other parameters remain the same.

b. Compute the time to thaw if temperature difference remains the same.

8.17. The hamburger in Example 8.5 is rolled into the shape of a ball of the same volume and frozen.

a. Determine the volume of this ball.

b. Compute the time to freeze this spherical shaped hamburger assuming all other parameters are the same as in Example 8.5.

Refrigerant Charts and Tables

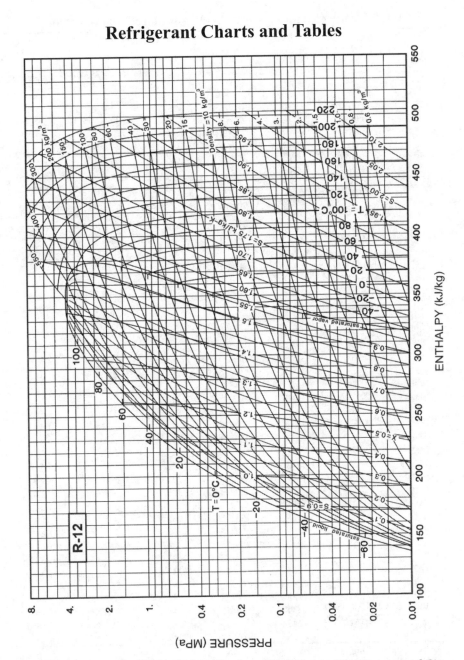

Figure 8.04. Pressure-enthalpy diagram for Refrigerant 12. (Courtesy of the American Society of Heating, Refrigeration and Air-Conditioning Engineers.)

Table 8.02. Selected properties of R-12[c] (dichlorodifluoromethane).

t (°C)	P (MPa)	ρ (kg/m³) Liquid	v (m³/kg Vapor)	Enthalpy (h) kJ/kg Liquid	Vapor	Entropy (s) kJ/(kg K) Vapor
−60.0	0.023	1572	0.6371	146.7	324.4	1.615
−50.0	0.039	1544	0.3836	155.3	329.2	1.600
−45.0	0.051	1530	0.3035	159.7	331.6	1.593
−40.0	0.064	1516	0.2428	164.0	334.0	1.588
−35.0	0.081	1502	0.1963	168.4	336.4	1.582
−30.0	0.100	1487	0.1603	172.8	338.8	1.578
−29.8[a]	0.101	1487	0.1590	173.0	338.9	1.578
−28.0	0.109	1481	0.1482	174.6	339.8	1.576
−26.0	0.119	1476	0.1372	176.4	340.7	1.575
−24.0	0.129	1470	0.1271	178.1	341.7	1.573
−22.0	0.139	1464	0.1180	179.9	342.6	1.572
−20.0	0.151	1458	0.1097	181.7	343.5	1.570
−18.0	0.163	1452	0.1020	183.5	344.5	1.569
−16.0	0.176	1446	0.0950	185.3	345.4	1.568
−14.0	0.189	1439	0.0886	187.1	346.3	1.566
−12.0	0.204	1433	0.0827	189.0	347.3	1.565
−10.0	0.219	1427	0.0773	190.8	348.2	1.564
−8.0	0.235	1421	0.0723	192.6	349.1	1.563
−6.0	0.252	1415	0.0677	194.5	350.0	1.562
−4.0	0.270	1408	0.0635	196.3	350.9	1.561
−2.0	0.289	1402	0.0596	198.1	351.8	1.560
0.0	0.308	1396	0.0559	200.0	352.7	1.559
10.0	0.423	1363	0.0413	209.4	357.1	1.555
12.0	0.449	1356	0.0390	211.3	357.9	1.554
14.0	0.477	1349	0.0368	213.2	358.8	1.554
16.0	0.505	1343	0.0348	215.2	359.6	1.553
18.0	0.535	1336	0.0329	217.1	360.4	1.552
20.0	0.567	1329	0.0311	219.0	361.2	1.552
22.0	0.599	1322	0.0295	221.0	362.0	1.551
24.0	0.633	1314	0.0279	222.9	362.8	1.550
26.0	0.669	1307	0.0264	224.9	363.6	1.550
28.0	0.705	1300	0.0251	226.9	364.4	1.549
30.0	0.744	1293	0.0238	228.9	365.2	1.549
32.0	0.784	1285	0.0226	230.9	365.9	1.548
34.0	0.825	1277	0.0214	232.9	366.7	1.548
36.0	0.868	1270	0.0203	234.9	367.4	1.547
38.0	0.913	1262	0.0193	237.0	368.1	1.547
40.0	0.959	1254	0.0184	239.0	368.8	1.546
42.0	1.007	1246	0.0175	241.1	369.5	1.545
44.0	1.057	1238	0.0166	243.2	370.2	1.545
46.0	1.109	1230	0.0158	245.3	370.8	1.544
48.0	1.162	1222	0.0151	247.4	371.5	1.544
111.8[b]	4.125	565	0.0018	347.4	347.4	1.427

[a] = normal boiling point   [b] = critical point
[c] Abridged data taken from ASHRAE. 1997. *Handbook of Fundamentals,* Chapter 19: Thermophysical properties of refrigerants. Courtesy of the American Society of Heating, Refrigerating and Air-Conditioning Engineers.

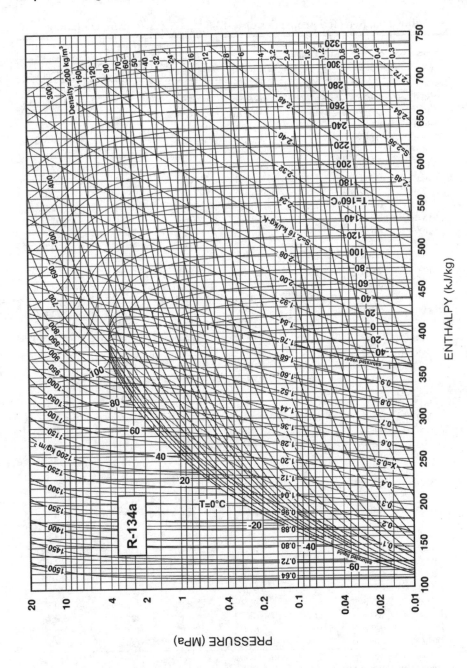

Figure 8.05. Pressure-enthalpy diagram for Refrigerant 134a. (Courtesy of the American Society of Heating, Refrigeration and Air-Conditioning Engineers.)

Food & Process Engineering Technology

Table 8.03. Selected properties of R-134a[c] (1.1,1.2-tetrafluorethane).

t (°C)	P (MPa)	ρ (kg/m³) Liquid	v (m³/kg Vapor)	Enthalpy (h) (kJ/kg) Liquid	Enthalpy (h) (kJ/kg) Vapor	Entropy (s) (kJ/kg K) Vapor
−60.0	0.016	1471	1.0770	124.0	361.5	1.802
−50.0	0.029	1443	0.6056	136.2	367.8	1.781
−40.0	0.051	1415	0.3610	148.6	374.2	1.765
−30.0	0.084	1386	0.2260	161.1	380.5	1.752
−28.0	0.093	1380	0.2068	163.6	381.7	1.750
−26.1[b]	0.101	1374	0.1902	166.1	382.9	1.748
−26.0	0.102	1374	0.1896	166.2	382.9	1.748
−24.0	0.111	1368	0.1741	168.7	384.2	1.746
−22.0	0.122	1362	0.1601	171.3	385.4	1.744
−20.0	0.133	1356	0.1474	173.8	386.7	1.742
−18.0	0.145	1350	0.1360	176.4	387.9	1.740
−16.0	0.157	1344	0.1256	179.0	389.1	1.738
−14.0	0.171	1338	0.1161	181.6	390.3	1.737
−12.0	0.185	1332	0.1075	184.2	391.6	1.735
−10.0	0.201	1326	0.0996	186.8	392.8	1.734
−8.0	0.217	1319	0.0925	189.4	394.0	1.732
−6.0	0.234	1313	0.0859	192.0	395.2	1.731
−4.0	0.253	1307	0.0799	194.7	396.3	1.730
−2.0	0.272	1300	0.0744	197.3	397.5	1.729
0.0	0.293	1294	0.0694	200.0	398.7	1.727
10.0	0.414	1260	0.0495	213.5	404.4	1.722
12.0	0.443	1253	0.0464	216.3	405.5	1.722
14.0	0.473	1246	0.0435	219.0	406.6	1.721
16.0	0.504	1239	0.0408	221.8	407.7	1.720
18.0	0.537	1232	0.0383	224.6	408.8	1.719
20.0	0.572	1225	0.0360	227.4	409.8	1.718
22.0	0.608	1218	0.0339	230.2	410.9	1.718
24.0	0.646	1210	0.0319	233.1	411.9	1.717
26.0	0.685	1203	0.0300	235.9	413.0	1.716
28.0	0.727	1195	0.0283	238.8	414.0	1.716
30.0	0.770	1187	0.0267	241.7	414.9	1.715
32.0	0.815	1179	0.0252	244.6	415.9	1.714
34.0	0.863	1171	0.0237	247.5	416.9	1.714
36.0	0.912	1163	0.0224	250.4	417.8	1.713
38.0	0.963	1155	0.0212	253.4	418.7	1.712
40.0	1.017	1147	0.0200	256.4	419.6	1.712
42.0	1.072	1138	0.0189	259.4	420.4	1.711
44.0	1.130	1129	0.0179	262.4	421.3	1.710
46.0	1.190	1120	0.0169	265.4	422.1	1.709
48.0	1.253	1111	0.0160	268.5	422.9	1.709
50.0	1.318	1102	0.0151	271.6	423.6	1.708
52.0	1.385	1093	0.0143	274.7	424.4	1.707
101.0[b]	4.056	513	0.0020	389.8	389.8	1.559

[a] = normal boiling point   [b] = critical point

[c] Abridged data taken from ASHRAE. 1997. *Handbook of Fundamentals,* Chapter 19: Thermophysical properties of refrigerants. Courtesy of the American Society of Heating, Refrigerating and Air-Conditioning Engineers.

Psychrometrics

9

Abstract. This chapter includes basic coverage of psychrometric properties and psychrometric processes. Emphasis is upon properties and processes relative to the environment and to processing of biological materials. The chapter also includes a discussion of steam properties and use of steam tables.

Keywords. Cooling, drying, dew point temperature, enthalpy, heating, humidity ratio, psychrometrics, steam quality, relative humidity, wet bulb temperature, steam, steam-air mixtures, steam tables.

9.1 Introduction

Air is a mixture of many different gases (a mixture we call dry air) and water vapor. If pressures do not greatly exceed atmospheric pressure, the perfect gas relationships are valid for these air-water vapor mixtures. These ideal gas relationships are used to evaluate thermodynamic properties of the mixtures. This field of study is called **psychrometrics**.

An understanding of psychrometrics is important in the drying and storage of selected food products. Proper drying conditions are necessary to control the drying rate and resulting quality of dried product. In addition, specific psychrometric conditions have been identified for optimum storage of many fresh and dried products. These are further discussed in other chapters. Psychrometric properties are also important in assessing environmental conditions relative to plant and animal health.

9.2 Relationships Derived from the Perfect Gas Law

The properties of air/water vapor mixtures are based upon ideal gas relationships. Thus, we will review the basic relationships needed to define important psychrometric properties. The **perfect gas law** may be written in different forms as:

$$PV = N R_u T \qquad (9.01)$$

$$PV = N M R T \qquad (9.02)$$

$$Pv = R T \qquad (9.03)$$

$$PV = m R T \qquad (9.04)$$

where: m = mass of the gas, kg
M = molecular weight of the gas, kg/kmol
N = number of moles of the gas
P = pressure, kPa

R = gas constant for a particular gas, R_u/M, kPa m^3/kg K

R_u = universal gas constant, R_u = 8.314 kPa m^3/kmol K (or 8.314 kJ/kmol K)

T = absolute temperature, K

v = specific volume of the gas, m^3/kg

V = total volume of the gas, m^3

Units for the gas constants R and R_u can be expressed in several different forms. The units given above for R_u are probably the most descriptive; however, using unit factors to convert units, we can also obtain units of kN m/kmol K without affecting the numeric value of 8.314. Similarly, R may be expressed in units of kPa m^3/kg K, kN m/kg K, or kJ/kg K without affecting the numeric value. Molecular weights and gas constants for air and water vapor (using the units given above) are: M_a = 28.96, R_a = 0.28706, M_w = 18.015, and R_w = 0.46152.

For a mixture of several gases, Equations 9.01 to 9.04 may be written separately for each gas. If Equation 9.01 is used, the equation for the total mixture becomes:

$$P = (N_1 + N_2 + N_3 + ...) R_u T/V \qquad (9.05)$$

For air containing water vapor, the total pressure is given by:

$$P = P_a + P_w \qquad (9.06)$$

where P_a is the partial pressure of the dry air (including all its component gases) and P_w is the partial pressure of the water vapor. These two partial pressures may be written (using Equation 9.01) as:

$$P_a = N_a R_u T/V \qquad (9.07)$$

$$P_w = N_w R_u T/V \qquad (9.08)$$

The partial pressure of water vapor is a very important parameter in psychrometrics. It is frequently used to calculate other psychrometric properties. For example, **relative humidity** (ϕ) is defined as the ratio of the amount of water vapor in the air (N_w) to the amount the air will hold when saturated at the same temperature (N_{ws}). Thus:

$$\phi = \frac{N_w}{N_{ws}} \qquad (9.09)$$

Using Equation 9.08, we can rewrite Equation 9.09 as:

$$\phi = \frac{P_w \dfrac{V}{R_u T}}{P_{ws} \dfrac{V}{R_u T}} = \frac{P_w}{P_{ws}} \qquad (9.10)$$

The partial pressure of water vapor at saturation (P_{ws}) is a function only of temperature. However, this relationship is complex, involving multiple exponential and logarithmic terms (Wilhelm, 1976).

Another psychrometric parameter of interest is the **humidity ratio** (W). The humidity ratio is the ratio of the mass of water vapor in the air to the mass of the dry air:

$$W = \frac{m_w}{m_a} \tag{9.11}$$

Referring to the ideal gas equation in the form of Equation 9.04, we can write:

$$W = \frac{m_w}{m_a} = \frac{P_w \dfrac{V}{R_w T}}{P_a \dfrac{V}{R_a T}} = \frac{R_a P_w}{R_w P_a} = \frac{0.28706 P_w}{0.46152 P_a} = 0.622 \frac{P_w}{P_a} \tag{9.12}$$

The partial pressure of the dry air (P_a) is the difference between atmospheric pressure and the partial pressure of the water vapor, also called vapor pressure:

$$P_a = P - P_w \tag{9.13}$$

Thus:

$$W = 0.622 \frac{P_w}{P - P_w} \tag{9.14}$$

or, solving for P_w:

$$P_w = \frac{P W}{0.622 + W} \tag{9.15}$$

The **degree of saturation** (μ) is another psychrometric parameter that is sometimes used. It is the humidity ratio divided by the humidity ratio at saturation:

$$\mu = \frac{W}{W_s} \tag{9.16}$$

A final parameter that can be determined from the perfect gas law is the **specific volume** (v) of the moist air. The specific volume is defined in terms of a unit mass of dry air. Thus, using Equations 9.04 and 9.13:

$$v = \frac{V}{m_a} = \frac{m_a R_a \dfrac{T}{P_a}}{m_a} = \frac{R_a T}{P_a} = \frac{R_a T}{P - P_w} \tag{9.17}$$

Substituting from Equation 9.15 for P_w:

$$v = \frac{R_a T}{P - \dfrac{P W}{0.622 + W}} = \frac{R_a T}{P}\left(1 + 1.608\,W\right) \tag{9.18}$$

9.3 Other Important Parameters

The **dew point temperature** (t_{dp}) is the temperature at which moisture begins to condense if air is cooled at constant pressure. The dew point temperature is directly related to partial pressure of the water vapor (P_w); however, that relationship is complex, involving several logarithmic terms (ASHRAE, 1997). Since P_w is also related to the humidity ratio W, this means that specifying any one of the three parameters t_{dp}, P_w, and W specifies all three.

The **wet-bulb temperature** (t_{wb}) is the temperature measured by a sensor (originally the bulb of a thermometer) that has been wetted with water and exposed to air movement that removes the evaporating moisture. The evaporating water creates a cooling effect. When equilibrium is reached, the wet-bulb temperature will be lower than the ambient temperature. The difference between the two (the **wet bulb depression**) depends upon the rate at which moisture evaporates from the wet bulb. The evaporation rate, in turn, depends upon the moisture content of the air. The evaporation rate decreases as the air moisture content increases. Thus, a small wet bulb depression indicates high relative humidity, while a large wet bulb depression is indicative of low relative humidity.

The **enthalpy** (h) of moist air is one of the most frequently used psychrometric parameters. It is a measure of the energy content of the air and depends upon both the temperature and the moisture content of the air. It is determined by adding the enthalpy of the moisture in the air ($W h_w$) to the enthalpy of the dry air (h_a):

$$h = h_a + W h_w = c_{pa} t + W\left(h_{fg} + c_{pw} t\right) \tag{9.19}$$

or:

$$h = 1.006 t + W\left(2501 + 1.805 t\right) \tag{9.20}$$

Equation 9.20 is based upon a specific heat for air of 1.006 kJ/kg K and a zero value of h at $t = 0°C$. The enthalpy of water is based upon: a zero value of h at 0°C (liquid state); $h_{fg} = 2501$ kJ/kg at 0°C; and an average specific heat for water vapor of 1.805 kJ/kg K. Equation 9.20 provides a good approximation for the enthalpy of moist air over a wide range of temperatures; however, the error increases rapidly at temperatures above 100°C. Empirical relationships, charts, or tables must then be used to determine h.

9.4 Psychrometric Charts

If two independent psychrometric parameters are known, all the psychrometric parameters previously discussed can be computed numerically. However, numerical calculation is practical only if the calculation method is computerized. The fastest and easiest method of evaluating psychrometric properties is often the use of a **psychrometric chart**. The psychrometric chart shows selected psychrometric properties as a function of each other. Properties shown on most psychrometric charts are drybulb, wet-bulb, and dew point temperatures; relative humidity; humidity ratio; enthalpy; and specific volume. Figure 9.01 is a typical psychrometric chart. It covers the

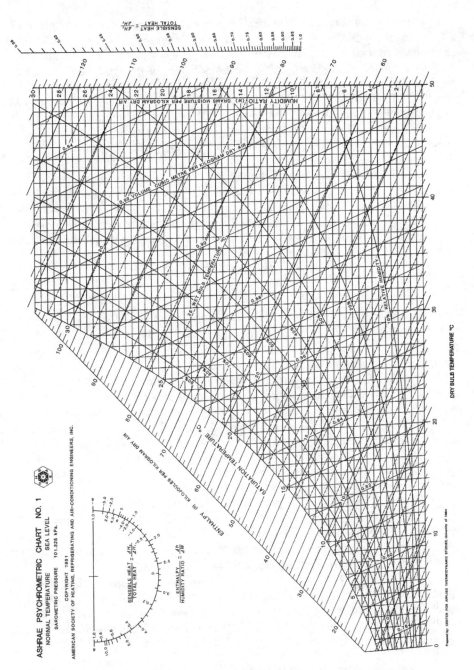

Figure 9.01. Psychrometric chart for normal temperatures (SI units). (Courtesy of the American Society of Heating, Refrigerating and Air-Conditioning Engineers.)

"normal temperature" range at standard atmospheric pressure. Other charts are available for higher and lower temperature ranges and for pressures above and below one atmosphere. In addition, different chart versions are available for these common psychrometric ranges. The general arrangement of all charts is the same; however, differences in appearance are obvious. The procedure for reading the psychrometric parameters differs little among the charts—except for the enthalpy and (occasionally) the wet-bulb temperature. We will use Figure 9.01 to gain an understanding of psychrometric charts. Before reading further, you should examine this figure closely. Identify the lines representing parameters such as dew point, wet-bulb and dry-bulb temperatures, humidity ratio, etc.

Each position on a psychrometric chart represents a unique state point. Any two independent psychrometric properties define such a state point. We will now use two properties to define a state point and then determine the values of the other psychrometric properties. Let us assume that we used a **psychrometer**, a device that measures wet-bulb and dry-bulb temperatures, and obtained the following measurements:

$$t_{wb} = 17.1°C$$

$$t = 24°C$$

To find the state point represented by these values, we follow a vertical line upward from $t = 24°C$ at the bottom of the chart. We then locate the point where this line intersects with an imaginary line just above, and parallel to, the dashed line sloping downward to the right from a wet-bulb temperature of 17.0°C. The intersection of the lines (circled on Figure 9.01) represents the desired state point. Note that the temperatures on the curved line at the upper left of the chart may represent either dew point (saturation temperature), wet-bulb, or dry-bulb temperatures. A constant wet-bulb temperature is represented by a line sloping downward to the right; a constant dew point temperature is represented by a horizontal line; and a constant dry bulb line is represented by a vertical (or near vertical) line. At saturation (100% relative humidity), the dry bulb, wet-bulb and dew point temperatures are equal. At any other condition, they are not equal and follow the order $t > t_{wb} > t_{dp}$.

We have now located the state point (indicated by the center of the circle on Figure 9.01). Moving left horizontally from this point, we find that the dew point is 13.0°C. Also, moving right along this horizontal line we find that the humidity ratio is 9.3 g/kg of dry air. Relative humidity is represented by lines curving upward to the right. Our state point appears to be exactly on the 50% line. Thus, $\phi = 50\%$.

Similarly, the specific volume is found by interpolating between the 0.85 and 0.86 constant specific volume lines which slope sharply downward to the right. We find that $v = 0.854$ m³/kg. The partial pressure of the water vapor can be calculated from Equation 9.15, noting that $P = 101.325$ kPa and W must be dimensionless (0.0093 kg/kg of dry air, instead of the 9.3 g/kg noted above):

$$P_w = \frac{101.325 \times 0.0093}{0.622 + 0.0093} = 1.493 \text{ kPa}$$

The psychrometric chart shown in Figure 9.01 is only one of several versions of psychrometric charts available. Two other charts are shown in Figures 9.02 and 9.03. Figure 9.02 covers lower temperature ranges not covered by Figure 9.01. Figure 9.03 is a greatly condensed chart that extends to higher temperatures. All these charts present the data in SI units. Similar charts are available using US units. Although there are some differences in chart arrangement, the same interpretation procedures apply for all psychrometric charts.

In reading the psychrometric chart, you should keep the following points in mind:

1. Enthalpy, humidity ratio, and specific volume are referenced to a *unit mass of dry air*.
2. On charts using US units, the humidity ratio may be given in pounds of moisture per pound of dry air or in grains of moisture per pound of dry air. Since one pound contains 7000 grains, the two measurements can be converted as needed. In SI units, the humidity ratio is expressed in either grams of water or kilograms of water per kilogram of dry air.
3. *Constant enthalpy and constant wet bulb lines are not parallel*, although there is only a slight difference in slope. Because of this, most charts do not show both constant wet-bulb and constant enthalpy lines. Only one parameter is usually plotted, although the other may be plotted at wide intervals. In the example used earlier, the enthalpy is 48 kJ/kg dry air. Note the short sloping lines along the right edge and bottom of the chart. These represent constant enthalpy lines corresponding to similar lines along the enthalpy scale at the upper left. By using a straight edge to align the point in the circle on Figure 9.01 with equal values of enthalpy along the bottom and upper left of the chart, we find that the enthalpy value is 48 kJ/kg dry air. Some charts use an enthalpy correction curve. These curves show the adjustment to correct for deviation between constant enthalpy and constant wet-bulb lines. On these charts, the constant wet-bulb line is followed to find a value for enthalpy from the enthalpy scale at upper left. That value is then adjusted by subtracting the value of the enthalpy correction.

9.4.1 Psychrometric Tables

Tabulated values of psychrometric properties (see Table 9.01) can also be used for analysis of psychrometric data. However, use of the tables is more time consuming than use of a chart. Use of the table also has limitations. For example, the wet bulb temperature cannot be directly related to any tabulated properties. However, we can use the table to determine other psychrometric properties at $t = 24°C$ and 50% relative humidity. This is the same point used in the chart analysis; however, we can expect the values of some properties to differ slightly from those determined by the chart. Results obtained using the table would normally be considered more accurate than those from a psychrometric chart.

To find the partial pressure (or vapor pressure) of water vapor in the air, we note that relative humidity is defined as $\phi = P_w/P_{ws}$ (Equation 9.10). At $t = 24°C$, the table gives $P_{ws} = 2.9852$. Solving for $P_w = \phi P_{ws} = 0.5(2.9852) = 1.4926$ kPa. This is essentially the same value found from the psychrometric chart. We can now use Equation 9.14 to solve for the humidity ratio (W) at 24°C and 50% relative humidity:

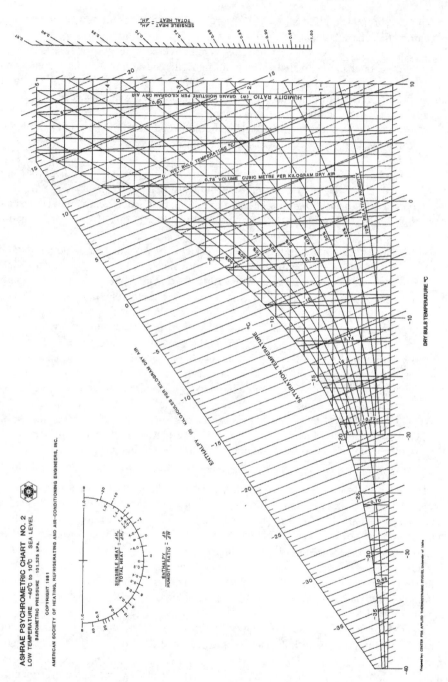

Figure 9.02. Psychrometric chart for low temperatures (SI units). (Courtesy of the American Society of Heating, Refrigerating and Air-Conditioning Engineers.)

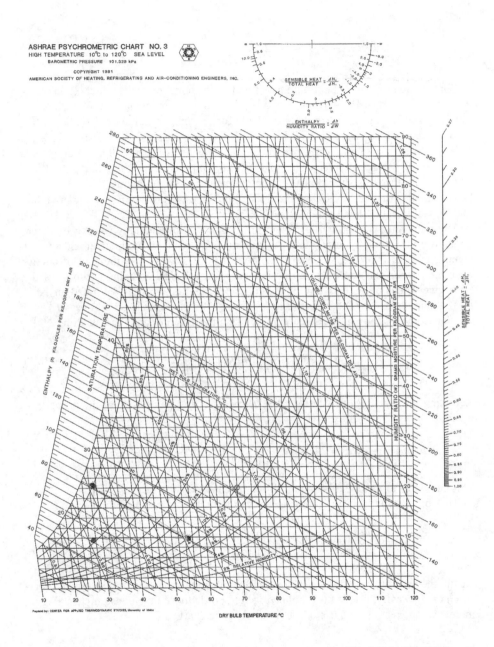

Figure 9.03. Psychrometric chart for high temperatures (SI units). (Courtesy of the American Society of Heating, Refrigerating and Air-Conditioning Engineers.)

$$W = 0.0622 \times \frac{P_w}{P - P_w} = 0.0622 \times \frac{1.4926}{101.325 - 1.4926} = 0.0093 \frac{\text{kg H}_2\text{O}}{\text{kg DA}}$$

Since the dew point temperature is defined as the temperature at which 100% relative humidity is reached as the air is cooled, this would be the temperature at which W_s = 0.0093 kg H_2O/kg DA. Searching the table for the temperature corresponding to W_s = 0.0093 kg H_2O/kg DA, we find that t_{dp} = 13°C at W_s = 0.009370 kg H_2O/kg DA. This is slightly above but very close to the look-up value of 0.0093 that we are using. If necessary, we could interpolate to find the temperature corresponding to W_s = 0.0093. Note that this should also be the temperature corresponding to P_{ws} = 1.4926 kPa. Note also that W_s = 0.018963 at 24°C; but since we have only 50% relative humidity, that moisture level is never reached.

The remaining two properties, specific volume (v) and enthalpy (h) can be determined from the table by noting that each are made up of an air component and a water component. For example, the energy content (h) of the wet air is the sum of energy from the dry air and energy from the moisture present. The enthalpy columns of the table give values of h_a (enthalpy of the dry air), h_s (enthalpy of the saturated air), and h_{as} (enthalpy added by the moisture to produce saturated air and equal to $h_s - h_a$). We can determine h at any moisture content by using these values and the equation:

$$h = h_a + \mu h_{as}, \text{ where } \mu = \frac{W}{W_s} \tag{9.21}$$

Rewriting the equation, substituting for μ, and inserting values for all the properties, we find:

$$h = h_a + \frac{W}{W_s} \times h_{as} = 24.146 + \frac{0.0093}{0.018963} \times 48.239 = 47.8 \frac{\text{kJ}}{\text{kg DA}}$$

This compares to a value of 48 found from the chart.

The solution for specific volume follows exactly the same procedure:

$$v = v_a + \frac{W}{W_s} \times v_{as} = 0.8416 + \frac{0.0093}{0.018963} \times 0.0256 = 0.8542 \frac{\text{m}^3}{\text{kg DA}}$$

Again, the resulting value is very close to the value determined from the psychrometric chart. Typically, use of the tabulated values, while more time consuming, will give more accurate results than use of the psychrometric chart.

Table 9.01. Selected thermodynamic properties of moist air.[a]

Temp (°C)	Humidity Ratio (kg_w/kg_da)	Volume (m³/kg_da)			Enthalpy (kJ/kg_da)			Condensed Water Enthalpy (kJ/kg)	Vapor Pressure (kPa)
t	W_s	v_a	v_{as}	v_s	h_a	h_{as}	h_s	h_w	p_{ws}
0	0.003789	0.7734	0.0047	0.7781	0.000	9.473	9.473	0.06	0.6112
2	0.004381	0.7791	0.0055	0.7845	2.012	10.970	12.982	8.49	0.7060
4	0.005054	0.7848	0.0064	0.7911	4.024	12.672	16.696	16.91	0.8135
6	0.005818	0.7904	0.0074	0.7978	6.036	14.608	20.644	25.32	0.9353
8	0.006683	0.7961	0.0085	0.8046	8.047	16.805	24.852	33.72	1.0729
9	0.007157	0.7990	0.0092	0.8081	9.053	18.010	27.064	37.92	1.1481
10	0.007661	0.8018	0.0098	0.8116	10.059	19.293	29.352	42.11	1.2280
11	0.008197	0.8046	0.0106	0.8188	11.065	20.658	31.724	46.31	1.3128
12	0.008766	0.8075	0.0113	0.8152	12.071	22.108	34.179	50.50	1.4026
13	0.009370	0.8103	0.0122	0.8225	13.077	23.649	36.726	54.69	1.4979
14	0.010012	0.8132	0.0131	0.8262	14.084	25.286	39.370	58.88	1.5987
15	0.010692	0.8160	0.0140	0.8300	15.090	27.023	42.113	63.07	1.7055
16	0.011413	0.8188	0.0150	0.8338	16.096	28.867	44.963	67.26	1.8185
17	0.012178	0.8217	0.0160	0.8377	17.102	30.824	47.926	71.44	1.9380
18	0.012989	0.8245	0.0172	0.8417	18.108	32.900	51.008	75.63	2.0643
19	0.013848	0.8274	0.0184	0.8457	19.114	35.101	54.216	79.81	2.1979
20	0.014758	0.8302	0.0196	0.8494	20.121	37.434	57.555	84.00	2.3389
21	0.015721	0.8330	0.0210	0.8540	21.127	39.908	61.035	88.18	2.4878
22	0.016741	0.8359	0.0224	0.8583	22.133	42.527	64.660	92.36	2.6448
23	0.017821	0.8387	0.0240	0.8627	23.140	45.301	68.440	96.55	2.8105
24	0.018963	0.8416	0.0256	0.8671	24.146	48.239	72.385	100.73	2.9852
25	0.020170	0.8444	0.0273	0.8717	25.153	51.347	76.500	104.91	3.1693
26	0.021448	0.8472	0.0291	0.8764	26.159	54.638	80.798	109.09	3.3633
27	0.022798	0.8501	0.0311	0.8811	27.165	58.120	85.285	113.27	3.5674
28	0.024226	0.8529	0.0331	0.8860	28.172	61.804	89.976	117.45	3.7823
29	0.025735	0.8558	0.0353	0.8910	29.179	65.699	94.878	121.63	4.0084
30	0.027329	0.8586	0.0376	0.8962	30.185	69.820	100.00	125.81	4.2462
35	0.036756	0.8728	0.0514	0.9242	35.219	94.236	129.455	146.71	5.6280
40	0.049141	0.8870	0.0698	0.9568	40.253	126.43	166.683	167.61	7.3838
45	0.065411	0.9012	0.0943	0.9955	45.289	168.87	214.164	188.51	9.5935
50	0.086858	0.9154	0.1272	1.0425	50.326	225.02	275.345	209.42	12.3503
55	0.115321	0.9296	0.1713	1.1009	55.365	299.77	355.137	230.33	15.7601
60	0.15354	0.9438	0.2315	1.1752	60.405	400.46	460.863	251.25	19.9439
65	0.20579	0.9580	0.3147	1.2726	65.446	538.55	603.995	272.18	25.0397
70	0.27916	0.9721	0.4328	1.4049	70.489	732.96	803.448	293.13	31.1986

[a]Abridged data taken from ASHRAE. 1997. Handbook of Fundamentals, Chapter 6. Courtesy of the American Society of Heating, Refrigerating and Air-Conditioning Engineers.

9.5 Processes on the Psychrometric Chart

The psychrometric chart is used in many applications both within and outside the food industry. It is used extensively to analyze product drying and air cooling, primarily because it is a simple and quick alternative to more costly methods. Drying with air is an extremely cost-effective method to reduce the moisture of a biological material, and the addition of a small amount of heat significantly improves the air's drying potential. Air at a particular temperature and pressure has a limit to its drying capability and so it is useful to understand the changes in its drying potential as moisture is added or removed by the food materials, people, animals, etc. Hot, dry environments for animals, including humans, can be made more comfortable by evaporative cooling, a low-cost method that lowers the air temperature as a trade-off for increasing humidity. The addition of moisture to the air is valuable in certain applications as seen in summertime greenhouse evaporative cooling. Fruit and vegetables harvested in hot weather often can be cooled with evaporatively cooled air to reduce respiration.

Large industrial plants, particularly food processing plants, generating waste heat and needing cooling often utilize cooling towers to reduce their refrigeration requirements. Cooling towers, operating on the evaporative cooling principle, provide a way to cool water by rejecting the unwanted heat to the atmosphere.

In all these applications, we are concerned with following a process that can be described on the psychrometric chart. By a *process* we mean moving from one state point to another state point on the chart. We will look at a few simple processes, and display the paths of these processes on small psychrometric charts in Figure 9.04. Selected relevant properties are also noted on each chart (Charts I, II, III, IV, V, VI). These are ideal processes assuming no heat transfer from the surroundings. In actual processes, there will always be some heat gain or loss.

a. **Heating or cooling**. These processes follow a constant moisture line (constant humidity ratio). Thus, temperature increases or decreases but moisture content and dew point are unchanged. Process A–B (Chart I) represents a heating process, while process A–B (Chart II) represents cooling. If cooled below the dew point (Chart III), the constant humidity ratio line is followed until the dew point (Point D) is reached. Further cooling follows the saturation (100% relative humidity) line until the final temperature (Point B) is reached. Moisture is condensed during the part of the process that follows the saturation line.

b. **Moisture addition** (i.e., evaporation) while using only energy from the air (Chart IV). Both drying and evaporative cooling follow this process. It is represented by a constant wet-bulb line (Process A–B.) Temperature, moisture content, etc., change but the wet-bulb temperature remains constant. This can be verified by an energy balance analysis. Note that enthalpy increases slightly in this process. This is due to energy present in the water before it is evaporated.

c. **Heating and drying** (Chart V). This combination of the processes shown in Charts I and IV is common in drying applications. Air is heated (Process A–B) and passed over the material to be dried (Process B–C). A second stage of heating (C–D) and drying (D–E) is sometimes included.

d. **Adiabatic mixing** (no heat transfer) of air (Chart VI). Moist air from two sources and at different state points is mixed to produce air at a third state point. Relationships among the properties at the three state points are established from mass and energy balances for the air and water components:

$$m_{aA} + m_{aB} = m_{aC} \qquad \text{air mass balance} \qquad (9.22)$$

$$m_{aA}W_A + m_{aB}W_B = m_{aC}W_C \qquad \text{water mass balance} \qquad (9.23)$$

$$m_{aA}h_A + m_{aB}h_B = m_{aC}h_C \qquad \text{energy balance} \qquad (9.24)$$

These equations are usually solved to relate specific properties to the specific masses involved. For example, we can use Equations 9.22 to 9.24 to obtain the following relationships:

$$\frac{m_{aA}}{m_{aC}} = \frac{h_C - h_B}{h_A - h_B} = \frac{W_C - W_B}{W_A - W_B} \qquad (9.25)$$

Subscripts A and B in the above equations represent entering air streams, while subscript C represents conditions after mixing. Note that this process does not follow a constant property line on the psychrometric chart. The position of Point C along the line between Points A and B is determined by the proportion of air at each state point included in the mix. If equal amounts of air are provided from each source, Point C will be at approximately the midpoint of the line. If 90% of the air is from state Point B, Point C will be approximately 90% of the distance from Point A and 10% of the distance from Point B. This scaled approach is useful as a quick estimate of the resulting state point. It is also useful as a quick verification of numerical calculations. However, use of the above equations to calculate the state point of mixed air is the preferred approach.

e. **Adiabatic Saturation**. The drying process was identified earlier as a constant wet-bulb process. While this is the generally accepted approach, a review of the adiabatic saturation process is provided here for added clarification. An adiabatic saturation process occurs when the humidity of air is increased as it flows through an insulated chamber as shown below. Water evaporates into the air as it passes through the chamber. If the chamber is long enough for equilibrium to occur, then the exit air will be saturated at an equilibrium temperature t^*.

With no heat transfer, the energy balance then becomes:

$$h_1 + (W_s - W_1)h_f = h_s$$

If the water temperature inside the chamber is equal to the exit temperature, the above equation for adiabatic saturation becomes:

$$h_1 + (W_s^* - W_1)h_f^* = h_s^*$$

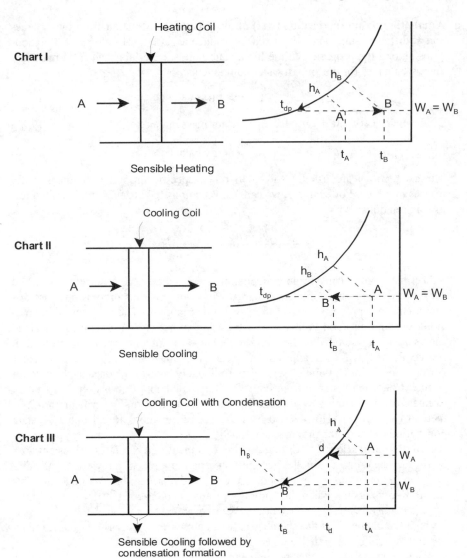

Figure 9.04. Examples of psychrometric processes (continued next page).

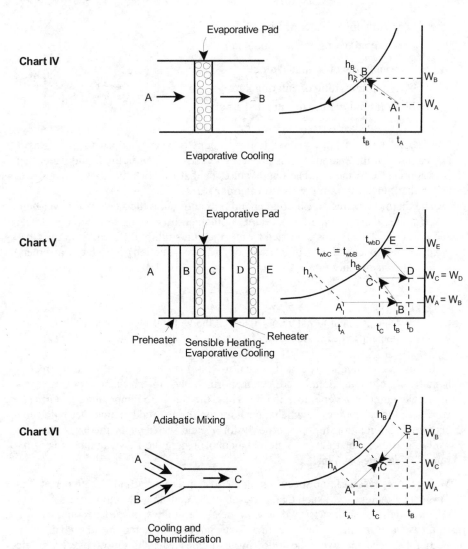

Chart IV — Evaporative Cooling

Chart V — Sensible Heating-Evaporative Cooling

Chart VI — Cooling and Dehumidification

Figure 9.04 (continued). Examples of psychrometric processes.

where: h_1 = enthalpy of entering air

h_f^* = enthalpy of saturated liquid at t^*

h_s^* = enthalpy of saturated air at t^*

W_1 = humidity ratio of entering air

W_s^* = humidity ratio of saturated air at t^*

(this is also W_2, since $t_2 = t^*$)

The second term of the equation is the amount of energy added to the air as it passes through the chamber. This is energy already present in the liquid water that is evaporated into the air. The temperature, t^*, that satisfies the above equation is called the **thermodynamic wet-bulb temperature**.

The thermodynamic wet-bulb temperature is not quite the same as the wet-bulb temperature. The wet-bulb temperature is obtained by cooling in a combined heat and mass transfer process governed by an equation slightly different from the adiabatic saturation equation. Comparison of the two equations introduces a dimensionless Lewis number Le:

$$Le = \frac{h}{kc_p}$$

where: h = surface heat transfer coefficient at the wet-bulb temperature (W/m^2 K)

c_p = specific heat of most air (J/kg K)

k = air-film coefficient of mass transfer (kg/m^2 s)

If this Lewis number is exactly equal to one, then the wet-bulb and thermodynamic wet-bulb temperatures are equal. Fortunately, for air-water vapor mixtures the Lewis number is very close to one. Thus, the wet-bulb temperature is normally considered the same as the adiabatic saturation, or thermodynamic wet-bulb temperature. This relationship is valid only for air and water vapor mixtures. It is not valid with other materials (e.g., air and alcohol) where the Lewis number may substantially deviate from one.

Most real processes do not occur along a constant property line. A number of factors influence each process such that, for example, a constant wet-bulb process is very difficult to attain. In such cases, we may not be able to follow the process on the chart. Instead, we identify the initial and final state points and determine the changes in properties between the two. The following examples will show how psychrometric charts may be used to evaluate processes.

Example 9.1

Air at 30°C and 10% relative humidity enters an evaporative cooler where moisture is evaporated until the temperature reaches 21°C. What is the relative humidity of the air as it leaves?

Solution:
The initial conditions (at $t_1 = 30°C$ and $\phi_1 = 10\%$) are (using Figure 9.01):

$t_{wb} = 13.3°C$

$h_1 = 37$ kJ/kg dry air

$w_1 = 2.6$ g/kg dry air

This method of moisture addition is a constant wet-bulb process (Chart IV of Figure 9.04.). By following a constant wet-bulb line to $t_2 = 21°C$, we find:

$\phi_2 = \underline{41\%}$ **ANSWER**

Example 9.2

Steam is added to air at 30°C and 10% relative humidity until the temperature reaches 38°C and the humidity ratio (W) is 18 g water/kg dry air. How much water is added to one kilogram of air?

Solution:
This process does not follow a constant property line. Instead, we define state point one (Example 9.1) and state point two from the given information. Thus, state point two has the following properties:

$t_2 = 38°C$ (given)

$W_2 = 18$ g/kg dry air (given)

$\phi_2 = 43\%$

$t_{wb} = 26.9°C$

$t_{dp} = 23.2°C$

$h_2 = 84.5$ kJ/kg dry air

The moisture added is

$W_2 - W_1 = 18 - 2.6 = \underline{15.4 \text{g/kg dry air}}$ **ANSWER**

Example 9.3

Air at 20°C, 50% relative humidity (State 1) is heated to 55°C (State 2). The heated air passes through a dryer and exits at a relative humidity of 90% (State 3). How much water is removed for each cubic meter of air entering the heater? How much heat is added during the heating process?

Solution:
The processes followed for the heating and drying are: (1) constant humidity ra-

tio (or dew point) for heating, and (2) constant wet-bulb temperature for drying. This is represented by processes A–B and B–C shown on Chart V of Figure 9.04. From Figure 9.01, the properties at each state point are:

Property	State 1	State 2	State 3
t (°C)	20[a]	55[a]	26.1
t_{wb} (°C)	13.7	24.8	24.8 [b]
t_{dp} (°C)	9.0	9.0 [b]	24.3
ϕ (%)	50[a]	7	90[a]
h (kJ/kg)	38.4	74.7	75.6
W (g H$_2$O/kg dry air)	7.3	7.3	19.5
v (m^3/kg dry air)	0.84	0.93	0.87

[a] Properties given in the problem statement.
[b] Properties unchanged from previous state point

From the table:

$$W_{rem} = W_3 - W_2 = 19.5 - 7.3 = 12.2 \text{ g H}_2\text{O/kg DA}$$

$$\dot{Q} = h_2 - h_1 = 74.7 - 38.4 = 36.3 \text{ kJ/kg DA}$$

We must now convert to volumetric values based upon the entering air:

$$W_{rem} = \frac{12.2 \dfrac{\text{g H}_2\text{O}}{\text{kg DA}}}{0.84 \dfrac{\text{m}^3}{\text{kg DA}}} = 14.5 \dfrac{\text{g H}_2\text{O}}{\text{m}^3} \qquad \textbf{ANSWER}$$

$$\dot{Q} = \frac{36.3 \dfrac{\text{kJ}}{\text{kg DA}}}{0.84 \dfrac{\text{m}^3}{\text{kg DA}}} = 43.2 \dfrac{\text{kJ}}{\text{m}} \qquad \textbf{ANSWER}$$

Example 9.4

Air at State Point 3 of Example 9.3 is cooled to 20°C.
(1) How much water is removed from the air?
(2) How much heat is removed?

Solution:
From Example 9.3, Point 3 is defined as: $t = 26.1$°C; $t_{dp} = 24.3$°C; $\phi = 90$%; and $h = 75.6$ kJ/kg. (These values are given in the table for the previous example.) Using Figure 9.01, we find $W=19.5$ g H$_2$O/kg DA.

From this point, the cooling process follows a horizontal line (constant W) to 100% relative humidity. Air is now at the dew point temperature (24.3°C). The process then follows the saturation ($\phi=100\%$) line to $t=t_{wb}=t_{dp}=20$°C. The enthalpy and humidity ratio at this point are 57.2 kJ/kg DA and 14.75 g H_2O/kg DA. Thus the answers are:

$$\Delta W = 19.5 - 14.75 = \underline{4.75 \text{ g } H_2O/\text{kg DA}} \qquad \text{ANSWER 1}$$

$$\dot{Q} = \Delta h = 75.1 - 57.2 = \underline{17.9 \text{ kJ/kg DA}} \qquad \text{ANSWER 2}$$

Example 9.5

If the exit flow rate for the air of Example 9.4 is 800 L/s, what are the rates of water and heat removal?

Solution:

At the exit conditions, $v = 0.85$ m^3/kg DA. Thus, the *mass* flow rate is:

$$\dot{m_a} = \frac{800\dfrac{L}{s}}{0.85\dfrac{m^3}{kg\,DA}\times 1000\dfrac{L}{m^3}} = 0.941\frac{kg\,DA}{s}$$

$$\Delta W = 4.75\frac{g\,H_2O}{kg\,DA}\times 0.941\frac{kg\,DA}{s} = \underline{4.47\frac{g\,H_2O}{s}} \qquad \text{ANSWER}$$

$$\dot{Q} = 17.9\frac{kJ}{kg\,DA}\times 0.941\frac{kg\,DA}{s} = 16.85\frac{kJ}{s} = \underline{16.85\,kW} \qquad \text{ANSWER}$$

Example 9.6

Air at 80°C and $\phi = 4\%$ (Point A) is mixed with air at 40°C and $\phi = 50\%$ (Point B). The ratio is 60% of air at 80°C to 40% at 40°C. What is the state point of the resulting mix (Point C)?

Solution:

We can use Equation 9.24 to find properties of the mixed air, but we must first use psychrometric charts to find the enthalpy and humidity ratios for Points A and B.

We must use the high temperature chart (Figure 9.03) for Point A. At $t = 80°C$ and $\phi = 4\%$, we find:

$$W_A = 12 \text{ g/kg DA} \qquad\qquad h_A = 115 \text{ kJ/kg DA}$$

For Point B, we may use either Figure 9.03 or 9.01; however, it is easier to read the property values from Figure 9.01. Using that figure, we find at $t = 40°C$ and $\phi = 50\%$:

$$W_B = 23.5 \text{ g/kg DA} \qquad\qquad h_B = 101 \text{ kJ/kg DA}$$

Air at properties of Point A represents 60% of the mix. Thus $\dfrac{m_{aA}}{m_{aC}} = 0.6$.

Using Equation 9.24, we can solve for h_c (or W_c) as $h_C = h_B + \dfrac{m_{aA}}{m_{aC}}\left(h_A - h_B\right)$

or:

$$h_C = 101 + 0.6\,(115 - 101) = 101 + 8.4 = \underline{109.4 \text{ kJ/kg DA}} \qquad \textbf{ANSWER}$$

$$W_C = 23.5 + 0.6\,(12 - 23.5) = 23.5 - 6.9 = \underline{16.6 \text{ g/kg DA}} \qquad \textbf{ANSWER}$$

Example 9.7

Air at 30°C and 60% relative humidity is cooled to 18°C.
(1) How much energy is removed from the air?
(2) Is any water removed? If so, how much?

Solution:
This process follows the path A–d–B shown on Chart III of Figure 9.04.
Initial conditions at point A from Figure 9.01 are:

$$t = 30°C \qquad\qquad W = 16 \text{ g/kg DA}$$
$$\phi = 60\% \qquad\qquad h = 70.8 \text{ KJ/kg DA}$$

As the air is cooled, the temperature drops until the air is saturated. At this point (Point d):

$$t = t_{wb} = t_{dp} = 21.3°C \qquad \text{and} \qquad \phi = 100\%$$

Continued cooling follows the saturation line to Point B where the properties are:

$$t = t_{wb} = t_{dp} = 18°C \qquad\qquad W = 13 \text{ g/kg DA}$$
$$\phi = 100\% \qquad\qquad h = 51 \text{ KJ/kg DA}$$

The energy removed from the air is: $\dot{Q} = h_A - h_B = 70.8 - 51 = \underline{19.8 \text{ KJ/kg DA}}$

Similarly, the water removed is: $\Delta W = W_A - W_B = 16 - 13 = \underline{3 \text{ g/kg DA}}$

ANSWERS

Example 9.8

Air at 50°C and a wet-bulb temperature of 30°C (Point A) is mixed with air at 24°C and 50% relative humidity (Point B) in proportions of 70% hot air and 30% cooler air. What are the properties of the air after mixing?

Solution:
The properties at Point C, the mixed air state point, can be computed using Equation 9.24.

Relevant properties at Points A and B are:

$$W_A = 18.7 \text{ g/kg DA} \qquad\qquad W_B = 9.3 \text{ g/kg DA}$$
$$h_A = 98.9 \text{ KJ/kg DA} \qquad\qquad h_B = 47.8 \text{ KJ/kg DA}$$

Solving Equation 9.24, noting that m_{aA} is 70% of the total mixture, m_{aC}, we have:

$$0.7 = \frac{h_C - 47.8}{98.9 - 47.8} \qquad \text{and} \qquad 0.7 = \frac{W_C - 9.3}{18.7 - 9.3}$$

and:

$$h_C = 0.7(98.9 - 47.8) + 47.8 \qquad W_C = 0.7(18.7 - 9.3) + 9.3$$

$$h_C = 83.6 \text{ KJ/kg DA} \qquad W_C = 15.9 \text{ g/kg DA}$$

Locating Point C from the values of h and W gives other property values as:

$$\phi_C = 30\% \qquad\qquad t = 42.4°C \qquad\qquad \textbf{ANSWER}$$

Example 9.9

Water is often cooled by evaporation into the air, using a cooling tower. Incoming hot water is sprayed into the air where a portion is evaporated, lowering the temperature of the remaining water by 10° to15°C. (Evaporation of 1 kg of water provides sufficient cooling to lower the temperature of approximately 56 kg of liquid water by 10°C.) Consider water entering a cooling tower at 40°C and leaving at 30°C. Air enters at 25°C with a relative humidity of 40% and exits at 34°C with 90% rh. For a water flow rate of 50 kg/s, and sufficient evaporation to meet the above conditions, determine the required air flow rate (kg/s) through the cooling tower.

Solution:
The solution of cooling tower problems consists of a combination of the evaporative cooling process on the psychrometric chart and an energy balance between air and water streams. The process describing the air humidification along

a constant wet-bulb line is needed to determine the enthalpy at the two state points. Read from psychrometric chart at 25°C dry bulb temperature and 40% rh, the enthalpy is 45.5 kJ/kg, and at 34°C and 90% rh the enthalpy is 113.5 kJ/kg. The energy lost by the cooling of water must equal energy gained by air. Thus:

$$\dot{m}_w\, c_{pw}\, \Delta t_w = \dot{m}_a\, \Delta h_a$$

$$\dot{m}_a = \dot{m}_w\, c_{pw}\, \frac{\Delta t_w}{\Delta h_a}$$

$$\dot{m}_a = 50\frac{kg}{s} \times 4.18\frac{kJ}{kg\,C}\left(\frac{(40-30)C}{(113.5-45.5)\frac{kJ}{kg}}\right)$$

$$\underline{\dot{m}_a = 30.7\frac{kg}{s}}\text{ of air}\qquad\qquad\textbf{ANSWER}$$

Note: This solution assumed a constant m_w, ignoring the approximately 2% of water that was evaporated. This approach greatly simplifies the solution and has little effect upon the computed air flow.

9.6 Ice-Water-Steam

Water in its three forms (solid, liquid, gas) is used extensively in food, agricultural, and other applications. The properties of water, in all three forms, make it well suited for many processing applications. In many applications we are concerned with the use of water in one or more of its forms for heating or cooling. To understand this use, we must first understand certain water properties that are relevant to these applications.

If ice at –20°C (or any other sub-freezing temperature) and atmospheric pressure is heated very slowly, its temperature would increase until the melting point (0°C, 32°F) is reached (Figure 9.05). It would then melt at that temperature. If additional heat is added after the ice is melted, the water temperature will increase until it reaches 100°C (212°F). At 100°C, the water will evaporate (boil) into gas (steam). Any further addition of heat will cause an increase in steam temperature. This process of heating and change of state is shown in Figure 9.05. The comparative energy requirements for heating (average specific heats) and change of state (latent heats) are also shown.

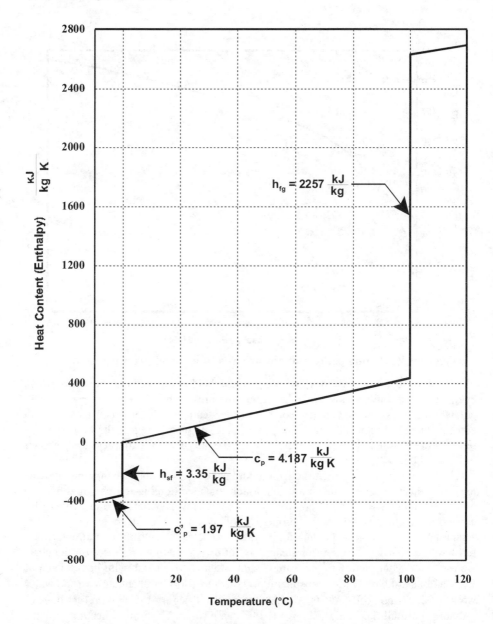

Figure 9.05. Heat content (enthalpy) of water at a pressure of one atmosphere as a function of temperature and state (solid, liquid, or gas).

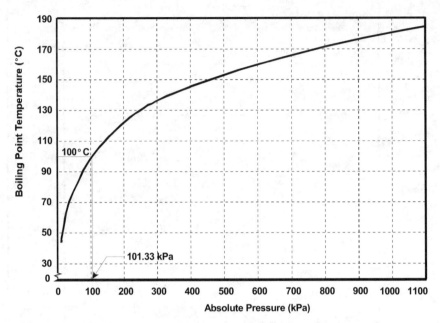

Figure 9.06. Boiling point temperature as a function of pressure for water.

The above example assumes that the water is held at atmospheric pressure. However, steam is usually produced and used at pressures higher than atmospheric. Thus, temperature, pressure, and energy content of the steam are all important factors to be considered. A key consideration here is the effect of pressure upon the boiling point temperature of water. This change in the boiling point of water with pressure is shown in Figure 9.06.

The energy required to melt the ice (latent heat of fusion) and to evaporate the water (latent heat of vaporization) are important considerations in the use of water for processing and environmental control applications. However, in this unit, we will be concerned exclusively with the properties of steam—either as pure steam ("dry steam") or a mixture of steam and liquid water droplets ("wet steam"). Figure 9.07 is a temperature enthalpy diagram for steam. By following heating processes on the chart we can get a better picture of the water-steam system. If we begin with liquid water at 25°C and heat it slowly (at atmospheric pressure) to 100°C, the enthalpy of the water would follow line A–B. At 100°C, the water would begin to evaporate (at constant pressure) until all the liquid is converted to steam (point C). Further heating will superheat the steam (line C–D). Similarly, heating water at a higher pressure of 600 kPa would produce line A–B–H–I–J. The curved dome containing points A, B, H, X, I and C is commonly called the **vapor dome**. To the left of the dome, liquid water is present. To the right of the dome is superheated (dry) steam. The curved line forming the left half of the dome represents saturated liquid; that on the right represents saturated vapor. Between these two lines is "wet" steam progressing from all liquid on the left to all vapor on the right. Note that above point X, there is no distinct change from liquid to gas. Point X is the critical point (22 120 kPa, 374.15°C). Above the critical point, the change from liquid to gas is gradual and cannot be identified as occurring at a specific point.

> Note: Strictly speaking, we do not follow the saturated liquid line during the heating process described above. The saturation line represents values of enthalpy at saturated temperature and pressure. The pressures along that saturation line and below Points B and H are less than 101.3 kPa and 600 kPa, respectively; and we are applying heat at a constant pressure of 101.3 or 600 kPa, respectively. However, the effect of pressure upon enthalpy is small. On the graph shown, we would be unable to detect any deviation from the saturated liquid line.

Beneath the vapor dome, a line of constant temperature is also a line of constant pressure. Thus, if either property is specified, the other is also known. In the superheat areas, this is not true. Both temperature and pressure must be specified to identify a specific state point in the superheated region. Figure 9.07 presents a good visual image of the pressure, temperature, enthalpy relationships. However, accurate values of these properties cannot be readily obtained from this figure. Tabulations of these properties, commonly called **steam tables**, are used to obtain accurate property values.

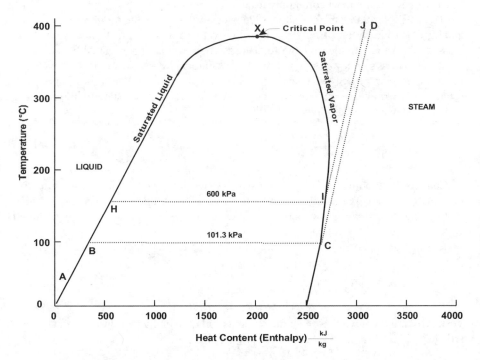

Figure 9.07. Temperature-Enthalpy diagram for water. The curve A–B–H–X–I–C is called a vapor dome. The region beneath the vapor dome represents a condition of wet steam.

9.7 Steam Tables

Tables 9.02, 9.03, and 9.04 are the three types of steam tables normally used. The first two tables show properties as a function of temperature (Table 9.02) and pressure (Table 9.03). Both tables give the same type of information; thus, the table to be used depends upon the known property (temperature or pressure). These tables represent conditions within the vapor dome. Table 9.04 gives properties for superheated steam. The choice of which table to use depends upon the conditions given. Any given combination of temperature and pressure may represent either wet steam (Tables 9.02 or 9.03) or superheated steam (Table 9.04). It may be necessary to look at each table before you find the correct state point. However, a notation that the steam is saturated or statement of a value for steam quality (see below) reveals that the wet steam tables (Table 9.02 or 9.03) should be used. For all tables, the properties of interest are temperature (t), pressure (P), enthalpy (h), and specific volume (v). Entropy (s) is an additional property often used in steam calculations. The commonly used subscripts are f for fluid properties, g for gaseous properties, and fg for the difference between fluid and gaseous properties. Use of the superheated steam tables is simply a matter of finding the appropriate state point given any two of the properties p, t, v, h, or s. Temperature and pressure are most commonly used.

To use Tables 9.02 and 9.03, it is often necessary to know the **quality** of the steam. Quality is an indication of how much of the wet steam is vapor. It is defined as the mass of the vapor divided by the total mass (liquid plus vapor). Quality is usually identified by the symbol x. At $x = 0$, we have saturated liquid. At $x = 1$, we have saturated vapor. For x between 0 and 1, we have a mixture of liquid and vapor (wet steam). If we know the enthalpy or specific volume for a given state point under the vapor dome, we can determine the quality, x:

$$x = \frac{v - v_f}{v_{fg}} \qquad \text{or} \qquad x = \frac{h - h_f}{h_{fg}} \qquad (9.26)$$

Conversely, the quality (x) can be used to determine the enthalpy or specific volume of wet steam. We shall make all calculations based upon a unit mass of water. Noting that the enthalpy of evaporated water (steam) is h_g and the enthalpy of liquid water is h_f, we find the enthalpy as follows:

1. Saturated steam ($x = 1$) (since we have only saturated vapor, the enthalpy is h_g):

$$h = x\,h_g = 1\,h_g = h_g$$

2. Saturated liquid ($x = 0$):

$$h = (1 - x)\,h_f = (1 - 0)\,h_f = h_f$$

3. Mixture (here we must take the amounts of liquid and vapor into account):

$$h = h_{liquid} + h_{vapor} = x\,h_g + (1 - x)\,h_f = x\,(h_g - h_f) + h_f$$

$$h = x\,h_{fg} + h_f = h_f + x\,h_{fg} \qquad (9.27)$$

The above example was for enthalpy. For specific volume, the same rule applies, e.g.:

$$v = x\,(v_g - v_f) + v_f = x\,v_{fg} + v_f = v_f + x\,v_{fg} \qquad (9.28)$$

Example 9.10

Find the enthalpy, specific volume, and pressure for steam at 175°C and a quality of 0.5. Locate the approximate position of this state point on Figure 9.07.

Solution:
We know the pressure and, with a quality of 0.5, we know that the steam is "wet." Thus, we choose Table 9.02, the table for wet steam properties as a function of temperature.

From the table, at 175°C, $P = \underline{892.4 \text{ kPa}}$ **ANSWER**

$v_f = 0.0011209 \text{ m}^3/\text{kg}$ $v_{fg} = 0.21542 \text{ m}^3/\text{kg}$

$h_f = 741.07 \text{ kJ/kg}$ $h_{fg} = 2030.7 \text{ kJ/kg}$

Solving for v and h:

$v = v_f + x\, v_{fg} = 0.0011209 + 0.5\,(0.21542) = \underline{0.1088 \text{ m}^3/\text{kg}}$ **ANSWER**

$h = h_f + x\, h_{fg} = 741.07 + 0.5\,(2030.7) = \underline{1756.4 \text{ kJ/kg}}$ **ANSWER**

At 175°C and an enthalpy of 1756.4 kJ/kg, the approximate state point location on Figure 9.07 is near the letter "P" of 600 kPa along line H–I.   **ANSWER**

Example 9.11

Find the temperature and enthalpy of steam at 300 kPa and 0.6506 m³/kg. Locate the approximate position of the state point on Figure 9.07.

Solution:
From Table 9.03 at 300 kPa, we see that $v_g = 0.6056 \text{ m}^3/\text{kg}$. v_g is the volume of saturated vapor at the given pressure. This value of $v_g = 0.6056$ is less than the specific volume given (0.6506). Since the specific volume of the steam is greater than that of saturated vapor, the steam must be superheated.

Using Table 9.04, at 300 kPa and the specific volume given, we find:

$t = 160°C$ $h = \underline{2781.8 \text{ kJ/kg}}$ **ANSWER**

For 160°C, 300 kPa, and 2781.8 kJ/kg, the state point location on Figure 9.07 is below, and to the right of Point I, between lines I–J and C–D.   **ANSWER**

Note: (1) If the value of v had not been given exactly in Table 9.04, it would have been necessary for us to interpolate between values in the table.

(2) If the value of v had been less than $v_g = 0.6056$, this would indicate that we have wet steam and we would have used Table 9.03 to find t (at 300 kPa), solve for the quality (x), and compute the enthalpy (h).

9.8 Steam -Air Mixtures

In this unit, we have examined systems involving steam (100% water vapor) and typical air and water vapor mixtures (low levels of water vapor.) We will now examine steam-air mixtures involving high water vapor concentrations. The issue of steam air mixtures in food processing is important because the temperature of a mixture of air and steam at any pressure is lower than the temperature of pure steam at the same pressure. Thus, the first step in batch processing with a retort, home canner, or pressure cooker is to vent until a steady stream of steam is produced. Failure to vent and purge the container of air will result in a mixture of air and water vapor, causing lower processing temperatures and, possibly, inadequate sterilization.

Our examination will make the simplifying assumption that ideal gas relationships apply. While not necessarily valid for all conditions, this assumption is a good approximation; and it will allow us to view the effect of increasing amounts of air in a steam environment. The trends we see will be valid even though the numeric values we calculate may differ slightly from the correct values.

Equations 9.05, 9.07, and 9.08 relate total and partial pressures, respectively, to the number of moles of gas present, the temperature, and the total volume. Using this relationship, we can solve for the partial pressure of water vapor in a steam-air mixture. We note that this mixture will be at a uniform temperature and that it occupies a fixed volume. Applying the above referenced equations, we find:

$$\frac{P_a}{P} = \frac{N_a R_u T / V}{N R_u T / V} = \frac{N_a}{N} = y_a \qquad \left(y_a = \text{mole fraction of air}\right) \qquad (9.29)$$

or
$$P_a = y_a P \qquad (9.30)$$

Using the above information we can solve for the partial pressure of water vapor (steam) at any mass ratio of water vapor. First, we note that the molecular weights of air and water are 28.96 and 18.015, respectively. We need these values to calculate the moles of air and water present in a given mixture.

If we assume a mixture of unit mass, at 200 kPa, containing a mass ratio of 0.2 air (20% air, by mass), we can compute P_w by the following steps.

The moles of air and water are:

$$N_a = \frac{m_a}{M_a} = \frac{0.2}{28.96} = 0.00690 \qquad \text{and} \qquad N_w = \frac{m_w}{M_w} = \frac{0.8}{18.015} = 0.04441$$

This results in a total of 0.05131 moles (0.00690 + 0.04441) in the system. The mole fractions of air and water in the system are then:

$$y_w = \frac{N_w}{N_t} = \frac{0.04441}{0.05131} = 0.8655 \qquad \text{and} \qquad y_a = \frac{N_a}{N_t} = \frac{0.0069}{0.5131} = 0.1345$$

The partial pressure of water vapor (steam) for this mixture is then:

$$P_w = y_w \times P_t = 0.8655 \times 200 = 173.1 \, \text{kPa}$$

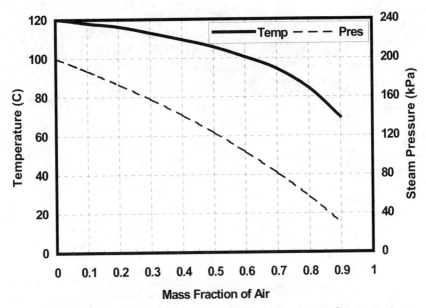

Figure 9.08. Effect of air upon steam partial pressure and temperature in steam-air mixtures at 200 kPa total pressure.

From the steam tables, the boiling points at 200 kPa and 173.1 kPa are 121.23°C and 115.6°C, respectively. Thus, the result of mixing air and steam in a ratio of 2 : 8 by mass results in almost a 6°C drop in the boiling point temperature at a total pressure of 200 kPa. This temperature drop could significantly affect a thermal processing operation. While a steam-air mixture containing 20% air is probably extreme, this does illustrate the effect of air in the mixture. Figure 9.08 shows the effect of differing air-steam mixtures (at 200 kPa) upon the steam partial pressure and boiling point temperature.

Example 9.12

We will consider the effect of failure to vent by examining the use (or misuse) of a home canner. A typical home canner is approximately 320 mm in diameter and 270 mm deep with a slightly domed lid. Figure 9.09 shows a cross-section representing a typical home canner containing several cans.

The typical operating procedure is to add hot water to a depth of about 25 mm, insert the cans to be processed, install the lid, heat, vent until continuous pure steam is observed, seal, and process for the required time. We will assume the following conditions for our example:

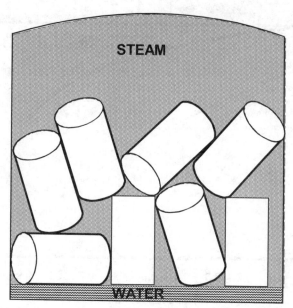

Figure 9.09. Sketch of home canner showing approximate proportions of water and steam.

- canner volume $(V_t) = 21.7$ L $= 0.0217$ m^3
- water volume $(V_w) = 2.0$ L $= 0.0020$ m^3 (for a depth of about 25 mm)
- three cans with a total volume $(V_c) = 2.8$ L $= 0.0028$ m^3
- initial temperature of all components $(t_i) = 25°C$
- processing pressure $(P_r) = 200$ kPa ("retort" processing pressure)
- canner immediately sealed without venting and heated until the pressure reaches 200 kPa

(Except for the initial temperatures and the small number of cans, all values above are realistic. In actual conditions, the water and can temperatures would probably be well above 25°C. However, we will make this assumption to simplify the problem.)

If the canner had been properly vented to insure pure steam inside, the inside temperature would be 120.2°C at 200 kPa. What is the temperature without the venting?

Solution:
We must first determine the mass and mole fractions of water and air in the container.

Water: From Table 9.05 at 25°C, we find $\rho_w = 997.1$ kg/m^3. Thus:

$$m_w = \rho_w \times V_w = 997.1 \frac{\text{kg}}{\text{m}^3} \times 0.002 \text{ m}^3 = 1.9942 \text{ kg}$$

Air: From Table 9.01 at 25°C, $v_a = 0.8444$ m³/kg, thus $\rho_a = 1.184$ kg/m³

(We could also determine v_a, but with less precision, from Figure 9.01 at 25°C and $W = 0$.) The volume of air in the canner (V_a) is that space not occupied by the cans or the water:

$$V_a = V_t - V_w - V_c = 21.7 - 2 - 2.8 = 16.9 \text{ L} = 0.0169 \text{ m}^3$$

$$m_a = \rho_a V_a = 1.184 \frac{\text{kg}}{\text{m}^3} \times 0.0169 \text{ m}^3 = 0.020014 \text{ kg}$$

We can now determine the number of moles of water and air present:

$$N_a = \frac{m_a}{M_a} = \frac{0.20014}{28.96} = 0.0006911 \quad \text{and} \quad N_w = \frac{m_w}{M_w} = \frac{1.9942}{18.015} = 0.1107$$

and

$$N_t = N_a + N_w = 0.0006911 + 0.1107 = 0.1114 \text{ Moles}$$

The mole fraction of water vapor and the resulting partial pressure of water vapor are:

$$y_w = \frac{N_w}{N_t} = \frac{0.1107}{0.1114} = 0.9938 \quad \text{and} \quad P_w = y_w P_w = 0.9938 \times 200 = 198.76 \text{ kPa}$$

Interpolating from Table 9.03, the temperature corresponding to a pressure of 198.76 kPa is 120.02°C. This is approximately 0.2° below the value for pure steam at 200 kPa (120.23°C). A difference of only 0.2° seems small; however, at the high temperatures used for processing, it can affect the required processing time. Thus, venting is important to insure that processing conditions are known.

Table 9.02. Properties of saturated steam and saturated water (temperature).
Computed using ASME software accompanying ASME Steam Tables (ASME, 1993).

Temperature		Pressure	Volume (m³/kg)			Enthalpy (kJ/kg)			Entropy (kJ/kg K)		
(°C)	(K)	(kPa)	Water	Evap.	Steam	Water	Evap.	Steam	Water	Evap.	Steam
t	T	p	v_f	v_{fg}	v_g	h_f	h_{fg}	h_g	s_f	s_{fg}	s_g
100.0	373.15	101.33	0.0010437	1.6720	1.6730	419.06	2256.9	2676.0	1.3069	6.0485	7.3554
105.0	378.15	120.80	0.0010477	1.4182	1.4193	440.17	2243.6	2683.7	1.3630	5.9332	7.2962
110.0	383.15	143.27	0.0010519	1.2089	1.2099	461.32	2230.0	2691.3	1.4185	5.8203	7.2388
115.0	388.15	169.06	0.0010562	1.0352	1.0363	482.50	2216.2	2698.7	1.4733	5.7099	7.1832
120.0	393.15	198.54	0.0010606	0.8905	0.8915	503.72	2202.2	2706.0	1.5276	5.6017	7.1293
125.0	398.15	232.1	0.0010652	0.7692	0.7702	524.99	2188.0	2713.0	1.5813	5.4957	7.0769
130.0	403.15	270.1	0.0010700	0.6671	0.6681	546.31	2173.6	2719.9	1.6344	5.3917	7.0261
135.0	408.15	313.1	0.0010750	0.5807	0.5818	567.68	2158.9	2726.6	1.6869	5.2897	6.9766
140.0	413.15	361.4	0.0010801	0.5074	0.5085	589.10	2144.0	2733.1	1.7390	5.1895	6.9284
145.0	418.15	415.5	0.0010853	0.4449	0.4460	610.59	2128.7	2739.3	1.7906	5.0910	6.8815
150.0	423.15	476.0	0.0010908	0.3914	0.3924	632.15	2113.2	2745.4	1.8416	4.9941	6.8358
155.0	428.15	543.3	0.0010964	0.3453	0.3464	653.77	2097.4	2751.2	1.8923	4.8989	6.7911
160.0	433.15	618.1	0.0011022	0.3057	0.3068	675.47	2081.3	2756.7	1.9425	4.8050	6.7475
165.0	438.15	700.8	0.0011082	0.2713	0.2724	697.25	2064.8	2762.0	1.9923	4.7126	6.7048
170.0	443.15	792.0	0.0011145	0.2414	0.2426	719.12	2047.9	2767.1	2.0416	4.6214	6.6630
175.0	448.15	892.4	0.0011209	0.21542	0.21654	741.07	2030.7	2771.8	2.0906	4.5314	6.6221
180.0	453.15	1002.7	0.0011275	0.19267	0.19380	763.12	2013.2	2776.3	2.1393	4.4426	6.5819
185.0	458.15	1123.3	0.0011344	0.17272	0.17386	785.26	1995.2	2780.4	2.1876	4.3548	6.5424
190.0	463.15	1255.1	0.0011415	0.15517	0.15632	807.52	1976.7	2784.3	2.2356	4.2680	6.5036
195.0	468.15	1398.7	0.0011489	0.13969	0.14084	829.88	1957.9	2787.8	2.2833	4.1822	6.4654
200.0	473.15	1554.9	0.0011565	0.12600	0.12716	852.37	1938.6	2790.9	2.3307	4.0971	6.4278
205.0	478.15	1724.3	0.0011644	0.11386	0.11503	874.99	1918.8	2793.8	2.3778	4.0128	6.3906
210.0	483.15	1907.7	0.0011726	0.10307	0.10424	897.73	1898.5	2796.2	2.4247	3.9293	6.3539
215.0	488.15	2106.0	0.0011811	0.09344	0.09463	920.63	1877.6	2798.3	2.4713	3.8463	6.3177
220.0	493.15	2319.8	0.0011900	0.08485	0.08604	943.67	1856.2	2799.9	2.5178	3.7639	6.2817
225.0	498.15	2550.	0.0011992	0.07715	0.07835	966.88	1834.3	2801.2	2.5641	3.6820	6.2461
230.0	503.15	2798.	0.0012087	0.07024	0.07145	990.27	1811.7	2802.0	2.6102	3.6006	6.2107
235.0	508.15	3063.	0.0012187	0.06403	0.06525	1013.83	1788.5	2802.3	2.6561	3.5195	6.1756
240.0	513.15	3348.	0.0012291	0.05843	0.05965	1037.60	1764.6	2802.2	2.7020	3.4386	6.1406
245.0	518.15	3652.	0.0012399	0.05337	0.05461	1061.58	1740.0	2801.6	2.7478	3.3579	6.1057

Temperature (°C) t	(K) T	Pressure (kPa) p	Volume (m³/kg) Water v_f	Evap. v_{fg}	Steam v_g	Enthalpy (kJ/kg) Water h_f	Evap. h_{fg}	Steam h_g	Entropy (kJ/kg K) Water s_f	Evap. s_{fg}	Steam s_g
250.0	523.15	3978.	0.0012513	0.04879	0.05004	1085.78	1714.7	2800.4	2.7935	3.2774	6.0708
255.0	528.15	4325.	0.0012632	0.04463	0.04590	1110.23	1688.5	2798.7	2.8392	3.1968	6.0359
260.0	533.15	4694.	0.0012756	0.04086	0.04213	1134.94	1661.5	2796.4	2.8849	3.1161	6.0010
265.0	538.15	5088.	0.0012887	0.03742	0.03871	1159.93	1633.5	2793.5	2.9306	3.0353	5.9658
270.0	543.15	5506.	0.0013025	0.03429	0.03559	1185.23	1604.6	2789.9	2.9764	2.9541	5.9305
275.0	548.15	5950.	0.0013170	0.03142	0.03274	1210.86	1574.7	2785.5	3.0223	2.8725	5.8947
280.0	553.15	6420.	0.0013324	0.02879	0.03013	1236.84	1543.6	2780.4	3.0683	2.7903	5.8586
285.0	558.15	6919.	0.0013487	0.02638	0.02773	1263.21	1511.3	2774.5	3.1146	2.7074	5.8220
290.0	563.15	7446.	0.0013659	0.02417	0.02554	1290.01	1477.6	2767.6	3.1611	2.6237	5.7848
295.0	568.15	8004.	0.0013844	0.02213	0.02351	1317.27	1442.6	2759.8	3.2079	2.5389	5.7469
300.0	573.15	8593.	0.0014041	0.020245	0.021649	1345.05	1406.0	2751.0	3.2552	2.4530	5.7081
305.0	578.15	9214.	0.0014252	0.018502	0.019927	1373.40	1367.7	2741.1	3.3029	2.3656	5.6685
310.0	583.15	9870.	0.0014480	0.016886	0.018334	1402.39	1327.6	2730.0	3.3512	2.2766	5.6278
315.0	588.15	10561.	0.0014726	0.015383	0.016856	1432.09	1285.5	2717.6	3.4002	2.1856	5.5858
320.0	593.15	11289.	0.0014995	0.013980	0.015480	1462.60	1241.1	2703.7	3.4500	2.0923	5.5423
325.0	598.15	12056.	0.0015289	0.012666	0.014195	1494.03	1194.0	2688.0	3.5008	1.9961	5.4969
330.0	603.15	12863.	0.0015615	0.011428	0.012989	1526.52	1143.6	2670.2	3.5528	1.8962	5.4490
335.0	608.15	13712.	0.0015978	0.010256	0.011854	1560.25	1089.5	2649.7	3.6063	1.7916	5.3979
340.0	613.15	14605.	0.0016387	0.009142	0.010780	1595.47	1030.7	2626.2	3.6616	1.6811	5.3427
345.0	618.15	15545.	0.0016858	0.008077	0.009763	1632.52	966.4	2598.9	3.7193	1.5636	5.2828
350.0	623.15	16535.	0.0017411	0.007058	0.008799	1671.94	895.7	2567.7	3.7800	1.4376	5.2177
355.0	628.15	17577.	0.0018085	0.006051	0.007859	1716.63	813.8	2530.4	3.8489	1.2953	5.1442
360.0	633.15	18675.	0.0018959	0.005044	0.006940	1764.17	721.3	2485.4	3.9210	1.1390	5.0600
365.0	638.15	19833.	0.0020160	0.003996	0.006012	1817.96	610.0	2428.0	4.0021	0.9579	4.9579
370.0	643.15	21054.	0.0022136	0.002759	0.004973	1890.21	452.6	2342.8	4.1108	0.7036	4.8144
371.0	644.15	21306.	0.0022778	0.002446	0.004723	1910.50	407.4	2317.9	4.1414	0.6324	4.7738
372.0	645.15	21562.	0.0023636	0.002075	0.004439	1935.57	351.4	2287.0	4.1794	0.5446	4.7240
373.0	646.15	21820.	0.0024963	0.001588	0.004084	1970.50	273.5	2244.0	4.2326	0.4233	4.6559
374.0	647.15	22081.	0.0028427	0.000623	0.003466	2046.72	109.5	2156.2	4.3493	0.1692	4.5185
374.15	647.30	22120.	0.00317	0.0	0.00317	2107.37	0.0	2107.4	4.4429	0.0	4.4429

Table 9.03. Properties of saturated steam and saturated water (pressure).

Press. (kPa)	Temp. (°C)	Volume (m³/kg)			Enthalpy (kJ/kg)			Entropy (kJ/kg K)		
		Water	Evap.	Steam	Water	Evap.	Steam	Water	Evap.	Steam
p	t	v_f	v_{fg}	v_g	h_f	h_{fg}	h_g	s_f	s_{fg}	s_g
1.0	6.983	0.0010001	129.21	129.21	29.34	2485.0	2514.4	0.1060	8.8706	8.9767
10.0	45.833	0.0010102	14.674	14.675	191.83	2392.9	2584.8	0.6493	7.5018	8.1511
20.0	60.086	0.0010172	7.649	7.650	251.45	2358.4	2609.9	0.8321	7.0774	7.9094
100.0	99.632	0.0010434	1.6927	1.6937	417.51	2257.9	2675.4	1.3027	6.0571	7.3598
110.0	102.317	0.0010455	1.5482	1.5492	428.84	2250.8	2679.6	1.3330	5.9947	7.3277
120.0	104.808	0.0010476	1.4271	1.4281	439.36	2244.1	2683.4	1.3609	5.9375	7.2984
130.0	107.133	0.0010495	1.3240	1.3251	449.19	2237.8	2687.0	1.3868	5.8847	7.2715
140.0	109.315	0.0010513	1.2353	1.2363	458.42	2231.9	2690.3	1.4109	5.8356	7.2465
150.0	111.37	0.0010530	1.1580	1.1590	467.13	2226.2	2693.4	1.4336	5.7898	7.2234
160.0	113.32	0.0010547	1.0901	1.0911	475.38	2220.9	2696.2	1.4550	5.7467	7.2017
180.0	116.93	0.0010579	0.9762	0.9972	490.70	2210.8	2701.5	1.4944	5.6678	7.1622
200.0	120.23	0.0010608	0.8844	0.8854	504.70	2201.6	2706.3	1.5301	5.5967	7.1268
220.0	123.27	0.0010636	0.8088	0.8098	517.62	2193.0	2710.6	1.5627	5.5321	7.0949
240.0	126.09	0.0010663	0.7454	0.7465	529.6	2184.9	2714.5	1.5929	5.4728	7.0657
260.0	128.73	0.0010688	0.6914	0.6925	540.9	2177.3	2718.2	1.6209	5.4180	7.0389
280.0	131.20	0.0010712	0.6450	0.6460	551.4	2170.1	2721.5	1.6471	5.3670	7.0140
300.0	133.54	0.0010735	0.6045	0.6056	561.4	2163.2	2724.7	1.6716	5.3193	6.9909
350.0	138.87	0.0010789	0.5229	0.5240	584.3	2147.4	2731.6	1.7273	5.2119	6.9392
400.0	143.62	0.0010839	0.4611	0.4622	604.7	2133.0	2737.6	1.7764	5.1179	6.8943
450.0	147.92	0.0010885	0.4127	0.4138	623.2	2119.7	2742.9	1.8204	5.0343	6.8547
500.0	151.84	0.0010928	0.3736	0.3747	640.1	2107.4	2747.5	1.8604	4.9588	6.8192
550.0	155.47	0.0010969	0.3414	0.3425	655.8	2095.9	2751.7	1.8970	4.8900	6.7870
600.0	158.84	0.0011009	0.3144	0.3155	670.4	2085.0	2755.5	1.9308	4.8267	6.7575
650.0	161.99	0.0011046	0.29138	0.29249	684.1	2074.7	2758.9	1.9623	4.7681	6.7304
700.0	164.96	0.0011082	0.27157	0.27268	697.1	2064.9	2762.0	1.9918	4.7134	6.7052
750.0	167.76	0.0011116	0.25431	0.25543	709.3	2055.5	2764.8	2.0195	4.6621	6.6817
800.0	170.41	0.0011150	0.23914	0.24026	720.9	2046.5	2767.5	2.0457	4.6139	6.6596
900.0	175.36	0.0011213	0.21369	0.21481	742.6	2029.5	2772.1	2.0941	4.5250	6.6192
1000.	179.88	0.0011274	0.19317	0.19429	762.6	2013.6	2776.2	2.1382	4.4446	6.5828
1100.	184.07	0.0011331	0.17625	0.17738	781.1	1998.5	2779.7	2.1786	4.3711	6.5497
1200.	187.96	0.0011380	0.16206	0.16320	798.4	1984.3	2782.7	2.2161	4.3033	6.5194
1300.	191.61	0.0011438	0.14998	0.15113	814.7	1970.7	2785.4	2.2510	4.2403	6.4913
1400.	195.04	0.0011489	0.13957	0.14072	830.1	1957.7	2787.8	2.2837	4.1814	6.4651

Press. (kPa) p	Temp. (°C) t	Volume (m³/kg)			Enthalpy (kJ/kg)			Entropy (kJ/kg K)		
		Water v_f	Evap. v_{fg}	Steam v_g	Water h_f	Evap. h_{fg}	Steam h_g	Water s_f	Evap. s_{fg}	Steam s_g
1500.	198.29	0.0011539	0.13050	0.13166	844.7	1945.2	2789.9	2.3145	4.1261	6.4406
1600.	201.37	0.0011586	0.12253	0.12369	858.6	1933.2	2791.7	2.3436	4.0739	6.4175
1800.	207.11	0.0011678	0.10915	0.11032	884.6	1910.3	2794.8	2.3976	3.9775	6.3751
2000.	212.37	0.0011766	0.09836	0.09954	908.6	1888.6	2797.2	2.4469	3.8898	6.3367
2200.	217.24	0.0011850	0.08947	0.09065	931.0	1868.1	2799.1	2.4922	3.8093	6.3015
2400.	221.78	0.0011932	0.08201	0.08320	951.9	1848.5	2800.4	2.5343	3.7347	6.2690
2600.	226.04	0.0012011	0.07565	0.07686	971.7	1829.6	2801.4	2.5736	3.6651	6.2387
2800.	230.05	0.0012088	0.07018	0.07139	990.5	1811.5	2802.0	2.6106	3.5998	6.2104
3000.	233.84	0.0012163	0.06541	0.06663	1008.4	1793.9	2802.3	2.6455	3.5382	6.1837
3500.	242.54	0.0012345	0.05579	0.05703	1049.8	1752.2	2802.0	2.7253	3.3976	6.1228
4000.	250.33	0.0012521	0.04850	0.04975	1087.4	1712.9	2800.3	2.7965	3.2720	6.0685
4500.	257.41	0.0012691	0.04277	0.04404	1122.1	1675.6	2797.7	2.8612	3.1579	6.0191
5000.	263.91	0.0012858	0.03814	0.03943	1154.5	1639.7	2794.2	2.9206	3.0529	5.9735
5500.	269.93	0.0013023	0.03433	0.03563	1184.9	1605.0	2789.9	2.9757	2.9552	5.9309
6000.	275.55	0.0013187	0.03112	0.03244	1213.7	1571.3	2785.0	3.0273	2.8635	5.8908
6500.	280.82	0.0013350	0.028384	0.029719	1241.1	1538.4	2779.5	3.0759	2.7768	5.8527
7000.	285.79	0.0013513	0.026022	0.027373	1267.4	1506.0	2773.5	3.1219	2.6943	5.8162
7500.	290.50	0.0013677	0.023959	0.025327	1292.7	1474.2	2766.9	3.1657	2.6153	5.7811
8000.	294.97	0.0013842	0.022141	0.023525	1317.1	1442.8	2759.9	3.2076	2.5395	5.7471
9000.	303.31	0.0014179	0.019078	0.020495	1363.7	1380.9	2744.6	3.2867	2.3953	5.6820
10000.	310.96	0.0014526	0.016589	0.018041	1408.0	1319.7	2727.7	3.3605	2.2593	5.6198
11000.	318.05	0.0014887	0.014517	0.016006	1450.6	1258.7	2709.3	3.4304	2.1291	5.5595
12000.	324.65	0.0015268	0.012756	0.014283	1491.8	1197.4	2689.2	3.4972	2.0030	5.5002
13000.	330.83	0.0015672	0.011230	0.012797	1532.0	1135.0	2667.0	3.5616	1.8792	5.4408
14000.	336.64	0.0016106	0.009884	0.011495	1571.6	1070.7	2642.4	3.6242	1.7560	5.3803
15000.	342.13	0.0016579	0.008682	0.010340	1611.0	1004.0	2615.0	3.6859	1.6320	5.3178
16000.	347.33	0.0017103	0.007597	0.009308	1650.5	934.3	2584.9	3.7471	1.5060	5.2531
17000.	352.26	0.0017696	0.006601	0.008371	1691.7	859.9	2551.6	3.8107	1.3748	5.1855
18000.	356.96	0.0018399	0.005658	0.007498	1734.8	779.1	2513.9	3.8765	1.2362	5.1128
19000.	361.43	0.0019260	0.004751	0.006678	1778.7	692.0	2470.6	3.9429	1.0903	5.0332
20000.	365.70	0.0020370	0.003840	0.005877	1826.5	591.9	2418.4	4.0149	0.9263	4.9412
21000	369.78	0.0022015	0.002822	0.005023	1886.3	461.3	2347.6	4.1048	0.7175	4.8223
22000.	373.69	0.0026714	0.001056	0.003728	2011.1	184.5	2195.6	4.2947	0.2852	4.5799
22120.	374.15	0.00317	0.0	0.00317	2107.4	0.0	2107.4	4.4429	0.0	4.4429

Table 9.04. Properties of superheated steam (temperature and pressure).
Computed using ASME software accompanying ASME Steam Tables (ASME, 1993).

Pressure p (kPa)		60	80	100	120	140	160	180	200	220
						Temperature, t (°C)				
1.0	v	153.71	162.95	172.19	181.42	190.66	199.89	209.12	218.35	227.58
	h	2613.3	2650.9	2688.6	2726.5	2764.6	2802.9	2841.4	2880.1	2919.0
	s	9.3001	9.4096	9.5136	9.6125	9.7070	9.7975	9.8843	9.9679	10.048
5.0	v	30.711	32.565	34.417	36.267	38.117	39.966	41.814	43.662	45.509
	h	2612.6	2650.3	2688.1	2726.1	2764.3	2802.6	2841.2	2879.9	2918.8
	s	8.5555	8.6655	8.7698	8.8690	8.9636	9.0542	9.1412	9.2248	9.3054
10.0	v	15.336	16.266	17.195	18.123	19.050	19.975	20.900	21.825	22.750
	h	2611.6	2649.5	2687.5	2725.6	2763.9	2802.3	2840.9	2879.6	2918.6
	s	8.2334	8.3439	8.4486	8.5481	8.6430	8.7338	8.8208	8.9045	8.9852
20.0	v		8.1172	8.5847	9.0508	9.516	9.980	10.444	10.907	11.370
	h		2648.0	2686.3	2724.6	2763.1	2801.6	2840.3	2879.2	2918.2
	s		8.0206	8.1261	8.2262	8.3215	8.4127	8.5000	8.5839	8.6647
40.0	v		4.0424	4.2792	4.5146	4.7489	4.9825	5.2154	5.4478	5.6800
	h		2644.9	2683.8	2722.6	2761.4	2800.3	2839.2	2878.2	2917.4
	s		7.6937	7.8009	7.9023	7.9985	8.0903	8.1782	8.2625	8.3435
60.0	v			2.8440	3.0025	3.1599	3.3166	3.4726	3.6281	3.7833
	h			2681.3	2720.6	2759.8	2798.9	2838.1	2877.3	2916.6
	s			7.6085	7.7111	7.8083	7.9008	7.9891	8.0738	8.1552
80.0	v			2.1262	2.2464	2.3654	2.4836	2.6011	2.7183	2.8350
	h			2678.8	2718.6	2758.1	2797.6	2836.9	2876.3	2915.8
	s			7.4703	7.5742	7.6723	7.7655	7.8544	7.9395	8.0212
100.0	v			1.6955	1.7927	1.8886	1.9838	2.0783	2.1723	2.2660
	h			2676.2	2716.5	2756.4	2796.2	2835.8	2875.4	2915.0
	s			7.3618	7.4670	7.5662	7.6601	7.7495	7.8350	7.9169
150.0	v				1.1876	1.2529	1.3173	1.3811	1.4444	1.5073
	h				2711.2	2752.2	2792.7	2832.9	2872.9	2912.9
	s				7.2693	7.3709	7.4667	7.5574	7.6439	7.7266

Pressure p (kPa)		\multicolumn{9}{c}{Temperature, t (°C)}
		60	80	100	120	140	160	180	200	220
200.0	v					0.9349	0.9840	1.0325	1.0804	1.1280
	h					2747.8	2789.1	2830.0	2870.5	2910.8
	s					7.2298	7.3275	7.4196	7.5072	7.5907
300.0	v					0.6167	0.6506	0.6837	0.7164	0.7486
	h					2738.8	2781.8	2824.0	2865.5	2906.6
	s					7.0254	7.1271	7.2222	7.3119	7.3971
400.0	v						0.4837	0.5093	0.5343	0.5589
	h						2774.2	2817.8	2860.4	2902.3
	s						6.9805	7.0788	7.1708	7.2576
500.0	v						0.3835	0.4045	0.4250	0.4450
	h						2766.4	2811.4	2855.1	2890.0
	s						6.8631	6.9647	7.0592	7.1478
600.0	v						0.3166	0.3346	0.3520	0.3690
	h						2758.2	2804.8	2849.7	2893.5
	s						6.7640	6.8691	6.9662	7.0567
800.0	v							0.2471	0.2608	0.2740
	h							2791.1	2838.6	2884.2
	s							6.7122	6.8148	6.9094
1000.0	v							0.1944	0.2059	0.2169
	h							2776.5	2826.8	2874.6
	s							6.5835	6.6922	6.7911
2000.0	v									0.1020
	h									2819.9
	s									6.3829
3000.0	v									
	h									
	s									
5000.0	v									
	h									
	s									

Pressure p (kPa)		Temperature, t (°C)								
		240.	260.	280.	300.	400.	500.	600.	700.	800.
1.0	v	236.82	246.05	255.28	264.51	310.66	356.81	402.97	449.12	495.27
	h	2958.1	2997.4	3037.0	3076.8	3279.7	3489.2	3705.6	3928.9	4158.7
	s	10.1262	10.2014	10.2743	10.3450	10.671	10.961	11.2243	11.4663	11.6911
10.0	v	23.674	24.598	25.521	26.445	31.062	35.679	40.295	44.910	49.526
	h	2957.8	2997.2	3036.8	3076.6	3279.6	3489.1	3705.5	3928.8	4158.7
	s	9.0630	9.1383	9.2113	9.2820	9.6083	9.8984	10.1616	10.4036	10.6284
20.0	v	11.832	12.295	12.757	13.219	15.529	17.838	20.146	22.455	24.762
	h	2957.4	2996.9	3036.5	3076.4	3279.4	3489.0	3705.4	3928.7	4158.7
	s	8.7426	8.8180	8.8910	8.9618	9.2882	9.5784	9.8416	10.0836	10.3085
40.0	v	5.9118	6.1435	6.3751	6.6065	7.7625	8.9176	10.072	11.227	12.381
	h	2956.7	2996.3	3036.0	3075.9	3279.1	3488.8	3705.3	3928.6	4158.6
	s	8.4217	8.4973	8.5704	8.6413	8.9680	9.2583	9.5216	9.7636	9.9885
60.0	v	3.9383	4.0931	4.2477	4.4022	5.1736	5.9441	6.7141	7.4839	8.2535
	h	2956.0	2995.6	3035.4	3075.4	3278.8	3488.6	3705.1	3928.5	4158.5
	s	8.2336	8.3093	8.3826	8.4536	8.7806	9.0710	9.3343	9.5764	9.8013
80.0	v	2.9515	3.0678	3.1840	3.3000	3.8792	4.4574	5.0351	5.6126	6.1899
	h	2955.3	2995.0	3034.9	3075.0	3278.5	3488.4	3705.0	3928.4	4158.4
	s	8.0998	8.1757	8.2491	8.3202	8.6475	8.9380	9.2014	9.4436	9.6685
100.0	v	2.3595	2.4527	2.5458	2.6387	3.1025	3.5653	4.0277	4.4898	4.9517
	h	2954.6	2994.4	3034.4	3074.5	3278.2	3488.1	3704.8	3928.2	4158.3
	s	7.9958	8.0719	8.1454	8.2166	8.5442	8.8348	9.0982	9.3405	9.5654
150.0	v	1.5700	1.6325	1.6948	1.7570	2.0669	2.3759	2.6845	2.9927	3.3008
	h	2952.9	2992.9	3033.0	3073.3	3277.5	3487.6	3704.4	3927.9	4158.0
	s	7.8061	7.8826	7.9565	8.0280	8.3562	8.6472	8.9108	9.1531	9.3781
200.0	v	1.1753	1.2224	1.2693	1.3162	1.5492	1.7812	2.0129	2.2442	2.4754
	h	2951.1	2991.4	3031.7	3072.1	3276.7	3487.0	3704.0	3927.6	4157.8
	s	7.6707	7.7477	7.8219	7.8937	8.2226	8.5139	8.7776	9.0201	9.2452

Pressure p (kPa)		Temperature, t (°C)								
		240.	260.	280.	300.	400.	500.	600.	700.	800.
300.0	v	0.7805	0.8123	0.8438	0.8753	1.0314	1.1865	1.3412	1.4957	1.6499
	h	2947.5	2988.2	3028.9	3069.7	3275.2	3486.0	3703.2	3927.0	4157.3
	s	7.4783	7.5562	7.6311	7.7034	8.0338	8.3257	8.5898	8.8325	9.0577
400.0	v	0.5831	0.6072	0.6311	0.6549	0.7725	0.8892	1.0054	1.1214	1.2372
	h	2943.9	2985.1	3026.2	3067.2	3273.6	3484.9	3702.3	3926.4	4156.9
	s	7.3402	7.4190	7.4947	7.5675	7.8994	8.1919	8.4563	8.6992	8.9246
500.0	v	0.4647	0.4841	0.5034	0.5226	0.6172	0.7108	0.8039	.08968	0.9896
	h	2940.1	2981.9	3023.4	3064.8	3272.1	3483.8	3701.5	3925.8	4156.4
	s	7.2317	7.3115	7.3879	7.4614	7.7948	8.0879	8.3526	8.5957	8.8213
600.0	v	0.3857	0.4021	0.4183	0.4344	0.5136	0.5918	0.6696	0.7471	0.8245
	h	2936.4	2978.7	3020.6	3062.3	3270.6	3482.7	3700.7	3925.1	4155.9
	s	7.1419	7.2228	7.3000	7.3740	7.7090	8.0027	8.2678	8.5111	8.7368
800.0	v	0.2869	0.2995	0.3119	0.3241	0.3842	0.4432	0.5017	0.5600	0.6181
	h	2928.6	2972.1	3014.9	3057.3	3267.5	3480.5	3699.1	3923.9	4155.0
	s	6.9976	7.0807	7.1595	7.2348	7.5729	7.8678	8.1336	8.3773	8.6033
1000.0	v	0.2276	0.2739	0.2480	0.2580	0.3065	0.3540	0.4010	0.4477	0.4943
	h	2920.6	2965.2	3009.0	3052.1	3264.4	3478.3	3697.4	3922.7	4154.1
	s	6.8825	6.9680	7.0485	7.1251	7.4665	7.7627	8.0292	8.2734	8.4997
2000.0	v	0.1084	0.1144	0.1200	0.1255	0.1511	0.1756	0.1995	0.2232	0.2467
	h	2875.9	2928.1	2977.5	3025.0	3248.7	3467.3	3689.2	3916.5	4149.4
	s	6.4943	6.5941	6.6852	6.7696	7.1296	7.4323	7.7022	7.9485	8.1763
3000.0	v	0.0682	0.0728	0.0771	0.0812	0.0993	0.1161	0.1323	0.1483	0.1641
	h	2822.9	2885.1	2942.0	2995.1	3232.5	3456.2	3681.0	3910.3	4144.7
	s	6.2241	6.3432	6.4479	6.5422	6.9246	7.2345	7.5079	7.7564	7.9857
5000.0	v			0.0422	0.0453	0.0578	0.0685	0.0786	0.0884	0.0981
	h			2856.9	2925.5	3198.3	3433.7	3664.5	3897.9	4135.3
	s			6.0886	6.2105	6.6508	6.9770	7.2578	7.5108	7.7431
10000.0	v					0.0264	0.0328	0.0383	0.0436	0.0486
	h					3099.9	3374.6	3622.7	3866.8	4112.0
	s					6.2182	6.5994	6.9013	7.1660	7.4058

Table 9.05. Thermodynamic properties of water at the saturation pressure.[a]

Temperature (°C) t	(K) T	Density (kg/m³) ρ	Specific Heat (kJ/kg K) C_p	Thermal Conductivity (W/m K) k	Thermal Diffusivity (m²/s) α	Absolute Viscosity (N s/m²) μ	Kinematic Viscosity (m²/s) ν	Prandtl number Pr
0	273.15	999.9	4.226	0.558	0.131×10^{-6}	1.7936×10^{-3}	1.789×10^{-6}	13.7
5	278.15	1000.0	4.206	0.568	0.135×10^{-6}	1.5347×10^{-3}	1.535×10^{-6}	11.4
10	283.15	999.7	4.195	0.577	0.137×10^{-6}	1.2964×10^{-3}	1.300×10^{-6}	9.43
15	288.15	999.1	4.187	0.587	0.141×10^{-6}	1.1356×10^{-3}	1.146×10^{-6}	8.10
20	293.15	998.2	4.182	0.597	0.143×10^{-6}	0.9934×10^{-3}	1.006×10^{-6}	6.96
25	298.15	997.1	4.178	0.606	0.146×10^{-6}	0.8806×10^{-3}	0.884×10^{-6}	6.07
30	303.15	995.7	4.176	0.615	0.149×10^{-6}	0.7924×10^{-3}	0.805×10^{-6}	5.38
35	308.15	994.1	4.175	0.624	0.150×10^{-6}	0.7198×10^{-3}	0.725×10^{-6}	4.82
40	313.15	992.2	4.175	0.633	0.151×10^{-6}	0.6580×10^{-3}	0.658×10^{-6}	4.34
45	318.15	990.2	4.176	0.640	0.155×10^{-6}	0.6051×10^{-3}	0.611×10^{-6}	3.95
50	323.15	988.1	4.178	0.647	0.157×10^{-6}	0.5550×10^{-3}	0.556×10^{-6}	3.55
55	328.15	985.7	4.179	0.652	0.158×10^{-6}	0.5099×10^{-3}	0.517×10^{-6}	3.27
60	333.15	983.2	4.181	0.658	0.159×10^{-6}	0.4717×10^{-3}	0.478×10^{-6}	3.00
65	338.15	980.6	4.184	0.663	0.161×10^{-6}	0.4354×10^{-3}	0.444×10^{-6}	2.76
70	343.15	977.8	4.187	0.668	0.163×10^{-6}	0.4040×10^{-3}	0.415×10^{-6}	2.55
75	348.15	974.9	4.190	0.671	0.164×10^{-6}	0.3766×10^{-3}	0.366×10^{-6}	2.23
80	353.15	971.8	4.194	0.673	0.165×10^{-6}	0.3520×10^{-3}	0.364×10^{-6}	2.25
85	358.15	968.7	4.198	0.676	0.166×10^{-6}	0.3285×10^{-3}	0.339×10^{-6}	2.04
90	363.15	965.3	4.202	0.678	0.167×10^{-6}	0.3089×10^{-3}	0.326×10^{-6}	1.95
95	368.15	961.9	4.206	0.680	0.168×10^{-6}	0.2922×10^{-3}	0.310×10^{-6}	1.84
100	373.15	958.4	4.211	0.682	0.169×10^{-6}	0.2775×10^{-3}	0.294×10^{-6}	1.75
120	393.15	943.5	4.232	0.685	0.171×10^{-6}	0.2354×10^{-3}	0.244×10^{-6}	1.43
140	413.15	926.3	4.257	0.684	0.172×10^{-6}	0.2010×10^{-3}	0.212×10^{-6}	1.23
160	433.15	907.6	4.285	0.680	0.173×10^{-6}	0.1716×10^{-3}	0.191×10^{-6}	1.10
180	453.15	886.6	4.396	0.673	0.172×10^{-6}	0.1520×10^{-3}	0.173×10^{-6}	1.01
200	473.15	862.8	4.501	0.665	0.170×10^{-6}	0.1392×10^{-3}	0.160×10^{-6}	0.95

[a] Based upon data from Raznjevic (1976).

List of Symbols

c_p	specific heat capacity at constant pressure, J/(kg K) or kJ/(kg K)
h	enthalpy, kJ/kg
h_{as}	$(h_s - h_a)$, enthalpy difference between saturated and dry air, kJ/kg
h_f	enthalpy of saturated liquid, kJ/kg
h_{fg}	$(h_g - h_f)$, latent heat of vaporization, kJ/kg
h_g	enthalpy of saturated vapor, kJ/kg
Le	Lewis Number, dimensionless
m	mass, kg
M	molecular weight, kg/kmol
N	number of moles
P	pressure, Pa
R	gas constant for a particular gas, kPa m³/(kg K)
R_u	gas constant, universal, 8.314 kJ/(kmol K)
s	entropy, kJ/(kg K)
t	temperature, °C
T	absolute temperature, K
v	specific volume, m³/kg
V	volume, m³
W	humidity ratio, g H₂O/kg DA or kg H₂O/kg DA
x	steam quality, kg vapor/kg total
y	mole fraction
θ	time, s
μ	degree of saturation, dimensionless
ϕ	relative humidity, percent or decimal

Subscripts

1, 2	position identification
a	air (or dry air)
dp	dew point
f	fluid state
fg	difference between properties at fluid and gaseous states
g	gaseous state
rem	removed
s	steam, or saturated
t	total
w	water
wb	wet-bulb
ws	water at saturation

Superscript

*	a property at the thermodynamic wet-bulb temperature
as	saturated air

References

1. ASHRAE. 1977. ASHRAE Brochure on Psychrometry. ASHRAE, Atlanta, GA.
2. ASHRAE. 1997. *Handbook of Fundamentals*, Chapter 6: Psychrometrics. ASHRAE, Inc., Atlanta, GA.
3. ASME. 1993. *Steam Tables*. 6th ed. with software for calculating steam properties. ASME, New York, NY.
4. Cengel, Yunus A., and Michael A. Boles. 1989. *Thermodynamics: An Engineering Approach*. McGraw-Hill Book Company, New York, NY.
5. Raznjevic, Kuzman. 1976. *Handbook of Thermodynamic Tables and Charts*. Hemisphere Publishing Corp., Washington, DC.
6. Van Wylen, Gordon J., and Richard E. Sonntag. 1986. *Fundamentals of Classical Thermodynamics*. John Wiley & Sons, New York, NY.
7. Wilhelm, Luther R. 1976. Numerical calculations of psychrometric properties in SI units. *Transactions of the ASAE* 19(2): 318-321, 325.

Problems

9.1. Use a psychrometric chart to complete the following table.

t_{db} (°C)	t_{wb} (°C)	t_{dp} (°C)	ϕ (%)	h (kJ)/(kg)	v (m³/(kg)	W (g H$_2$O)/(g air)
21	17					
21		17				
21			30			
		18		81		
27		18				
10			20			

9.2. A psychrometer measures wet bulb and dry bulb temperatures of 20°C and 30°C, respectively. What is:

     a. the dew point temperature?   c. the relative humidity?

     b. the humidity ratio?   d. the enthalpy?

9.3. For a dew point of 24°C and dry bulb of 30°C, find:

     a. relative humidity   c. humidity ratio

     b. enthalpy   d. vapor pressure

9.4. Air inside a room is at 20°C with a t_{wb} = 15°C. Will condensation occur if the air contacts a surface at 10°C?

9.5. A 4m × 7m × 2.5m room contains air at 27°C and atmospheric pressure. The partial pressure of the water vapor in the air is 1.5 kPa. Find:

     a. the wet bulb temperature   d. the dew point

     b. the humidity ratio   e. the enthalpy per kg of dry air

     c. the specific volume

9.6. One kilogram of air at 20°C and 70% relative humidity is heated to 40°C with no moisture added or removed.

a. What is the relative humidity of the heated air?

b. If this air is maintained at a pressure of 1 atmosphere (101.325 kPa) during the heating process, what is the percentage change in volume due to the heating?

9.7. Air at 25°C and a relative humidity of 40% is to be cooled until condensation begins.

a. How low can it be cooled?

b. What happens if the initial relative humidity is 90%?

9.8. A large balloon contains air at 44°C and 10% relative humidity. The contents are slowly cooled.

a. How much heat must be removed to cool the air to 15°C?

b. To what temperature must the air be cooled before condensation begins?

9.9. Evaporative cooling by forcing air through trailer loads of snap beans is sometimes used during shipments. Assume the following conditions:

Air enters at 27°C and 70% relative humidity.

It leaves at 27°C and 95% relative humidity.

a. How much heat is removed per 1000 m³ of air entering the trailer?

b. How much water is removed per 1000 m³ of air?

9.10. In hot, dry areas evaporative cooling is often very effective. Consider a system where water for evaporation is added by spraying into a duct containing air at 45°C and 20% relative humidity.

a. If the resulting air-vapor mixture must not exceed 60% relative humidity, how much can the temperature be lowered by evaporative cooling?

b. If the air flow rate is 0.50 m³/s, what must be the flow rate of the water added for evaporation?

c. Show this process on a psychrometric chart.

9.11. In a building heating/cooling system, air flows over cooling coils for moisture removal and is then reheated as necessary to maintain a cooling air temperature of 21°C. If the air temperature as it crosses the coils is 13°C, what will be the relative humidity of the cooling air?

9.12. Air at 55°C and a wet-bulb temperature of 26°C passes through a humidifier and exits at 80% relative humidity. For this process, find:

a. the change in temperature of the air

b. the change in moisture content of the air

c. the change in specific volume

d. the change in dew point temperature

e. the change in enthalpy

9.13. Air at 15°C and 50% relative humidity is mixed with an equal amount of air at 35°C and 50% relative humidity. Determine the temperature and relative humidity of the mixed air. Repeat for a mixture containing 80% of the 15°C air and 20% of the 35°C air.

9.14. Ambient air at 15°C and 50% relative humidity is heated to 50°C. This heated air is than mixed with an equal amount of ambient air (at 15°C and 50% relative humidity). Determine the temperature and relative humidity of the mixed air. Repeat for a mixture containing 80% of the heated air and 20% of the ambient air.

9.15. Air at 22°C and 90% relative humidity (Point 1) is passed over cooling coils and cooled to 5°C (Point 2). It is then heated to 45°C (Point 3). The heated air is forced through a drier, exiting at 80% relative humidity (Point 4).

a. Give the values of the following properties at State Point 2: t_{wb}, t_{dp}, h, v, W.

b. How much water per unit mass of dry air is removed by the drying air in the drying process?

c. How much heat, per unit mass of dry air, is removed from the air in the cooling process?

9.16. Show that each term of Equation 9.19 can be written in units of kJ/kg DA.

9.17. Using the latent heat of fusion of water, calculate the amount of energy needed to melt 50 kg of ice at 0°C. If the ice is initially at –15°C, how much energy would be needed?

9.18. Use the steam tables to find the enthalpy of steam under the following conditions.

State	P (kPa)	t (°C)	h (kJ/kg)
Liquid	300	133.5	
Liquid	10	45.8	
Vapor	300	133.5	
Vapor	200	300	
Vapor	400	800	

9.19. What is the enthalpy of 1 kg of "wet" steam in a 0.2 m³ container at:

a. 100°C   c. 800 kPa

b. 4000 kPa   d. 175°C

Note: First determine the quality (x). Since $0 \le x \le 1$, any computed value of $x > 1$ indicates a physically impossible condition.

9.20. What is the enthalpy of an 80% vapor and 20% liquid mixture at 100°C?

9.21. Superheated steam at 200 kPa and 160°C is cooled at constant pressure

a. What are the initial values of t, h, and v?

b. What are the values of t, h, and v when the steam is cooled to saturated vapor?

    c. What are the values of t, h, and v when it is cooled to a quality of 0.5?

    d. What are the values of t, h, and v when it is cooled to saturated liquid?

    e. If additional cooling occurs, will the temperature change? If so, how?

9.22. Plot enthalpy (h) as a function of quality (x) for steam at:

    a. 100°C   c. 130°C

    b. 120 kPa   d. 400 kPa

9.23. Complete the following table of steam properties.

Item	t (°C)	P (kPa)	v (m³/kg)	h (kJ/kg)	x	State
A	170	792		2047.9		
B	400	200				
C	140				0.9	
D	140	150				
E		140				SL
F		140			0.5	
G	121				0.1	
State codes:	SL = saturated liquid			SV = saturated vapor		
	SH = superheated vapor			WS = wet steam		

9.24. Calculate the partial pressure of water vapor and the corresponding temperature for a steam air mixture that is 10% air by mass with a total pressure of 400 kPa.

9.25. Repeat the previous problem for a mixture that is 20% air by mass.

Drying and Dehydration

10

Abstract. This chapter reviews basic concepts of drying and dehydration, including mass balance analyses. Equilibrium moisture content, water activity, and related parameters are discussed. Drying methods and drier types are briefly discussed.

Keywords. Dehydration, driers, drying, equilibrium moisture content, evaporation, water activity.

10.1 Introduction

Removing water from food and agricultural products constitutes a significant portion of the processing activity for persons working in the food and agricultural processing industries. Two major moisture removal methods are **drying** (or dehydration) to produce a solid product and **evaporation** to produce a more concentrated liquid. The words drying and dehydration are often used interchangeably, especially when referring to food products; however, only the word drying is commonly used when referring to processing of non-food products. Applications range from on-farm drying of grain, fruits, and vegetables to large scale commercial drying of fruits, vegetables, snack food products, milk products, coffee, and other products. Although certain basic factors are involved in all drying processes, the equipment and techniques vary greatly depending upon the product and other factors. In this unit, we will consider some basic factors affecting drying and briefly examine some drying methods.

Evaporation is the removal of some water from a liquid product to produce a more concentrated liquid. Applications include concentration of milk, fruit juices, and syrup products. Most evaporation systems are large-scale commercial operations, although small-scale farm operations still exist for production of maple, sorghum, and sugar cane syrups. The governing principles of evaporator operation will be briefly examined in this unit.

10.2 Moisture Content

No agricultural product in its natural state is completely dry. Some water is always present. This moisture is usually indicated as a percent moisture content for the product. Two methods are used to express this moisture content. These methods are wet basis (m) and dry basis (M). In addition, the content may be expressed as a percent or as a decimal ratio. We will use all four forms (wet basis, dry basis, percent, and decimal ratio) in analyzing moisture or food products.

The general governing equations for indicating moisture content are:

$$m = \frac{m_w}{m_w + m_d} = \frac{m_w}{m_t} \qquad (10.01)$$

$$M = \frac{m_w}{m_d} \qquad (10.02)$$

where: m = decimal moisture content wet basis (wb)
M = decimal moisture content dry basis (db)
m_d = mass of dry matter in the product
m_w = mass of water in the product
m_t = total mass of the product, water plus dry matter

The percent moisture content is found by multiplying the decimal moisture content by 100.

In addition, relationships between wet and dry moisture content on a decimal basis can be derived from Equations 10.01 and 10.02. Those relationships are:

$$M = \frac{m}{1 - m} \qquad \text{or} \qquad m = \frac{M}{1 + M} \qquad (10.03)$$

Use of the wet basis measurement is common in the grain industry where moisture content is typically expressed as percent wet basis. However, use of the wet basis has one clear disadvantage—the total mass changes as moisture is removed. Since the total mass is the reference base for the moisture content, the reference condition is changing as the moisture content changes. On the other hand, the amount of dry matter does not change. Thus, the reference condition for dry basis measurements does not change as moisture is removed.

For a given product, the moisture content dry basis is always higher than the wet basis moisture content. This is obvious from a comparison of Equations 10.01 and 10.02. The difference between the two bases is small at low moisture levels, but it increases rapidly at higher moisture levels.

A final note regarding moisture content relates to high moisture materials such as fruits and vegetables. Many of these products have moisture contents near 0.90 (or 90%) (wb). On a dry basis this would be 900% if expressed as a percentage. For products of this type, moisture is often given as "mass of water per unit mass of dry product," the decimal basis we discussed earlier.

Example 10.1

A bin holds 2000 kg of wet grain containing 500 kg of water. This grain is to be dried to a final moisture content of 14% (wb).
a. What are the initial and final moisture contents of the grain (wet basis, dry basis, decimal and percent)?
b. How much water is removed during drying?

Solution:
Using Equations 10.01 and 10.02 the initial moisture content is:

$$m = \frac{m_w}{m_t} = \frac{500}{2000} = 0.25 \text{ or } \underline{25\% \text{ wet basis (wb)}} \qquad \textbf{ANSWER}$$

$$M = \frac{m_w}{m_d} = \frac{500}{2000 - 500} = \underline{0.3333} \text{ or } \underline{33.33 \% \text{ dry basis (db)}} \quad \textbf{ANSWER}$$

The final moisture content was stated as 14% (wb), or $m = 0.14$. Using Equation 10.03, we can solve for the moisture content on a dry basis:

$$\textbf{ANSWER}$$
$$M = \frac{0.14}{1 - 0.14} = \frac{0.14}{0.86} = \underline{0.1628} \text{ or } \underline{16.28\% \text{ (db)}}$$

The amount of water in the dried grain may be found using either Equation 10.01 or 10.02 and the appropriate final moisture content noted above. For our example, we will use both methods. We will first use the dry basis moisture of $M = 0.1628$. Noting that the bin contains 1500 kg of dry matter (2000 – 500), Equation 10.02 gives:

$$m_w = m_d \times M = 1500 \times 0.1628 = 244 \text{ kg}$$

Alternatively, using Equation 10.01 and $m = 0.14$, we find the same solution:

$$m_w = m \times (m_w + m_d) = 0.14 \times (m_w + 1500) = 0.14 m_w + 210$$

$$0.86 m_w = 210 \implies m_w = 244 \text{ kg}$$

Thus, the water removed is: $m_{w\,rem} = 500 - 244 = \underline{256 \text{ kg}}$ **ANSWER**

Many different techniques are available for measuring the moisture content of a material. The technique used in a given instance depends upon the material being studied, equipment available, and the time available for the measurement. The most straightforward method of moisture measurement is to use a drying oven. A sample of the product is heated at a specified temperature and pressure (usually atmospheric pressure or a specified vacuum) for a specified time to remove all moisture (i.e., dry until there is no further weight loss). The loss in mass of the sample represents the moisture removed from the product. The temperature, drying time, and pressure are dependent upon the product being analyzed. Microwave drying ovens and chemical analysis are also used for some moisture measurement applications. An extensive list of standards for moisture measurement is provided by AOAC (1990).

10.3 Equilibrium Moisture Content

A material held for a long time at a fixed temperature and relative humidity will eventually reach a moisture content that is in equilibrium with the surrounding air. This does not mean that the material and the air have the same moisture content. It simply means that an equilibrium condition exists such that there is *no net exchange* of moisture between the material and the air. This **equilibrium moisture content** (*EMC* or M_e) is a function of the temperature, the relative humidity, and the product. These equilibrium moisture relationships are normally expressed mathematically. Numerous equations have been proposed to represent the EMC curves for various products (Iglesias and Chirfe, 1982; ASAE, 2000). No single equation is suitable for all products; however, most products can be represented by one of several equations available. Four of these equations are listed below. Halsey's equation (Equation 10.04) and Henderson's equation (Equation 10.05) are two of the less complicated equations. Temperature is not a parameter in Halsey's equation. Thus, different constants must be used for each product and temperature of interest. Note also that the constants are valid only for the equation listed and should not be adapted for other equations. Grains and related products are often represented by the slightly more complicated Modified Henderson Equation (Equation 10.06), the Modified Halsey Equation (Equation 10.07), the Modified Oswin Equation, or the Guggenheim-Anderson-DeBoer (GAB) equation (ASAE, 2000). The relative humidity defined by these equations is commonly called the **equilibrium relative humidity** (*ERH*). Thus, *ERH* is the relative humidity for equilibrium between air and a specific product at a given temperature.

$$ERH = \exp\left(\frac{-K}{M_e^N}\right) \qquad\qquad \text{Halsey} \qquad\qquad (10.04)$$

$$ERH = 1 - \exp\left(-K\, t\, M_e^N\right) \qquad\qquad \text{Henderson} \qquad\qquad (10.05)$$

$$ERH = 1 - \exp\left(-K(t+C)M_e^N\right) \qquad \text{Modified Henderson} \qquad (10.06)$$

$$ERH = \exp\left(\frac{\exp(K + C\,t)}{M_e^N}\right) \qquad \text{Modified Halsey} \qquad (10.07)$$

where: *ERH* = relative humidity, decimal
         M_e = equilibrium moisture content, percent, dry basis
         t = temperature, °C
         K, N, C = are constants determined for each material
                (see Tables 10.01 and 10.02)

A typical set of equilibrium moisture curves are presented in Figure 10.01. These curves are computed using Equation 10.06 and the constants from Table 10.01 for shelled corn. Note that curves begin at 20% relative humidity and are terminated before reaching 100% relative humidity. Prediction curves are generally written to describe conditions in the middle ranges of relative humidity. They do not predict well for extreme conditions. In addition, reliable experimental data are difficult to obtain in those regions.

Table 10.01. Constants for Modified Henderson and Halsey Equations. (From ASAE, 2000.)

Grain	K	N	C	Equation
Beans, pinto	4.4181	1.7571	−0.011875	10.07
Beans, white	0.1633	1.567	87.46	10.06
Canola meal	0.000103	1.6129	89.99	10.06
Corn, shelled	6.6612×10^{-5}	1.9677	42.143	10.06
Popcorn	1.5593×10^{-4}	1.5978	60.754	10.06
Peanut, kernel	3.9916	2.2375	−0.017856	10.07
Pumpkin seed, adsorption	3.3725×10^{-5}	3.4174	1728.729	10.06
Pumpkin seed, desorption	3.3045×10^{-5}	3.3645	1697.76	10.06
Rice, med grain	3.5502×10^{-5}	2.31	27.396	10.06
Soybean	2.87	1.38	−0.0054	10.07
Wheat, hard red	4.3295×10^{-5}	2.1119	41.565	10.06

Table 10.02. Selected EMC relationships for food products. Constants are valid only for the equation number listed. (From Iglesias and Chirfe, 1982.)

Product	Temperature	rh range	Equation	K	N
Apple	30°C	0.10 - 0.75	10.05	0.1091	0.7535
Apple[a]	19.5°C	0.10 - 0.70	10.04	4.4751	0.7131
Banana	25°C	0.10 - 0.80	10.05	0.1268	0.7032
Chives	25°C	0.10 - 0.80	10.04	11.8931	1.1146
Grapefruit	45°C	0.10 - 0.80	10.05	0.1519	0.6645
Mushrooms	20°C	0.07 - 0.75	10.04	7.5335	1.1639
Mushrooms[a]	25°C	0.10 - 0.80	10.04	11.5342	1.1606
Peach	20 - 30°C	0.10 - 0.80	10.05	0.0471	1.0096
Peach	40°C	0.10 - 0.80	10.05	0.0440	1.1909
Peach	50°C	0.10 - 0.80	10.05	0.0477	1.3371
Pear	25°C	0.10 - 0.80	10.05	0.0882	0.7654
Tomato	17°C	0.10 - 0.80	10.04	10.587	0.9704

[a]Desorption isotherm data. All other data is for sorption (moisture addition) measurements.

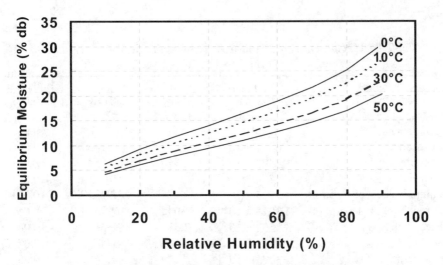

Figure 10.01. Equilibrium moisture curves for shelled corn.
Computed from ASAE data (ASAE, 2000).

Example 10.2

Compute the equilibrium moisture content for popcorn at 20°C and 50% relative humidity.

Solution:
We first rearrange Equation 10.06 to express equilibrium moisture in terms of the other parameters:

$$M_e = \sqrt[N]{\frac{\ln(1 - ERH)}{-K(t + C)}} = \left(\frac{\ln(1 - ERH)}{-K(t + C)}\right)^{\frac{1}{N}}$$

We now substitute values of K, N, and C from Table 10.01 into the equation and solve for M_e at 20°C and 50% relative humidity:

$$M_e = \left(\frac{\ln(1 - 0.5)}{= -1.5593 \times 10^{-4}(20 + 60.754)}\right)^{\frac{1}{1.5978}} = \left(\frac{\ln(0.5)}{-0.01259}\right)^{0.62586}$$

$$= \left(\frac{-0.6931}{-0.01259}\right)^{0.6258} = (55.047)^{0.62586} = \underline{12.19\% \ (db)} \qquad \textbf{ANSWER}$$

10.4 Water Activity (a_w)

The amount of water in food and agricultural products affects the quality and per-ishability of these products. However, perishability is not directly related to moisture content. In fact, perishability varies greatly among products with the same moisture content. A much better indicator of perishability is the availability of water in the product to support degradation activities such as microbial action. The term **water activity** is widely used in the food industry as an indicator of water available in a product. See Labuza (1984) or Troller and Christian (1978) for further information. Water activity (a_w) is defined as:

$$a_w = \frac{P_w}{P_{ws}} \quad \text{or} \quad a_w = \phi \quad \text{since} \quad \phi = \frac{P_w}{P_{ws}}$$

where: ϕ = the relative humidity, decimal
  P_w = the partial pressure of water vapor at the specified conditions
  P_{ws} = the partial pressure of water vapor at saturation and the temperature specified

Thus, water activity is the equilibrium relative humidity (*ERH*) in decimal form for a product at a given temperature and moisture content. Figure 10.01 can then be con-sidered as a plot of equilibrium moisture content as a function of a_w, if we change the x-axis scale to decimal form. A more common method for representing the effect of a_w is shown in Figure 10.02. The shape of this graph is typical of water activity graphs although the moisture content scale may vary greatly among products. The key feature of this relationship is that actual moisture content increases rapidly with a_w at the higher values of water activity.

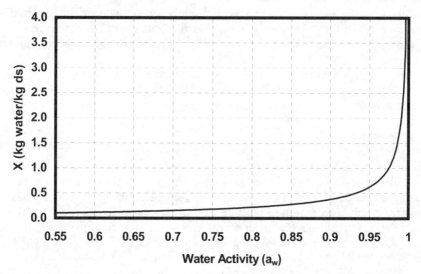

Figure 10.02. Water activity curve for fresh, diced sweet potato cubes.

The physical significance of a_w may not be immediately clear from the above equation. Thus, we will examine a conceptually simple method of determining a_w. If we take a sample of a food product and place it in an enclosed container at a fixed temperature, the product will exchange moisture with the air surrounding it. After a period of time, as with the equilibrium moisture example noted in the previous section, an equilibrium condition will occur. The product no longer has any net change in moisture. The water activity is equal to the decimal relative humidity at that condition.

10.5 Controlling Factors for Drying

Two separate phenomena are involved in drying. First, moisture must move from the interior of a material to the surface of that material. Second, the surface water must be evaporated into the air. These two steps involve two very different phenomena. Movement of water from the interior to the surface must occur in one of two manners —capillary action or diffusion. Movement by capillary action would only occur during early stages of drying. As the drying process continues, internal moisture movement would occur by molecular diffusion of water vapor within the material. Removal of water from the surface involves evaporation of water from the surface into the surrounding air. The evaporation rate depends upon the condition of drying air and the concentration of water at the surface.

Air drying involves the passing of air over the object(s) to be dried. Typically, the air is heated prior to entering the drying region. Consider the drying process for a high moisture product such as an apple slice. The surface of the slice will be visibly covered with water immediately after slicing. As this water evaporates, the surface becomes slightly dry. Moisture cannot move from the interior of the slice as rapidly as it can evaporate at the surface. Thus the governing factor in later stages of drying is the diffusion rate of moisture within the slice.

Factors affecting the drying rate will vary slightly depending upon the type of drying system used. However, in general, the following factors must be considered:

1. nature of the material: physical and chemical composition, moisture content, etc.;
2. size, shape, and arrangement of the pieces to be dried;
3. wet-bulb depression ($t - t_{wb}$), or relative humidity, or partial pressure of water vapor in the air (all are related and indicate the amount of moisture already in the air);
4. air temperature; and
5. air velocity (drying rate is approximately proportional to $u^{0.8}$).

Another factor that must be considered in drying solid materials is case hardening. This problem can occur if the initial stage of drying occurs at low relative humidity and high temperature. Under these conditions, moisture is removed from the surface of the material much faster than it can diffuse from within the material. The result is formation of a hardened relatively impervious layer on the surface of the material. Formation of such a layer causes subsequent drying to be much slower than it would otherwise be.

10.6 Air Drying Methods

Many different drying systems have been developed to meet the needs for drying different materials. A few of the more common systems are described in the following sections.

10.6.1 Bin Drying

Bin drying systems are common in on-farm grain drying operations. The bin is filled with grain and drying air is forced up through the grain from a plenum chamber beneath the perforated floor of the bin. The grain on the bottom is dried first. As drying progresses a layer of drying grain separates the dried grain from the undried grain. This region of drying grain is called a drying front. This drying front progresses upward through the bin of grain until all grain is dried. Figure 10.03 shows a representation of this process. Other on-farm drying methods include stirring of grain in the bin during drying and use of continuous flow dryers to dry grain before storage. The arrangement shown in Figure 10.03 is very useful for studying drying systems since it can be readily analyzed for mass and energy balances.

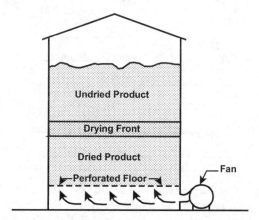

**Figure 10.03. Bin drying diagram showing the drying front
with about half the product dried.**

10.6.2 Cabinet Drying

Cabinet dryers are usually small, insulated units with a heater, circulating fan, and shelves to hold the product to be dried. The small dehydration units sold for home use are small-scale examples of this type of dryer. Different designs are used, but the general procedure is to force heated air over multiple trays. Small-scale cabinet dryers are typically single pass units. However, greater energy efficiencies can be obtained if some of the heated air is recirculated. This is especially true in later stages of drying when the moisture removal rate is low and the exit air retains considerable moisture-holding capacity. Figure 10.04 shows the basic operation of a cabinet dryer with recirculation. Energy savings of 50% or more can be achieved with recirculation.

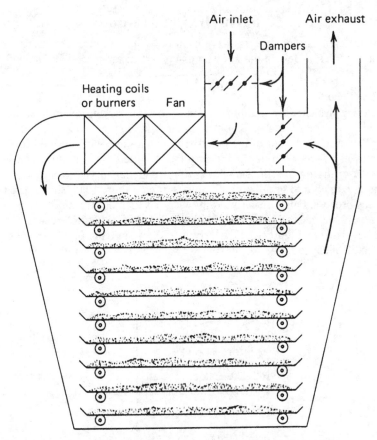

Figure 10.04. Sketch of a cabinet dryer with recirculation.
(*Food Engineering Fundamentals*, **J. C. Batty and S. L. Folkman, 1983. © by
John Wiley & Sons, Inc. Reprinted by permission of John Wiley & Sons, Inc.)**

10.6.3 Tunnel Drying

Tunnel dryers are a large-scale modification of the cabinet dryer concept. The drying chamber is a tunnel with multiple carts containing trays of the product being dried. New carts of undried product are loaded at one end of the tunnel as carts of dried product are removed from the other end. Air flow in these dryers may be parallel or counter to the movement of carts in the tunnel. Figure 10.05 shows examples of parallel and counter flow tunnel dryers.

10.6.4 Drum Drying

Large rotating drums are used for drying slurries (liquids with a high solids content). A thin film of the slurry is deposited on the bottom of a rotating drum as it passes through the slurry. The slowly rotating drum is heated and sometimes held under a vacuum. The dried product is scraped from the drum before the rotating surface re-enters the slurry. Figure 10.06 shows four different configurations of drum dryers.

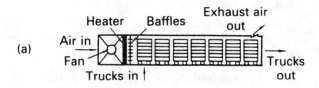

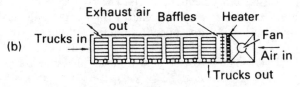

Figure 10.05. Tunnel dryer sketches showing (a) parallel and
(b) counter flow operation (from Brennan et al. 1990).

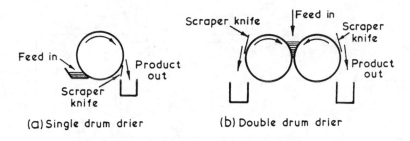

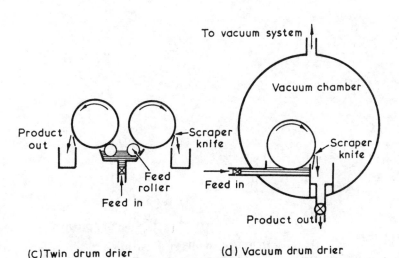

Figure 10.06. Different drum dryer configurations (from Brennan et al. 1990).

10.6.5 Other Drying

Numerous other air drying techniques are also used. The major function of all such systems is to move air over the product in such a manner that the product is dried as economically as possible without damage.

10.7 Special Drying Methods

10.7.1 Spray Drying

Spray drying is used to dry liquid products. The product to be dried is sprayed into a stream of heated air. Water evaporates into the air leaving the dry particles to be collected. The two major operations of concern in spray drying are droplet atomization and powder collection. To optimize drying, droplets should be small and uniform in size. Thus special procedures must be used to insure that atomization is satisfactory.

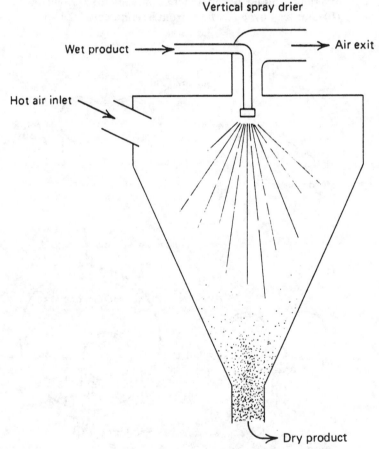

Figure 10.07. Spray dryer illustration.
(*Food Engineering Fundamentals*, J. C. Batty and S. L. Folkman, 1983. © by John Wiley & Sons, Inc. Reprinted by permission of John Wiley & Sons, Inc.)

Collection of the dried powder also requires special techniques. The powder particles are small and move easily within an air stream. Collection chambers or special filters are normally used. Figure 10.07 shows a simple representation of a spray dryer. Actual operations are more complex, and many different configurations are available.

10.7.2 Vacuum Drying
In vacuum drying, the product is placed inside a chamber where the pressure is reduced to produce a vacuum. Since the total pressure in the chamber is very low, the partial pressure of the water vapor in the chamber is also very low. This low partial pressure causes a large partial pressure difference between the water in the product and the surroundings. Thus water moves more readily from the product to the surrounding environment in the chamber. Drying under vacuum conditions permits drying at a lower temperature. This characteristic of vacuum drying is very important for products that may suffer significant flavor changes at higher temperatures.

10.7.3 Freeze Drying
Freeze drying involves the removal of moisture from a frozen product without thawing that product. The temperature must be below freezing for that product (to insure that the product remains frozen) and the vapor pressure must be maintained at a very low level to permit moisture removal by sublimation. Because of the low temperature, low pressure, and low drying rate, freeze drying is quite expensive compared to many other drying methods. However, freeze drying can produce high quality dried products. Thus, it is the preferred drying method for some high value materials. Figure 10.08 shows a representation of a freeze dryer. "Freezer burn," sometimes seen in frozen foods, is an example of undesirable freeze drying. This very slow type of freeze drying can occur when inadequately protected food is stored in a freezer for extended periods.

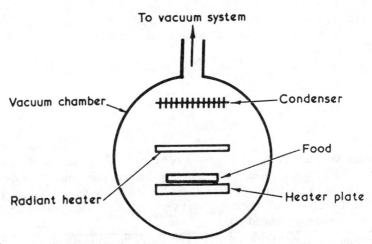

Figure 10.08. Representation of freeze drying components.
Low temperature and pressure are required. (From Brennan et al. 1990.)

Example 10.3

A counter flow dryer unit uses heated air to dry apple slices. The slices enter at a rate of 200 kg/h and a moisture content of $m_1 = 0.9$. The "dried" slices have a moisture content of $M_2 = 0.10$. The drying air enters at 50°C and exits at 25°C and 90% relative humidity.

(1) Find the water removed, $\dot{m}_{wrem}$, kg/h.

(2) Find the entering air flow rate, m³/min.

Solution:

Analysis of this problem requires calculation of mass balances for dry matter, water, and dry air. We begin by calculating the amount of dry matter (solids) and water entering and leaving with the slices. Since we know the moisture content and the input rate, we can determine the amount of water and dry matter in the entering slices:

$$m_1 = 0.9 = \frac{\dot{m}_{w1}}{\dot{m}_{T1}} = \frac{\dot{m}_{w1}}{200} \text{ giving } \dot{m}_{w1} = 200 \times 0.90 = 180 \frac{\text{kg H}_2\text{O}}{\text{h}}$$

Next solve for the entering dry matter. Since only water is removed, the dry matter in the "dried" product is the same as that entering in the undried slices:

$$\dot{m}_{D1} = \dot{m}_{T1} - \dot{m}_{w1} = 200 - 180 = 20 \frac{\text{kg DM}}{\text{h}} = \dot{m}_{D2}$$

Knowing the moisture content and the amount of dry matter in the "dried" slices, we can now calculate the output rate of the product:

$$M_2 = \frac{\dot{m}_{w2}}{\dot{m}_{D2}} = 0.01 = \frac{\dot{m}_{w2}}{20} \text{ giving } \dot{m}_{w2} = 20 \times 0.10 = 2.0 \frac{\text{kg H}_2\text{O}}{\text{h}}$$

The water removed from the apple slices is then:

$$\dot{m}_{wrem} = \dot{m}_{w1} - \dot{m}_{w2} = 180 - 2 = \underline{178 \frac{\text{kg H}_2\text{O}}{\text{h}}} \qquad \textbf{ANSWER 1}$$

We know that the drying air follows a constant wet-bulb process as it gains moisture from the apple sliced. Using the temperature and humidity of the exit air, we can go to a psychrometric chart, find the wet-bulb temperature, and follow the constant wet-bulb line to the inlet air temperature. Using this process we find the following air properties:

Location	t_{db} (°C)	t_{wb} (°C)	ϕ (%)	v (m³/kg DA)	W (g H₂O/kg DA)
Entering	50	23.7		0.925	7.7
Exiting	25	23.7	90		18

For use in our solution, we need to convert the humidity ratio to units of kg H_2O/kg DA (divide the table values by 1000).

We can now calculate the moisture gained by each unit mass of dry air:

$$\Delta W = W_1 - W_2 = 0.018 - 0.007 = 0.0103 \frac{\text{kg } H_2O}{\text{kg DA}}$$

Knowing the total water gain by the air and the gain by each kilogram of the air, we can now calculate the air flow rate:

$$\dot{m}_{DA} = \frac{178 \dfrac{\text{kg } H_2O}{\text{h}}}{0.0103 \dfrac{\text{kg } H_2O}{\text{kg DA}}} = 17\,280 \frac{\text{kg DA}}{\text{h}} = 288 \frac{\text{kg DA}}{\text{min}}$$

Using the calculated mass flow rate and the entering air specific volume from the psychrometric chart, and listed in the table above, we can determine the volumetric air flow rate:

$$\dot{Q} = 288 \frac{\text{kg DA}}{\text{min}} \times 0.925 \frac{\text{m}^3}{\text{kg DA}} = 266 \frac{\text{m}^3}{\text{min}} \qquad \textbf{ANSWER 2}$$

Example 10.4

Repeat Example 10.3 with all parameter values the same except that the "dried" slices exit at a moisture content of $m_2 = 0.10$ (wet basis instead of dry basis).

Solution:
We follow a solution process very similar to that of the previous example. Input parameters are exactly the same as before. Thus:

$$\dot{m}_{D1} = \dot{m}_{D2} = 200 - 180 = 20 \frac{\text{kg DM}}{\text{h}}$$

Solving for the water in the "dried" slices:

$$m_2 = 0.10 = \frac{\dot{m}_{w2}}{\dot{m}_{T2}} = \frac{\dot{m}_{w2}}{\dot{m}_{w2} + \dot{m}_{D2}} = \frac{\dot{m}_{w2}}{\dot{m}_{w2} + 20}$$

$$0.1\dot{m}_{w2} + 2 = \dot{m}_{w2} \qquad \Rightarrow \qquad \dot{m}_{w2} = 2.22 \frac{\text{kg } H_2O}{\text{h}}$$

The moisture removed is then:

$$\dot{m}_{wrem} = \dot{m}_{w1} - \dot{m}_{w2} = 180 - 2.22 = 177.78 \, \frac{\text{kg H}_2\text{O}}{\text{h}} \qquad \textbf{ANSWER}$$

Continuing as in the previous example, we find:

$$\dot{m}_{DA} = 287.7 \, \frac{\text{kg DA}}{\text{min}} \quad \text{and} \quad \dot{Q} = 266.1 \, \frac{\text{m}^3}{\text{min}} \qquad \textbf{ANSWER}$$

Note that the results differ little between these two examples. That is because, at low moisture content, there is little difference between the wet basis and dry basis measurements. The difference would be much greater if an exit moisture content of 0.20 had been used in the examples.

10.8 Introduction to Evaporation

An important step in the production of many food products is the removal of water to produce a more concentrated liquid. The term used in the food industry to define this operation is **evaporation**. Examples of evaporated food products are evaporated milk, syrups, and various fruit juice concentrates. The basic principle involved in the evaporation process is the application of heat to evaporate free water present in the product. The configuration of the equipment used to accomplish this concentration defines the evaporator type.

10.8.1 Open (Atmospheric) and Vacuum Evaporators

The earliest evaporators were open kettles or pans placed over an open flame. Maple syrup, sweet sorghum syrup, and sugar cane syrup were produced using open evaporators during the early history of the United States. Figure 10.09 shows a sketch of an open pan evaporator used for sorghum syrup evaporation during the early 1900s (Walton et al., 1938). Evaporators very similar to that shown in Figure 10.09 continue to be used by many sorghum syrup producers in the United States. The primary difference is that few processors use wood as a heat source. Most now use gas (natural or LP) or steam as the direct heat source for their evaporators.

Two major disadvantages of open evaporators are higher operating temperatures and higher energy cost in comparison to vacuum evaporation systems. While acceptable for syrup production, the temperatures required to boil a product, thus evaporating water, are sufficient to produce undesirable flavors for many food products. In addition, such evaporation requires huge amounts of energy—more than 2200 kJ for every kilogram of water evaporated.

The problems noted above for open evaporators can be avoided by using vacuum evaporators. By evaporating at a lower pressure, the boiling point is lowered. This reduces the possibility of undesirable flavors. In addition, vacuum evaporators can be placed in series. These multiple effect evaporators use the vapor from one evaporator to provide energy for evaporation in the next evaporator in the series. This combination results in a significant reduction in energy use, although initial cost is greater.

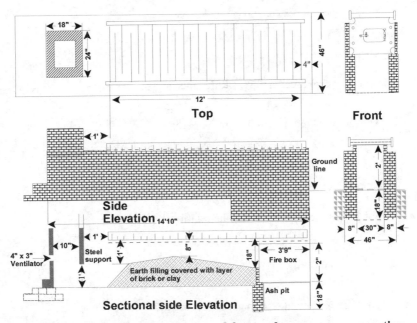

Figure 10.09. Open pan evaporator used for sorghum syrup evaporation (modified from Walton et al., 1938).

Example 10.5

A small open pan evaporator is used to produce sorghum syrup. Juice ($m = 0.87$ wb) enters at the rate of 800 kg/h. The finished syrup leaving the evaporator contains 80% solids. Five percent of the entering solids are removed as impurities during the evaporation process.
(1) Find the production rate of the syrup (kg/h).
(2) Find the mass of water removed per unit mass of syrup.
(3) Find the energy required per hour to evaporate the water removed.
(4) Find the steam flow required for evaporation if 20% of the heat is lost to surroundings. The steam enters at 350 kPa (saturated) and exits at a quality of 0.10.

Solution:
As with dryer analysis, the solution requires *mass* and *energy* balances. However, one unique difference from previous examples is that the dry matter mass balance must account for the solids removed. For the solids balance:

Solids (dry matter) entering (m_{DI}):

$$m_{w1} = 0.87 \times 800 = 696 \text{ kg H}_2\text{O/h}$$

$$m_{D1} = m_{T1} - m_{w1} = 800 - 696 = 104 \text{ kg DM/h}$$

$$(\text{or } m_{D1} = 0.13 \times 800 = 104)$$

Impurities removed are 5% of the entering solids, thus:

$$m_1 = 0.05 \times m_{D1} = 0.05 \times 104 = 5.2 \text{ kg DM/h}$$

The solids remaining in the product are:

$$m_{D2} = m_{D1} - m_1 = 104 - 5.2 = 98.8 \text{ kg DM/h}$$

$$\text{or } m_{D2} = m_{D1} - 0.5 \times m_{D1} = 0.95 \times m_{D1} = 0.95 \,(104) = 98.8$$

We can now determine the syrup output.

For 80% solids we can write the relationship as $0.80 = \dfrac{\dot{m}_{D2}}{\dot{m}_{T2}}$

Thus, $\dot{m}_{T2} = \dfrac{\dot{m}_{D2}}{0.80} = \dfrac{98.8}{0.80} = 123.5 \, \dfrac{\text{kg product}}{\text{h}}$ **ANSWER 1**

The amount of water in the product can now be determined as:

$$\dot{m}_{w2} = \dot{m}_{T2} - \dot{m}_{D2} = 123.5 - 98.8 = 24.7 \, \frac{\text{kg H}_2\text{O}}{\text{h}}$$

Knowing the water input ($\dot{m}_{w1}$) and water output ($\dot{m}_{w2}$), we can now determine the water removed:

$$\dot{m}_{wrem} = \dot{m}_{w1} - \dot{m}_{w2} = 696 - 24.7 = 671.3 \, \frac{\text{kg H}_2\text{O}}{\text{h}}$$

Converting to water removed per unit mass of syrup, we have:

$$\frac{\dot{m}_{wrem}}{\dot{m}_{T2}} = \frac{671.3}{123.5} = 5.44 \, \frac{\text{kg H}_2\text{O}}{\text{kg syrup}}$$ **ANSWER 2**

We can use the latent heat of the evaporated water to determine the energy needed for evaporation. Assuming an average evaporation temperature of 105°C we find that $h_{fg} = 2244 \text{ kJ/kg}$.

Thus, $\dot{Q} = 2244 \text{ kJ/kg} \times 671.3 \text{ kg/h} = 1\,506\,400 \text{ kJ/h} = \underline{418.4 \text{ kW}}$

ANSWER 3

We can now compute the required steam flow. The energy output per unit mass (kg) of steam is:

$$\Delta h_s = h_g - [h_f + x\, h_{fg}] = 2731.6 - [584.3 + 0.1 \times 2147.7]$$

$$= 2731.6 - 799. = 1932.6 \text{ kJ/kg steam}$$

Knowing the energy required for evaporation ($\dot{Q}$) and the energy per unit mass of steam (Δh_s), we can solve for the required steam flow $\dot{m}_S$:

$$\dot{m}_S \times \Delta h_s = \dot{m}_S [1932.6 \text{ kJ/kg steam}] = \dot{Q} = 1\,506\,400 \text{ kJ/h}$$

$$\dot{m}_S = 1\,506\,400 / 1932.6 = 779.5 \text{ kg steam/h} \quad \text{(with no losses)}$$

Taking the 20% loss into account the above value represents only 80% of the required flow rate. Thus the required total steam flow rate is:

$$\dot{m}_{sT} = \frac{\dot{m}_S}{0.80} = \frac{779.5}{0.80} = 974.3 \frac{\text{kg steam}}{\text{h}} \qquad \textbf{ANSWER 4}$$

10.8.2 Controlling Factors for Evaporation

Analysis of evaporator systems is relatively complex. In addition to the normal mass and energy balances that must be satisfied, other thermodynamic parameters must also be considered. These include boiling point and latent heat of vaporization of the raw and finished products. The boiling point of any liquid increases as pressure increases. Thus, vacuum evaporators, which operate below atmospheric pressure, require lower operating temperatures than those required for the same product in an open evaporator. The presence of sugars and/or other components in the liquid being concentrated increases the boiling point of that material at any given pressure. As the concentration of the liquid increases, so does the boiling point. This increase in boiling point is commonly referred to as **boiling point rise**. It is a function of the amount and type of constituents in the liquid. The combination of evaporator pressure and boiling point rise must be considered in determining the actual boiling point in the evaporator.

The latent heat of vaporization (h_{fg}) is the energy required to evaporate a unit mass of liquid at its boiling point. The value of h_{fg} for water at atmospheric pressure is 2257 kJ/kg; however, it does not remain constant as the boiling point changes. It decreases slightly as the boiling point increases. At any evaporator pressure (and boiling point), h_{fg} is quite large. Thus, substantial energy is required for evaporation processes.

Because h_{fg} of food products is large, evaporators require substantial amounts of energy input. This energy must be transferred from the energy source (commonly steam) to the liquid being evaporated. Thus, the heat transfer rate must be as great as possible in the heat exchanger area of the evaporator. This is a major consideration in evaporator design. In addition, foaming of the product and fouling of the heat exchanger surface can have significant adverse effects upon the heat transfer rate. Foaming occurs during concentration of some food products. This can substantially reduce the surface heat transfer coefficient (and the rate of heat transfer from the heat exchanger surface to the fluid.) Fouling of the heat transfer surface can create added resistance to heat flow, thus reducing the heat transfer rate.

Properties of raw material and finished product are major factors that enter into evaporator design and selection. Maximum temperature and length of time exposed to that temperature are significant in determining product quality for some products. Evaporators must therefore operate within specified temperature limitations and yet allow for rapid evaporation. Viscosity is another important parameter since more viscous fluids tend to have higher boiling points and lower heat transfer rates.

10.8.3 Multiple Effect Evaporators

To reduce overall energy costs, evaporators may be placed in series such that the vapor from one evaporator is the heat source to evaporate water from the next unit in the series. Figure 10.10 shows how evaporators could be connected to provide a multiple effect system. In this system steam for evaporation is required for the first unit only. The latent heat of vaporization of the condensing steam provides energy to evaporate water in the first stage of the evaporator. Vapor from this stage is condensed in the next effect to vaporize the water there. This continues through all effects. Because we recycle the vapor into subsequent evaporator stages, we could make the following gross estimate of energy requirements: "in a multiple effect system, one kilogram of steam input will evaporate as many kilograms of water as there are effects." This would imply that for a triple effect system, one kilogram of steam would produce three kilograms of vapor. This simplification is an aid in showing the advantage of multiple effects, but it gives a misleading (high) indication of the vapor produced. Aside from inefficiencies and heat losses, the latent heat of vaporization of water is not constant. It increases as the boiling point decreases. Thus, at every effect in the system, less vapor is evaporated in the current effect than was condensed from the previous effect.

The system shown in Figure 10.10 is called a forward feed system. The heat source and the product being concentrated flow in parallel. In this system, the pressure and temperature decrease with each effect. This decrease is necessary to permit use of vapor from one effect as the heat source for the next effect. The vapor can only be used if the boiling point in the next effect is lower. The boiling point can only be lower if the pressure is lower; thus, $P_1 > P_2 > P_3$ and $T_1 > T_2 > T_3$. An advantage of this system is that flow between effects occurs because of the pressure differences.

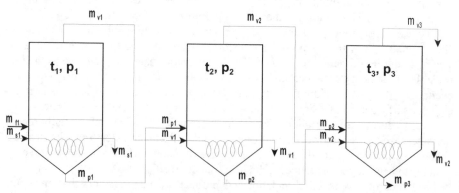

Figure 10.10. Multiple effect (three effects) forward feed evaporator system.

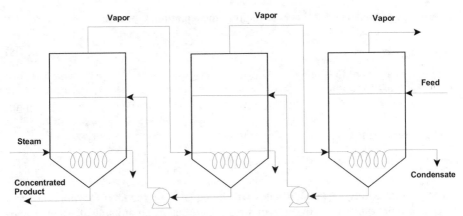

Figure 10.11. Backward feed multiple effect evaporator.

A different multiple effect arrangement, a backward flow system, is shown in Figure 10.11. Here, the product being concentrated flows counter to the flow of vapor used as the heat source. The number of effects (evaporators in the series) may vary depending upon the application. Economy is usually the controlling factor. Steam costs are a major component of operating costs and multiple effects significantly reduce steam requirements. However, the increased efficiency of more effects is eventually offset by the increased initial and maintenance costs of the added effects.

10.8.4 Mass and Energy Balances

Mass and energy balances are key components in analyses of any evaporator system. For multiple effect systems, this results in multiple equations that must be solved. Such an analysis is beyond the scope of our study. We will only examine a simplified analysis of a single effect system following the notation of Figure 10.12. The feed, product, vapor, and steam flow rates are represented by subscripts as indicated. Similarly, mass ratios of solids in the feed and product streams are X_f and X_p, respectively.

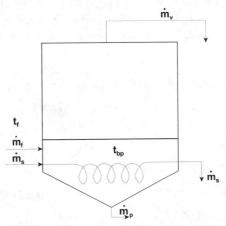

Figure 10.12. Notation for analysis of a single effect evaporator.

A total mass balance for this system gives the equation:

$$\dot{m}_f = \dot{m}_p + \dot{m}_v \qquad (10.08)$$

A similar analysis of the solids balance gives:

$$\dot{m}_f X_f = \dot{m}_p X_p \qquad (10.09)$$

And a water balance gives:

$$\dot{m}_f(1 - X_f) = \dot{m}_p(1 - X_p) + \dot{m}_v \qquad (10.10)$$

Entering and exiting steam flow rates will be equal. The required magnitude of this flow is a function of the flow rate of feed material and the amount of water evaporated. An energy analysis is necessary to determine the steam flow required.

The energy balance analysis is somewhat more complicated. We will simplify the analysis by assuming that the evaporator is perfectly insulated. Thus, all energy from the steam is used to heat the feedstock to the boiling point and then evaporate the desired amount of water. An overall energy balance then becomes:

$$\dot{m}_s \, \Delta h_s = \dot{m}_s \, c_{pf}\left(t_{bp} - t_f\right) + \dot{m}_v \, \Delta h_{fs} \qquad (10.11)$$

Example 10.6

A single-effect evaporator is used to concentrate syrup from 10% to 70% solids. The production rate is 50 kg/h. The evaporation occurs at a pressure of 50 kPa (a boiling point of 81.3°C for pure water). The feed syrup enters at a temperature of 20°C. Energy for evaporation is provided by steam entering as saturated vapor at 200 kPa and exiting as saturated liquid at the same pressure. What steam flow is required to accomplish the evaporation if we assume no energy losses?

Solution:

We must first perform a mass balance to determine the amount of water evaporated. Performing a solids balance (Equation 10.09) we have:

$$0.1\dot{m}_f = 0.7\dot{m}_p = 0.7(50 \text{ kg/h}) = 35 \text{ kg/h}$$

$$\dot{m}_f = 350 \text{ kg/h}$$

Then, solving for $\dot{m}_v$ using Equation 10.10:

$$\dot{m}_v = 350(1 - 0.1) - 50(1 - 0.7) = 350(0.9) - 50(0.3) = 300 \text{ kg/h}$$

or by using Equation 10.08:

$$\dot{m}_v = \dot{m}_f + \dot{m}_p = 350 - 50 = 300 \text{ kg/h}$$

Knowing the amount of water evaporated in the concentration process, we can now determine the energy required to heat the feedstock to the boiling point and evaporate the water. The boiling point of a sugar solution is a function of pressure, sugar content, and type(s) of sugar present. The boiling point rise is less than 1°C at relatively low sugar concentrations and increases rapidly at concentration above 70% (Pancoast and Junk, 1980). At a concentration of 70% the boiling point rise would be near 5°C for a sucrose solution. For simplicity, we will ignore the increase in boiling point temperature as the syrup is concentrated and use 82°C as the approximate boiling point temperature of a 10% sugar solution at 50 kPa. This is a 0.7°C increase above the boiling point of pure water.

We analyze the energy balance using Equation 10.11, which states that:

Steam Energy = Energy for Heating + Energy for Evaporation

From steam tables:

at 200 kPa, h_{fg} = 2201.6 kJ/kg (for condensing steam)

at 82°C, h_{fg} = 2303.8 kJ/kg (for boiling solution)

We now have all parameters needed for a solution of Equation 10.11 except for the specific heat c_{pf}. At 82°C water has a specific heat of 4.2 kJ/kg K, and a 10% sucrose solution has a specific heat that is 95% of that for pure water. Thus:

$$c_{pf} = 4.2(0.95) = 3.99 \text{ kJ/kg K}.$$

Substituting into Equation 10.11, we find:

$$\dot{m}_s \times 2201.6 = 350 \times 3.99(82 - 20) + 300 \times 2303.8 = 86\,583 + 691\,140 = 777\,723$$

$$\dot{m}_s = \underline{353.2 \text{ kg/h}} \qquad \textbf{ANSWER}$$

Note that the energy for evaporation is almost eight times larger than the energy required to heat the solution from 20°C to 82°C. Thus, energy for evaporation is the primary energy factor in evaporator systems; and our act of ignoring the boiling point rise had little effect upon the answer obtained.

List of Symbols

a_w water activity, decimal

c_p specific heat capacity at constant pressure, J/(kg K) or kJ/(kg K)

C, N, K equilibrium moisture equation constants (see Tables 10.01 and 10.02).

EMC equilibrium moisture content, decimal or percent

ERH equilibrium relative humidity, decimal or percent

h_{fg} $(h_f - h_g)$, latent heat of vaporization, kJ/kg

m mass, kg

m moisture content wet basis (wb), decimal or percent

M moisture content dry basis (db), decimal or percent

M_e equilibrium moisture content (db), decimal or percent

$\dot{m}$ mass flow rate, kg/s

P pressure, kPa

rh relative humidity, decimal or percent

t temperature, °C

T absolute temperature, K

X mass ratio (mass fraction), decimal

ϕ relative humidity, decimal or percent

Subscripts

bp boiling point

d dry

f feed

p product

rem removed

s steam, saturation

t total

v vapor

w water

wb wet-bulb

ws water at saturation

References

1. AOAC. 1990. *Official Methods of Analysis of the Association of Analytical Chemists*, 15th ed. Kenneth Helrich, ed. AOAC, Arlington, VA.
2. ASAE. 2000. *ASAE Standards* D245.5: Moisture relationships of grains. ASAE, St. Joseph, MI.
3. Batty, J. C., and S. L. Folkman. 1983. *Food Engineering Fundamentals*. John Wiley & Sons, New York, NY.
4. Brennan, J. G., J. R. Butters, N. D. Cowell, and A. E. V. Lilly. 1990. *Food Engineering Operations*, 3rd ed. Elsevier, London, UK.
5. Brooker, D. B., F. W. Bakker-Arkema, and C. W. Hall. 1974. *Drying Cereal Grains*. AVI, Westport, CT.
6. Charm, S. E. 1971. *The Fundamentals of Food Engineering*. AVI, Westport, CT.

7. Farrall, Arthur W. 1963. *Engineering for Dairy and Food Products.* John Wiley & Sons, Inc., New York, NY.

8. Iglesias, H. A., and J. Chirfe. 1982. *Handbook of Food Isotherms.* Academic Press, New York, NY.

9. Labuza, I. P. 1984. *Moisture Sorption: Practical Aspects of Isotherm Measurement and Use.* American Association of Cereal Chemists, St. Paul, MN.

10. Minton, Paul E. 1986. *Handbook of Evaporation Technology.* Noyes Publications, Park Ridge, NJ.

11. Pancoast, Harry M., and W. Ray Junk. 1980. *Handbook of Sugars*, 2nd ed. AVI, Westport, CT.

12. Troller, J. A., and J. H. B. Christian. 1978. *Water Activity and Food.* Academic Press, New York, NY.

13. Van Arsdel, W. B., M. J. Copley, and A. I. Morgan, Jr. 1973. *Food Dehydration Volume 1: Drying Methods and Phenomena*, 2nd ed. AVI, Westport, CT.

14. Van Arsdel, W. B., M. J. Copley, and A. I. Morgan, Jr. 1973. *Food Dehydration Volume 2: Practices and Applications*, 2nd ed. AVI, Westport, CT.

15. Walton, C. F., E. K. Ventre, and S. Byall. 1938. *Farm Production of Sorgo Sirup.* USDA Farmers' Bulletin 1791. GPO, Washington, DC.

Problems

10.1. Show the relationship between moisture content wet basis (m) and dry basis (M) by plotting M as a function of m for values of m between 0 and 0.95.

10.2. Show how the equation used to solve for M_e in Example 10.2 can be obtained from Equation 10.06.

10.3. Air at 75°C (167°F) and a dew point temperature of 20°C (68°F) is used to dry apple leather in a counter flow arrangement. The air leaves at 90% relative humidity. The leather enters at a rate of 100 kg/hr and 85% moisture (wb). The dried product contains 20% moisture (wb).

   a. How much dried product is produced per hour?

   b. How much water is removed hourly?

   c. What air flow rate is needed to accomplish the drying?

10.4. Repeat problem 10.3, assuming a finished product of 25% moisture (wb).

10.5. Repeat problem 10.3, assuming a finished product with 0.2 kg H_2O/kg of dry matter.

10.6. Mashed potatoes at 40% moisture content (wb) are to be air dried to 12% moisture. The output rate is 500 kg/hr of the 12% moisture content (wb) product. The drying air enters at 55°C and 10% relative humidity and is removed at 80% relative humidity.

   a. Find the moisture content of the potatoes on a dry basis before and after drying.

   b. What is the water removal rate, kg/hr?

   c. What is the temperature of the exiting air?

d. Find the volumetric flow rate of the inlet air.

e. If the drying air was heated from an initial temperature of 27°C, what was its initial relative humidity?

10.7. Sliced apples at 88% moisture (wb) are to be dried to 25% moisture in a counter flow dryer. Drying air enters at 90°C (194°F) and 34°C (93°F) wet bulb. If the air leaves at 60% relative humidity, what air flow rate is required to dry 1000 kg/hr (2200 lb/hr) of sliced apples?

10.8. A small, steam heated, open pan evaporator is used to produce sorghum syrup. In the process, 8 kg of juice produces 1 kg of syrup. The production rate is 100 kg/hr of syrup that contains 76% solids. Five percent of the solids in the raw juice is removed as impurities during the process.

a. How many kilograms of water are removed per kilogram of syrup?.

b. Find the juice supply rate needed to maintain the production rate.

c. How much energy is required per hour to evaporate the water?

d. What steam flow is required if saturated steam is supplied at 350 kPa and leaves at 10% quality? (Assume that 20% of the energy from the steam is lost.)

10.9. The equilibrium moisture content of some materials is related to relative humidity by the following equation:

$$1 - \phi = \exp\left[- K(t + C)M_e^N\right]$$

where C, K, and N are constants for a given material, t is the temperature (°C), N is the relative humidity (decimal), and M_e is the equilibrium moisture content (% dry basis). Values of constants for selected materials are given in Table 10.01. Plot the equilibrium moisture content as a function of relative humidity for any one of these products at temperatures of 0°C, 10°C, 30°C, and 50°C.

10.10. An evaporator is used to concentrate juice of sugar cane to produce syrup. Complete the table below for the various combinations of juice input, juice sugar content, syrup production and syrup sugar content. The sugar content is expressed in °Brix, which represents the percent sugars present in the solution.

| Condition | Juice | | Syrup | |
	Input (kg/h)	° Brix	° Brix	Output (kg/h)
A	1000	15°	70°	
B	1000	15°		150
C		15°	65°	300
D	1000		70°	100

Energy Use in Food Processing

11

Abstract. *This chapter provides a brief overview of energy use in the food chain from production to processing through preparation in homes and restaurants.*

Keywords. *Energy, energy costs, energy use distribution, food systems, industry comparisons.*

11.1 Introduction

The U.S. consumer has readily available an abundant quantity and selection of high quality food items produced in many diverse parts of the world. A supply of relatively low-cost energy is used to power equipment for production, handling, processing, and transport. In 100 years, the food system has seen a labor intensive industry replaced by energy-consuming mechanization. In 1910, one kilocalorie of energy was spent for every kilocalorie of energy contained in the final food product. Fifty years later, nine kilocalories of energy were used by the food system for each kilocalorie of produced food (Unklesbay and Unklesbay, 1982). The luxury we currently enjoy in having an abundant selection of modern foods has come at the cost of enormous usage of non-renewable energy.

The share of energy used in the U.S. food system, as shown in Figure 11.01, is 18% for on-farm production, 29% for processing, 10% for distribution, 26% for in-home preparation, and 17% for out-of-home preparation (Singh, 1986). The food processing industry directly uses nearly 1/3 of all the energy consumed and has a significant influence on the energy that is used later in the food system. Whether the processed product is frozen, aseptically packaged, or sold in fresh form will certainly have different energy consumption implications for subsequent storage and preparation methods.

Energy use in the U.S. food processing system has grown rapidly in the last 50 years. Food processing used 1.2×10^{15} kJ in 1940, 1.9×10^{15} kJ in 1950, 2.4×10^{15} kJ in 1960, and 3.5×10^{15} kJ in 1970 (Unklesbay and Unklesbay, 1982). This energy use growth rate of 3.3% per year was double the population growth rate over the same period. Industry's increasing use of energy was further impacted with higher fuel costs in the 1970s but prices have since returned to lower levels. Today's new food products and packages include microwaveable, individual servings, and shelf-stable foods—all energy-consuming items. Also, there is a trend to more convenience and away-from-home food consumption.

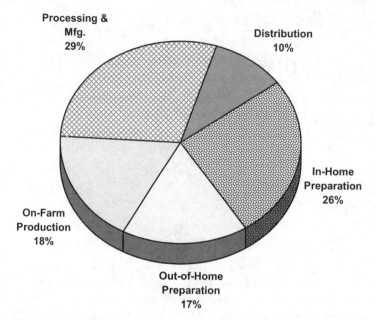

Figure 11.01. Share of energy used within the U.S. food system.

The trends of increasing energy use and cost affect various parts of the food system differently. A fresh fruit and vegetable company would be less affected by changes in energy costs than a company manufacturing a highly processed product. Companies relying heavily on energy-intensive processing will continue to use low-cost fuels and will have the opportunity to utilize energy-conserving processes and equipment. Although the cost of energy has decreased as a percentage of the final sale price, its absolute cost for certain industries is significant and would become even greater at higher fuel costs.

11.2 Energy Used by U.S. Industry

Manufacturing companies in the United States in 1993 employed 17 million people, used $61 billion of energy, added $1.5 trillion in value to raw materials to produce products valued at $3.1 trillion (USDC, 1993). The U.S. Department of Commerce compiles and publishes an annual survey of manufacturer statistics including the cost of purchased fuels. The statistics are arranged by industry groups according to the Standard Industrial Classification system (SIC). Table 11.01 lists the industrial groups that purchased the most fuel and electrical energy in 1993. The food group is the fourth largest industrial use of energy (Figure 11.02), moving up from a sixth-place ranking in 1981. It uses 9% of the industry's total energy, compared to 8% in 1981. Food manufacturing uses 9.0% of the employees to produce 13.5% of the value of shipments, highest of all industries. By any measure, the food industry is a significant part of U.S. manufacturing with continued growth expected to use even more energy in the future.

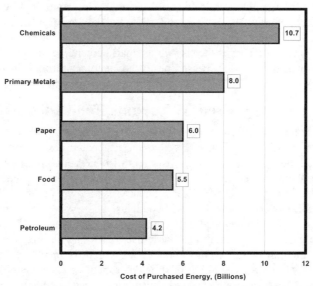

Figure 11.02. Cost of purchased energy ($\$ \times 10^9$ in 1993) for
five largest U.S. industry groups (USDC, 1993).

Table 11.01. Cost of purchased energy, employment, and value of shipments
for 10 leading energy-consuming U.S. industries.

Industry Group	Cost of Purchased Fuel & Electrical Energy ($\$ \times 10^6$)	All Employees ($\$ \times 10^3$)	Value Added ($\$ \times 10^6$)	Value of Shipments ($\$ \times 10^6$)
Chemicals	10 685.8	841.0	170 880	314 743
Primary metal	7 970.3	653.2	55 272	142 364
Paper	6 006.6	627.4	59 449	133 485
Food	5 504.6	1 521.9	165 987	423 367
Petroleum	4 201.9	113.7	23 014	164 715
Stone/clay/ glass	3 715.5	468.2	35 784	65 574
Transportation	3 100.1	1 583.4	165 551	414 914
Fabricated metal products	2 982.3	1 371.9	88 007	175 137
Rubber	2 928.0	938.7	63 378	122 776
Ind. machinery	2 600.7	1 748.9	140 987	277 867
Top 21 industries	60 916.6	16 957.9	1 496 395	3 128 364

Data from U.S. Department of Commerce Annual Survey of Manufacturers (1993).

Energy used by manufacturing industries has increased continually over the years, except for a decline in the 1970s after the Middle East oil embargo when unit prices of fuel rose by 50%. Since then, fuel costs have returned to a lower steady level. For most manufacturing companies fuel is only a small percentage of operating costs and so energy cost can be generally passed on to the customer through increased cost of the final product.

11.3 Energy Used by Various Food Industries

The U.S. Department of Commerce's SIC #20 divides the food and kindred products industry into nine groups with three to seven subcategories in each. Table 11.02 lists the 10 food industries buying the most fuel in 1993. Wet corn milling is by far the largest food processing energy user (Figure 11.03). The number two energy use is for poultry slaughtering and processing. This industry has grown significantly in size and has replaced meat packing which was second just 10 years earlier. Beet sugar was third in 1981 and by 1993 dropped below nine higher energy users. The number three through seven users in 1993 were also large users 10 years before. Sausage and prepared meats is the new entrant as the number six energy user in 1993.

The cost of fuel to process a dollar of shipped product varies among industries. Wet corn milling and beet sugar are energy intensive processes spending 5.5¢ to 6.9¢ for fuel per dollar of shipment (Figure 11.04). These two industries could be significantly affected by changes in fuel costs and potential changes in the processing system. Energy intensive industries could gain the most from developments of alternative processes using less energy. The next highest industry users are 2.0¢ for soybean oil milling and 1.8¢ for bread products. The food and kindred products industry average is 1.3¢ fuel cost per dollar of shipped product while all manufacturing industries average

Table 11.02. Cost of purchased energy and value of shipments
for 10 leading energy-consuming U.S. food industries.

Industry Group	Cost of Purchased Fuel & Electrical energy ($ × 10^6$)	Value of Shipments ($ × 10^6$)	Fuel Costs ($)/ Value of Shipment ($)
Wet corn milling	427.5	6 170	0.0694
Poultry	326.4	24 853	0.0132
Bread & cake	278.9	15 181	0.0184
Fluid milk	247.8	18 422	0.0135
Meat packing	264.3	49 487	0.0054
Canned fruit & vegetable	233.4	15 100	0.0155
Malt beverages	235.7	17 644	0.0134
Sausage & prepared meat	238.5	18 835	0.0127
Beet sugar	133.9	2 402	0.0558
Soybean oil	198.2	9 775	0.0203
All food & kindred products	5 504.6	423 368	0.0131

Data from U.S. Department of Commerce Annual Survey of Manufacturers (1993)

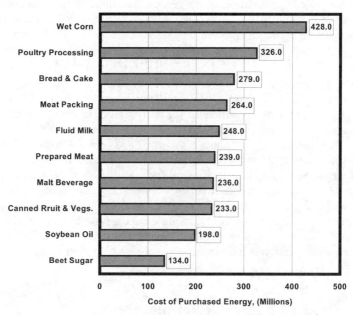

Figure 11.03. Cost of purchased energy in 1993 ($ $\times 10^6$) for 10 largest U.S. food industry groups (USDC, 1993).

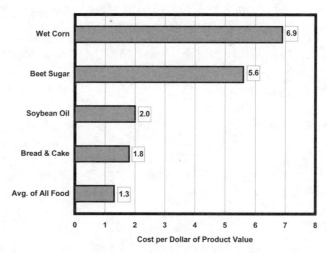

Figure 11.04. Energy cost (cents per dollar product value) for the most energy-intensive food industries (USDC, 1993).

energy cost is 2.0¢ per dollar of product. Energy use in specific industries and processing operations are explained in detail in a series of articles in Food Technology (1977) and for milk processing, freezing, canning, blanching, evaporation, membrane filtration, and irradiation by Singh (1986).

11.4 Post-Processing Energy Use

Energy use after processing, although not explicitly part of processing, is directly affected by the form of the product leaving the manufacturing plant. Thus, the products of the processing industry influence the energy used during distribution, storage, and preparation. The transport of frozen products over long distances and storage for long times requires extensive amounts of energy. Food preparation is performed by an extremely high number of small size units widely distributed in location and time of use. Food preparation operations requiring energy, such as heating, may be performed by individuals with little awareness of energy implications. The home cook, who is the largest user of energy in the food processing system, is often the least informed about wise use of energy. Energy use is also of little concern to the food service business, e.g.., fast food operators. The processing industry can have a major influence on energy use patterns in subsequent transportation, storage, and food preparation.

References

1. Food Technology. 1977. *Energy analysis in food process operations*. A series of six articles in *Food Technology* 31(3): 51-87.
2. Singh, R.P. 1986. *Energy in Food Processing*. Elsevier Science Publishing Co. Inc., New York, N.Y.
3. Unklesbay, N., and K. Unklesbay. 1982. *Energy Management in Foodservice*. AVI Publishing Co. Westport, CT. 437 pp.
4. USDC. 1993. *Annual Survey of Manufacturers*. Statistics for industry groups and industries. M93(AS)-1. Bureau of the Census. U.S. Dept Commerce, Washington D.C.

Problems

11.1. Explain energy distribution/needs between: processing and manufacturing, on-farm production, out-of-home preparation, in-home preparation, and distribution.

11.2. Why has the energy use in the U.S. food production increased more than the population growth in the last century?

11.3. List food companies that rely heavily on energy-intensive processing and would benefit most by using low-cost preservation processes and equipment.

11.4. List the industry group that used the most fuel and electrical energy in 1993.

11.5. Where did food production rank in fuel and electrical energy use in 1993? Has this been an increase or a decrease over the previous 12 years?

11.6. What percent of total energy did the food industry use in food production in 1993? Is this an increase or a decrease from 1981?

11.7. Despite the rapid increase in energy use, what percent of operating cost does it represent?

11.8. List the ten food industries buying the most fuel in 1993. How has this list changed since 1983?

11.9. Which industries would benefit most from changes in fuel costs and processing systems?

11.10. What is the average fuel cost per dollar of shipped product for the food industry? How does this compare to all manufacturing industries?

11.11. Why is the energy used for food preparation so high?

11.12. Are persons involved in food preparation knowledgeable of the amount of energy used (and needed) for food production? Why, or why not?

Appendix

Abstract. This appendix contains general reference information relevant to multiple chapters.

Keywords. SI units, useful conversions, useful constants, thermal properties, viscous properties, composition of food products.

A Precautionary Note!

This appendix contains tables listing selected properties of biological materials. We know that there is great variability in biological materials. Thermal and mechanical properties of apples, for example, vary greatly with maturity, and also among cultivars. Two apples of the same apparent maturity, harvested from the same tree at the same time, will almost certainly have somewhat different properties. Keep this variability in mind as you use the tables in this appendix. Some property values may be expressed to as many as four significant digits. However, actual values for any given sample of the material may differ from these tabulated values by 10%, 20%, or more, depending upon the product and the property being measured.

SI (Metric) Units

The SI (for Systeme International d'Unites) system of units is now the standard throughout most of the world. While it is the official system in the United States, the traditional US units (also called customary units) continue to be used. The SI system of units is based upon the metric system developed about 200 years ago. As technology progressed some inconsistencies in the metric system standards were causing problems with increasingly precise measurement requirements. These inconsistencies were resolved in 1960, and the modified system was given the SI designation. For most applications, the SI and the older metric system may be considered the same.

SI units consist of several basic units plus many derived units, some with special names. Some of the more common units are listed in Table A.1. To further simplify manipulation of numeric values, prefixes are often applied to SI units. These prefixes, shown in Table A.2, help to keep numeric values within a range convenient to use. (For example, 1375 m can be represented as 1.375 km.)

SI units may at first seem more difficult to use than conventional US units. However, after a short period of use, you will find that SI units are much easier to use than the US units. Our initial difficulty with SI units is simply that we are unfamiliar with these units and do not have a "feel" for the magnitude of measurements in SI units.

There are a number of rules for expressing numbers and units in the SI system. A few of those rules are as follows:

- Case (upper vs. lower, i.e., M vs. m) is important for SI and prefix symbols. See Tables A.1 and A.2.
- Number strings greater than four digits on either side of a decimal should be separated in groups of three digits. Examples are: 37 354 330; 45 637.2; 0.345 543. Do not use the comma as in 37,354,330.
- Numbers and units should be separated by a space (34.5 kg, 10^3 kPa, 545.23 kW). An exception to this rule is the expression of temperature in degrees Celsius. It should be written with no space (25.3°C, not 25.3° C).

References

1. ASAE. 2003 (published annually). ASAE Engineering Practice EP285: Use of SI (metric) units. American Society of Agricultural Engineers, St. Joseph, MI.
2. ASME. 1976. *ASME Orientation and Guide for Use of SI (Metric) Units* (ASME Guide SI-1). The American Society of Mechanical Engineers, New York, NY.
3. ASTM. 1974. *Metric Practice Guide* (E380-74). American Society for Testing and Materials, Philadelphia, PA.
4. Page, C. H., and P. Vigoureux. 1972. *The International System of Units (SI)*. NBS Special Publication 330. U.S. Department of Commerce, Washington, DC.

Table A.1. Common SI basic and derived units.

Quantity	SI Unit	SI Symbol	Formula
length	meter	m	
mass	kilogram	kg	
time	second	s	
electric current	ampere	A	
thermodynamic temp.	kelvin	K	
amount of matter	mole	mol	
luminous intensity	candela	cd	
plane angle	radian	rad	
acceleration, angular	radian per second squared		rad/s^2
acceleration, linear	meter per second squared		m/s^2
area	square meter	m^2	
density	kilogram per cubic meter		kg/m^3
energy	joule	J	N m
force	newton	N	$kg\ m/s^2$
frequency	hertz	Hz	s^{-1}
illumination	lux	lx	lm/m^2
inductance	henry	H	V s/A
kinematic viscosity	square meter per second		m^2/s
luminance	candela per square meter		cd/m^2
luminous flux	lumen	lm	cd sr
power	watt	W	J/s
pressure	kilopascal	kPa	kN/m^2
quantity of heat	joule	J	N m
stress	pascal	Pa	N/m^2
surface tension	newtons per meter		N/m
torque	newton meter		N m
velocity, angular	radian per second		rad/s
velocity, linear	meter per second		m/s
viscosity	newton-second per square meter		$N\ s/m^2$
voltage	volt	V	W/A
volume	cubic meter	m^3	
work	joule	J	N m

Table A.2. Prefixes that may be applied to SI units.

Multiple	Prefix	Symbol	Multiple	Prefix	Symbol
10^{12}	Tera	T	10^{-2}	centi	c[b]
10^9	giga	G	10^{-3}	milli	m[a]
10^6	mega	M[a]	10^{-6}	micro	μ[a]
10^3	kilo	k[a]	10^{-9}	nano	n
10^2	hecto	h[b]	10^{-12}	pico	p
10	deka	da[b]	10^{-15}	femto	f
10^{-1}	deci	d[b]	10^{-18}	atto	a

[a] These are the most commonly used prefixes.
[b] Use of these units in scientific applications is discouraged.

Table A.3. Useful conversion constants.

LENGTH
  1 inch = 2.54 cm
  1 meter = 3.281 ft = 39.37 in. = 10^{10} Å
  1 km = 0.6214 mile
  1 mile = 5280 ft = 80 chains = 320 rods

AREA
  1 acre = 43 560 ft^2 = 10 ch.^{2}
  1 ha = 0.01 km^2 = 10 000 m^2 = 2.471 acre
  1 m^2 = 10.76 ft^2 = 1550 in.^{2} = 10^6 mm^2

VOLUME
  1 acre ft = 43 560 ft^3 = 1233 m^3
  1 bushel = 1.245 ft^3
  1 gallon = 231 in.^{3} = 3.785 L
  1 ft^3 = 7.48 gallons = 28.32 L
  1 m^3 = 35.31 ft^3 = 1 000 L = 10^6 cm^3
  1 L = 61.02 in.^{3}

MASS
  1 kg = 2.205 lb_m = 35.27 oz
  1 lb_m = 453.5 g
        = 0.031 08 slug $(lb_f sec^2)/(ft)$
  1 ton = 2000 lb
  1 tonne = 1000 kg (a metric ton)

FORCE
  1 kg_f = 9.807 N = 2.205 lb_f
  1 lb_f = 32.17 poundal
  1 lb_f = 444 800 dynes = 4.448 N

VELOCITY
  1 ft/s = 0.6818 mi/h
  1 ft/s = 0.3048 m/s
  1 mi/h = 1.609 km/h

FLOW RATE
  1 ft^3/s = 449 gal/min = 0.028 32 m^3/s
        = 1.983 acre-ft/day
  1 ft^3/min = 0.000 471 9 m^3/s
        = 0.4719 L/s
  1 m^3/s = 35.31 ft^3/s = 1000 L/s

DENSITY
  1 lb_m/ft^3 = 0.016 02 gm/cm^3
        = 16.02 kg/m^3 = 0.1337 lb_m/gal
  1 kg/m^3 = 0.001 kg/L = 0.062 43 lb_m/ft^3

PRESSURE
  1 atm = 101.325 kPa = 14.696 lb_f/in.^{2}
        = 0.92 in. Hg
  1 bar = 1 × 10^5 Pa
  1 kPa = 0.1450 lb_f/in.^{2} = 4.022 in. H_2O
        = 102.15 mm H_2O
  1 lb_f/in.^{2} (psi) = 144 lb_f/ft^2
        = 2.31 ft of H_2O
        = 6.895 kPa = 27.72 in. H_2O

ENERGY
  1 BTU = 1 055 joule = 778.3 ft-lb_f
  1 joule = 0.2391 cal= 0.737 5 ft-lb_f
  1 kWh = 1.341 hp hr = 3.6 MJ
        = 3413 Btu

POWER
  1 hp = 0.7457 kW = 745.7 W
        = 2546 Btu/hr = 33 000 ft lb_f/min
  1 watt = 1 J/s = 3.41 Btu/hr

ENTHALPY & SPECIFIC HEAT
  1 kJ/kg = 0.4299 BTU/lb
  1 kJ/kg K = 0.238 85 BTU/lb °R

THERMAL CONDUCTIVITY/
  CONDUCTANCE
  1 Btu/hr ft °R = 12 Btu in./hr ft^2 °R
                = 1.7131 W/m K
  1 Btu/hr ft^2 °R = 5.678 W/m^2 K

HEAT FLOW
  1 Btu/hr ft^2 = 3.152 W/m^2

DYNAMIC VISCOSITY
  1 N s/m^2 (1 Pa s) = 10 poise (gm/cm s)
                = 0.672 lb_m/ft s
                = 0.02 088 lb_f s/ft^2
  Note: 1 kg/m s = 1 N s/m^2

KINEMATIC VISCOSITY
  1 ft^2/s = 0.0929 m^2/s
        = 929 stokes (cm^2/s)
  1 m^2/s = 10^4 stokes = 38 750 ft^2/hr
  1 stoke = 0.000 1 m^2/sec

TEMPERATURE
°C = 5/9 (°F–32)   K = °C + 273.16
°F = (1.8 × °C) +32   °R = °F + 459.69

Table A.4. Selected useful constants.

Symbol	Value	Comments
e	2.718 281 828 459...	Base of natural logarithms
g_c	1 kg m/N s^2	Gravitational constant
g	9.807 m/s^2	Gravitational acceleration (standard) metric
g	32.5174 ft/s^2	Gravitational acceleration (standard) USCS
M_a	28.96 kg/kmol	Molecular weight of air
M_w	18.015 kg/kmol	Molecular weight of water
R_a	0.287 06 kPa m^3/kg K	gas constant for air
R_w	0.461 52 kPa m^3/kg K	gas constant for water vapor
R_u	8.314 kPa m^3/kmol K	universal gas constant
ρ_{water}	62.4 lbm/ft^3	Commonly used density of water for
ρ_{water}	8.34 lbm/gal	general calculations where changes with
ρ_{water}	1000 kg/m^3	temperature are not considered.
ev	1.6022×10^{-19} C	electron volt or electron charge (coulombs)
F	96 845 C/mol	Faraday constant (coulombs/mole)
c	299 792 000 m/s	speed of light
h	6.6262×10^{-34} J/s	Planck's constant
π	3.141 592 653 590	Pi
N	6.022×10^{23} particles/mol	Avogadro's number
amu	1.6606×10^{-24} g	atomic mass unit
σ	5.67×10^{-8} W/m^{2}K^4	Stefan-Boltzmann constant
ln 10	2.303 585 093...	Natural log of 10
c_{pH2O}	4.18 kJ/kg K	at 20°C (varies with temperature)
c_{pice}	2.04 kJ/kg K	at 0°C (varies with temperature)
c_{pair}	1.004 kJ/kg K	Dry air at 20°C (varies with temperature)

Table A.5. Thermal properties of selected food products. [a]

Commodity	% water	Sp. Heat at Freezing (kJ/kg K) Above	Below	Freezing Point (°C)	Latent Heat of Fusion[b] (kJ/kg)
Vegetables					
Asparagus	92.4	3.94	2.01	-0.6	310
Beans, snap	90.3	3.94	2.39	-0.7	303
Brussels sprouts	86.0	3.68	1.67	-0.8	288
Cabbage	92.2	3.94	1.97	-0.9	309
Carrots	87.8	3.77	1.93	-1.4	294
Cauliflower	91.9	3.89	1.97	-0.8	308
Corn, sweet yellow	76.0	3.32	1.77	-0.6	255
Lettuce, iceberg	95.9	4.02	2.01	-0.2	321
Onions	89.7	3.77	1.93	-0.9	300
Peas, green	78.9	3.31	1.76	-0.6	264
Peppers, sweet green	92.2	3.94	1.97	-0.7	309
Potatoes, main crop	79.0	3.63	1.82	-0.6	265
Potatoes, sweet	72.8	3.14	1.68	-1.3	244
Tomatoes, mature green	93.0	3.98	2.01	-0.6	312
Tomatoes, ripe	93.8	3.98	2.01	-0.5	314
Fruits					
Apples, dried	31.8	2.27	1.14		107
Apples, fresh	83.9	3.60	1.84	-1.1	281
Apricots	86.3	3.68	1.93	-1.1	289
Bananas	74.3	3.35	1.76	-0.8	249
Blackberries	85.6	3.68	1.68	-0.8	287
Blueberries	84.6	3.60	1.88	-1.6	283
Oranges	82.3	3.77	1.93	-0.8	276
Peaches, fresh	87.7	3.77	1.93	-0.9	294
Raisins, seedless	15.4	1.97	1.07		52
Strawberries	91.6	3.89	1.94	-0.8	307
Meats					
Beef, sirloin, lean	71.7	3.08	1.55	-1.7	240
Beef, veal, lean	75.9	3.35	1.93		254
Bacon	31.6	2.09	1.26		106
Ham, country cured	55.9	2.72	1.37		187
Shoulder, whole lean	72.6	2.90	1.46	-2.2	243
Chicken	66.0	3.31	1.55	-2.8	221
Salmon, pink	76.4	2.97	1.63	-2.2	256
Dairy					
Butter	17.9	1.38	1.05		60
Cheese, cheddar	36.8	2.60	1.31	-12.9	123
Cream, half and half	80.6	3.68	1.85		270
Ice cream, vanilla	61.0	3.27	1.88	-5.6	204
Milk, skim	90.8	4.00	2.51		304
Milk, whole	87.7	3.85	1.94	-0.6	294
Other					
Eggs, whole	75.3	3.18	1.68	-0.6	252
Honey[c]	17.1	2.10	1.68		57
Maple syrup	32.0	2.05	1.30		107
Orange Juice	89.0	3.82	1.96	-0.4	298
Pecans	4.8	1.75	0.88		16

[a] Properties of selected commodities taken from ASHRAE. 1998. *Handbook of Refrigeration*, Chapter 8. Courtesy of the American Society of Heating, Refrigerating and Air-Conditioning Engineers.

[b] Computed from product of the latent heat of fusion (335 kJ/kg) and the moisture content shown (in decimal form).

[c] Specific heat values for honey were taken from ASHRAE. 1993. *Handbook of Fundamentals*, Chapter 30.

Table A.6. Composition of selected fruit products.[a]

Product	Water	Protein	Fat	Carbo-hydrate	Fiber[c]	Ash	Energy[d] (kJ/100g)
Apples, raw, with skin	83.93	0.19	0.36	15.25	0.77	0.26	245
Apples, dried, sulfured, uncooked	31.76	0.93	0.32	65.89	2.87	1.10	1,017
Applesauce, unsweetened	88.35	0.17	0.05	11.29	0.53	0.15	181
Applesauce, sweetened	79.58	0.18	0.18	19.91	0.46	0.14	318
Bananas, raw	74.26	1.03	0.48	23.43	0.50	0.80	384
Blueberries, raw	84.61	0.67	0.38	14.13	1.30	0.21	236
Blueberries, frozen, unsweetened	86.59	0.42	0.64	12.17	1.50	0.18	212
Dates	22.50	1.97	0.45	73.51	2.20	1.58	1,151
Melons, cantaloupe, raw	89.78	0.88	0.28	8.36	0.36	0.71	148
Oranges, raw	86.75	0.94	0.12	11.75	0.43	0.44	197
Peaches, raw	87.66	0.70	0.09	11.10	0.64	0.46	180
Peaches, canned, water pack	93.13	0.44	0.06	6.11	0.31	0.27	100
Peaches, canned, heavy syrup	79.28	0.45	0.10	19.94	0.29	0.24	310
Peaches, dehydrated, sulfured, cooked	62.04	2.01	0.42	34.14	1.63	1.39	557
Pears, raw	83.81	0.39	0.40	15.11	1.40	0.28	247
Strawberries, raw	91.57	0.61	0.37	7.02	0.53	0.43	127
Strawberries, frozen, unsweetened	89.97	0.43	0.11	9.13	0.79	0.37	147
Watermelon, raw	91.51	0.62	0.43	7.18	0.30	0.26	132

[a] From Gebhardt, Cutrufelli, and Matthews. 1982. *Composition of Foods: Fruits and Fruit Juices*. Agricultural Handbook Number 8-9, USDA, GPO, Washington, DC.

[b] Rounded to two decimal places. The sum of values may not always be 100%.

[c] Fiber is included in the carbohydrate value. Thus, values in this column should not be added separately to obtain the 100% total content.

[d] The energy value provided is physiological energy. Some energy is required for metabolism and for digestion of the product. The energy remaining after these losses is the physiological energy.

Table A.7. Composition of selected vegetable products.[a]

Product	Water	Protein	Fat	Carbo-hydrate	Fiber[c]	Ash	Energy[d] (kJ/100g)
Beans, snap, raw	90.27	1.82	0.12	7.14	1.10	0.66	129
Beans, snap, cooked, boiled, drained	89.22	1.89	0.28	7.89	1.43	0.73	147
Broccoli, raw	90.69	2.98	0.35	5.24	1.11	0.92	116
Broccoli, cooked, boiled, drained	90.20	2.97	0.28	5.57	1.20	0.99	123
Broccoli, frozen, chopped	91.46	2.81	0.29	4.79	1.10	0.66	110
Cabbage, raw	92.52	1.21	0.18	5.37	0.80	0.72	99
Cabbage, cooked, boiled, drained	93.60	0.96	0.25	4.77	0.60	0.43	90
Carrots, raw	87.79	1.03	0.19	10.14	1.04	0.87	181
Carrots, cooked, boiled, drained	87.38	1.09	0.18	10.48	1.47	0.87	188
Carrots, frozen, cooked, boiled, drained	89.88	1.19	0.11	8.25	1.18	0.58	150
Corn, sweet, raw	75.96	3.22	1.18	19.02	0.70	0.62	358
Corn, sweet, cooked, boiled, drained	69.57	3.32	1.28	25.11	0.60	0.72	454
Corn, sweet, canned, solids and liquid	81.90	1.94	0.45	14.83	0.49	0.89	257
Corn, sweet, canned, cream style	78.73	1.74	0.42	18.13	0.49	0.98	303
Corn, sweet, frozen, kernels, cut off cob, unprepared	74.92	3.02	0.77	20.80	0.62	0.48	369
Okra, raw	89.58	2.00	0.10	7.63	0.94	0.70	158
Okra, cooked, boiled, drained	89.91	1.87	0.17	7.21	0.90	0.84	133
Okra, frozen, unprepared	90.82	1.69	0.25	6.64	0.83	0.61	125
Onions, raw	90.82	1.18	0.26	7.32	0.44	0.42	141
Potatoes, raw, fresh	78.96	2.07	0.10	17.98	0.44	0.89	331
Potatoes, baked, flesh and skin	71.20	2.30	0.10	25.23	0.66	1.16	456
Potatoes, baked, flesh	75.42	1.96	0.10	21.56	0.38	0.97	390
Potatoes, baked, skin	47.31	4.29	0.10	46.07	2.28	2.24	830
Potatoes, mashed, from dehydrated flakes	76.3	1.90	5.60	15.02	0.47	1.18	472
Squash, summer, all varieties, raw	93.68	1.18	0.21	4.35	0.60	0.58	84
Squash, summer, all varieties, cooked, boiled, drained	93.70	0.91	0.31	4.31	0.60	0.77	85
Tomato paste	74.06	3.78	0.89	18.82	0.95	2.45	351
Tomato sauce	89.07	1.33	0.17	7.18	0.71	2.25	127
Tomatoes, green, raw	93.00	1.20	0.20	5.10	0.50	0.50	100
Tomatoes, red, ripe, raw	93.95	0.89	0.21	4.34	0.47	0.61	81
Tomatoes, red, ripe, cooked, boiled	92.40	1.12	0.27	5.63	0.77	0.58	105
Turnip greens, raw	91.07	1.50	0.30	5.73	0.80	1.40	111
Turnip greens, cooked, boiled, drained	93.20	1.14	0.23	4.36	0.61	1.07	85
Turnip greens, canned, solids and liquid	94.69	1.36	0.30	2.42	0.61	1.23	61

[a] From Haytowitz and Matthews. 1984. *Composition of Foods: Vegetables and Vegetable Products*. Agricultural Handbook Number 8-11, USDA, GPO, Washington, DC.

[b] Rounded to two decimal places. The sum of values may not always be 100%.

[c] Fiber is included in the carbohydrate value. Thus, values in this column should not be added separately to obtain the 100% total content.

[d] The energy value provided is physiological energy. Some energy is required for metabolism and for digestion of the product. The energy remaining after these losses is the physiological energy.

Table A.8. Heat of respiration for selected fresh fruits and vegetables
at various temperatures. [a]

Commodity	0°C	5°C	10°C	15°C	20°C	25°C
Apples, early cultivars	9.7-18	16-32	41-32	54-92	58-121	
Apples, late cultivars	5.3-11	14-21	20-31	28-58	351-386	
Apricots	16-17	19-27	33-56	63-102	303-581	
Asparagus	81-238	162-404	318-904	472-971	809-1484	
Beans, snap		101-104	162-173	252-276	351-386	
Berries, blackberries	47-68	85-136	155-281	208-432	388-582	
Berries, raspberries	52-74	92-114	82-165	244-301	400-727	
Berries, Strawberries	36-52	48-98	146-281	210-274	303-581	501-626
Brussels Spouts	46-71	96-144	187-251	283-317	267-564	
Carrots, Imperator, TX	46	58	93	117	209	
Carrots, Roots, Nantes, Can.	9.2	20		64-84		
Cauliflower, TX	53	61	100	1377	238	
Corn, sweet with husk, TX	126	230	332	483	856	1208
Lettuce, head, CA.	27-50	40-59	81-119	114-121	178	
Lettuce, leaf, TX	68	87	117	187	298	434
Peaches	12-19	19-27		98-126	176-304	242-361
Pears, late ripening	7.8-11	18-41	23-56	82-126	97-218	
Pears, early ripening	7.8-14	22-46	22-63	102-160	116-267	
Peas, green-in pod	90-139	163-226		530-600	728-1072	1018-1118
Tomatoes, TX, mature green				61	103	127 (27°C)
Tomatoes, TX, ripening				79	120	143 (27°C)
Tomatoes, CA, mature green					71-104	89-143

[a]Properties of selected commodities taken from ASHRAE. 1998. *Handbook of Refrigeration*,
Chapter 8. ASHRAE, Inc., Atlanta, GA. Courtesy of the American Society of Heating, Refrigerating and
Air-Conditioning Engineers.

Table A.9. Thermal properties of selected products.[a]

Product	t (°C)	k (W/m K)	ρ (kg/m^3)	c_p (kJ/kg K)	α (m^2/s)
Air [b] (at 101.3 kPa)	20	0.024	1.293	1.005	18.6×10^{-6}
Ice [b]	-20	2.43	948	1.95	1.32×10^{-6}
Ice [b]	0	2.22	917	2.10	1.14×10^{-6}
Water [b]	0	0.533	999.8	4.21	0.135×10^{-6}
Water [b]	20	0.599	998.2	4.18[f]	0.143×10^{-6}
Water [b]	100	0.684	958.4	4.21	0.170×10^{-6}
Steam [b] (at 101.3 kPa)	100	0.0242	0.60	2.03	19.0×10^{-6}
Mercury	20	8.2	13 546	0.139	4.36×10^{-6}
Half & half [c] [d]	20	0.47	1025	3.8	0.12×10^{-6}
Milk, whole [c] [d]	20	0.53	1029	3.9	0.13×10^{-6}
Milk, skimmed [c] [d]	20	0.57	1033	3.94	0.14×10^{-6}
Sucrose, 20% solution [e]	20	0.535	1079.9	3.72	0.133×10^{-6}
Sucrose, 40% [e]	20	0.470	1175.4	3.22	0.124×10^{-6}
Sucrose 60% [e]	20	0.404	1285.4	2.76	0.114×10^{-6}
Beef fat[b]	20	0.18	950	2.00	0.095×10^{-6}
Starch[b]	20	0.15	1500	1.25	0.08×10^{-6}

[a] Based upon data from references identified for each product. Note that thermal properties of milk products are highly variable, depending upon fat content.

[b] Locin, M., and R. L. Merson. 1979. *Food Engineering Principles and Selected Applications.* Academic Press, New York, NY.

[c] Wong, N. P. 1988. *Fundamentals of Dairy Chemistry.* Van Nostrand Reinhold Co., New York, NY.

[d] Davies, W. L. 1936. *The Chemistry of Milk.* Chapman & Hall Ltd., London, UK.

[e] Pancoast, H. M., and W. R. Junk. 1980. *Handbook of Sugars.* AVI, Westport, CT.

[f] The specific heat of water is slightly higher at the freezing and boiling points than at temperatures between those points.

Table A.10. Viscosities of selected materials.[a]

Material	t (°C)	μ (N s/m^2)	ρ (kg/m^3)	ν (m^2/s)
Air [b][c]	0	1.720×10^{-5}	1.290	1.330×10^{-5}
	25	1.839×10^{-5}	1.180	1.552×10^{-5}
	50	1.957×10^{-5}	1.100	1.786×10^{-5}
	100	2.179×10^{-5}	0.957	2.300×10^{-5}
Water [b]	0	1.792×10^{-3}	999.9	1.792×10^{-6}
	25	0.894×10^{-3}	997.1	0.897×10^{-6}
	50	0.549×10^{-3}	988.1	0.556×10^{-6}
	75	0.380×10^{-3}	974.8	0.390×10^{-6}
	100	0.283×10^{-3}	958.4	0.295×10^{-6}
Sucrose solution [d][e] 20%	0	3.818×10^{-3}	1084.4	3.52×10^{-6}
	25	1.710×10^{-3}	1078.4	1.59×10^{-6}
	50	0.974×10^{-3}	1067.9	0.912×10^{-6}
Sucrose solution [d][e] 40%	0	14.82×10^{-3}	1182.3	12.5×10^{-6}
	25	5.206×10^{-3}	1173.3	4.44×10^{-6}
	50	2.506×10^{-3}	1161.4	2.16×10^{-6}
Sucrose solution [d][e] 60%	0	235.7×10^{-3}	1294.7	182×10^{-6}
	25	44.02×10^{-3}	1283.0	34.3×10^{-6}
	50	14.06×10^{-3}	1269.6	11.1×10^{-6}
Milk, whole, homogenized [f][g]	0	4.28×10^{-3}	1032	4.15×10^{-6}
	25	1.85×10^{-3}	1028	1.80×10^{-6}
	50	1.08×10^{-3}	1018	1.06×10^{-6}
Milk, skim [h]	0	3.42×10^{-3}	1041	3.28×10^{-6}
	25	1.54×10^{-3}	1032	1.49×10^{-6}
	50	0.85×10^{-3}	1022	0.832×10^{-6}

[a] Based upon data from references identified for each product. Note that viscosity and density of milk products are highly variable, depending upon fat content.

[b] Geankoplis, C. J. 1993. *Transport Processes and Unit Operations.* Prentice-Hall, Englewood Cliffs, NJ.

[c] Holman, J. P. 1972. *Heat Transfer.* McGraw-Hill, New York, NY.

[d] Pancoast, H. M., and W. R. Junk. 1980. *Handbook of Sugars.* AVI, Westport, CT.

[e] Steffe, J. F. 1992. *Rheological Methods in Food Process Engineering.* Freeman Press, East Lansing, MI.

[f] Spreer, E., and A. Mixa. 1998. *Milk and Dairy Product Technology.* Marcel Dekker, Inc., New York, NY.

[g] Davies, W. L. 1936. *The Chemistry of Milk.* Chapman & Hall Ltd., London, UK.

[h] Whittaker, R., J. M. Sherman, and P. F. Sharp. 1927. Effect of temperature on the viscosity of skim milk. *Journal of Dairy Science* X: 361-371.

Comprehensive Nomenclature List

a	acceleration, m/s^2
a_w	water activity, dimensionless ratio
A	area, m^2
Bi	Biot number, dimensionless
c	speed of light, m/s
c_p	specific heat capacity at constant pressure, J/(kg K) or kJ/(kg K)
c'_p	specific heat capacity below freezing at constant pressure, J/(kg K) or kJ/(kg K)
C	constant in various equations
C	circumference, m
C	concentration, kmol/m^3
C	thermal conductance, W/(m^2 K)
COP	coefficient of performance, dimensionless
d	depth below the liquid surface, m
d	product thickness, m
d_p	penetration depth (microwave energy), cm
D	diameter, m
D	diffusivity, m^2/s
D	deformation, m
D	time required at a given temperature to destroy 90% of the spores of an organism
E	voltage, volts
E	energy per unit mass, J/kg
E	energy radiated, W/m^2
E	modulus of elasticity, N/m^2 or Pa
E_f	energy loss due to friction, J/kg
E_p	energy input from pump, J/kg
EMC	equilibrium moisture content, decimal or percent
ERH	equilibrium relative humidity, decimal or percent
f	frequency, Hz
f	friction factor
f_c	slope parameter for graph of can center temperature during cooling
f_d	Darcy friction factor, dimensionless, ($f_d = 4f_f$)
f_f	Fanning friction factor, dimensionless

f_h slope parameter for graph of can center temperature during heating

F force, N

F_0 time required at 121.1°C (250°F) to obtain a desired sterilization value

Fo Fourier number, dimensionless

FT freezing time, s

g gravitational acceleration, 9.81 m/s^2

g_c gravitational constant, 1 (kg m)/(N s^2)

Gr Grashof number, dimensionless

h enthalpy, kJ/kg

h height or length, m

h convective (surface) heat transfer coefficient, W/(m^2 K)

h_{as} (h_s - h_a), enthalpy difference between saturated and dry air, kJ/kg

h_f enthalpy of saturated liquid, kJ/kg

h_{fg} (h_g - h_f), latent heat of vaporization, kJ/kg

h_g enthalpy of saturated vapor, kJ/kg

h_{sf} (h_f - h_s), latent heat of fusion, kJ/kg

H total head, ft or m

H_f head loss due to friction, ft or m

H_p head added by the pump, ft or m

I electrical current flow, amperes

j an offset parameter or lag factor used in developing equation for heat penetration

J diffusion rate, kmol/(m^2 s)

k thermal conductivity, W/(m K)

K constant in various equations

K compressibility factor, dimensionless

L a characteristic length, m

L_e equivalent length, m

Le Lewis number, dimensionless

m mass, kg

m moisture content wet basis (wb), decimal or percent

$\dot{m}$ mass flow rate, kg/s

M moisture content dry basis (db), decimal or percent

M molecular weight

M_e equilibrium moisture content, dry basis , decimal or percent

N rotational speed, rpm

N number of moles

N number of organisms at any time, θ

N_o initial number of organisms (at $\theta = 0$)

Nu Nusselt number, dimensionless

P pressure, Pa

P permeability, cm^3 (STP) cm cm^{-2} s^{-1} (cm Hg)$^{-1}$

P Plank Equation constant, a function of product shape

P_d pressure at any depth (d) below the liquid surface, Pa

P_f fan power, W

P_m motor input power, W

P_s pressure at a liquid surface, Pa

P_w pump output power, W

ΔP pressure drop, Pa

ΔP_f pressure loss due to friction, Pa

Pe Peclet number, dimensionless

Pr Prandtl number, dimensionless

$\dot{q}$ heat transfer rate per unit area, W/m^2

Q energy, J

Q_R heat of respiration, kJ/kg day

$\dot{Q}$ volumetric flow rate, m^3/s

$\dot{Q}$ heat transfer rate, W

r radius, m

rh relative humidity, decimal or percent

R Plank Equation constant, a function of product shape

R gas constant for a particular gas, kPa m^3/(kg K)

R electrical resistance, ohms

R thermal resistance, (m^2 K)/W

R_T total resistance to heat flow, (m^2 K)/W

R_u gas constant, universal, 8.314 kJ/(kmol K)

Re Reynolds number, dimensionless

s entropy, kJ/(kg K)

SV sterilization value, decimal reductions, or log cycles

t temperature, °C

t_i' a pseudo initial temperature used in heat penetration analysis, °C

t_r retort temperature, °C

Δt temperature difference, °C

T absolute temperature, K

T temperature ratio, dimensionless, $(t_o - t)/(t_o - t_i)$

TT thawing time, s

u velocity, m/s

$\dot{u}$ thermal energy of mass crossing a boundary

U overall heat transfer coefficient, W/(m^2 K)

v specific volume, m^3/kg

V volume, m^3

ΔV volume change, m^3

W humidity ratio, g H_2O/kg DA or kg H_2O/kg DA

w specific weight, force/unit volume

x steam quality, kg vapor/kg total

X mass ratio (mass fraction) of a specified material

X horizontal distance, m

x,y,z coordinate direction
y mole fraction
Y vertical distance, m
z elevation above any selected reference level, m
z temperature difference required for thermal destruction to result in a change of one log cycle (or a 90% reduction in spores of the organism), °C
α thermal diffusivity, m^2/s
γ shear strain rate, s^{-1}
γ ratio of heat capacity
δ characteristic length, m
$\in$ equivalent height of pipe roughness, m
$\in$ strain $= D/L$, m/m or similar dimensionless ratio
$\in'$ dielectric constant
$\in''$ dielectric loss factor
η_f fan efficiency in decimal form
η_m motor efficiency in decimal form
η_p pump efficiency in decimal form
θ time, s, min, or hr
θ_o corrected zero for a process (58% of the come-up time), s or min
λ wavelength, m
μ degree of saturation, dimensionless
μ dynamic (or absolute) viscosity, Pa·s or (N s)/m^2
ν kinematic viscosity (μ/ρ), m^2/s
ρ density, kg/m^3
σ Stefan-Boltzmann constant, 5.669×10^{-8} W/(m^2 K^4)
σ stress $= F/A$, N/m^2 or Pa
τ shear stress, N/m^2 or Pa
ϕ relative humidity, percent or decimal

Subscripts

o property evaluated at $\theta = 0$
1, 2   initial and final values
1,2,3 position identification
a air (or dry air), or ash
b bulk (average)
bp boiling point
c cold fluid, infinite cylinder, or carbohydrates
d dry
d depth
dp dew point
D diameter
f friction
f fat, feed, fluid state, frozen product, or freezing point

fg	difference between properties at fluid and gaseous states
g	gaseous state
h	hot fluid
H	highest enthalpy value of refrigeration cycle
HP	heat pump operation
i	initial, or inside
L	liquid
lm	logarithmic mean
o	outside, surrounding or reference condition
p	plate, product, protein, or pump
r	retort
rem	removed
s	steam, or saturated
s	solid, or surface
T	total
v	vapor
w	wall, water
wb	wet-bulb
ws	water at saturation

Superscripts

*	a property at the thermodynamic wet-bulb temperature
as	saturated air
n	exponent in power law equation
N	exponent in equilibrium moisture equations

Index

The **bolded** page represents the most significant information.